Applied Sketching and Technical Drawing

by

Ronald J. Lutz
Professor of Industrial and Engineering Technology
Central Michigan University
Mount Pleasant, Michigan

South Holland, Illinois
THE GOODHEART-WILLCOX COMPANY, INC.
Publishers

ABOUT THE AUTHOR

Readers will discover APPLIED SKETCHING AND TECHNICAL DRAWING easy to understand and the activities exciting to complete because of the background and educational philosophy of the author.

Ron Lutz has developed a strong background in the areas of applied sketching and technical drawing from his teaching architectural, civil, and mechanical engineering curricula, from industrial experience, and from his graduate work relating to the teaching of engineering graphics.

Teaching experience includes 4 years at the junior high level, 4 years at the secondary level, and 10 years at the university level. This professional involvement has been recognized by numerous outstanding teaching awards.

Combining his background with an intense desire and commitment to simplify the learning process and to make learning fun, Ron Lutz has written APPLIED SKETCHING AND TECHNICAL DRAWING with precise language, dynamic illustrations, and meaningful learning activities.

Library of Congress Catalog Card Number 89-17043
International Standard Book Number 0-87006-764-8

1234567890-91-9876543210

Library of Congress Cataloging in Publication Data

Lutz, Ronald J.,
Applied sketching and drafting / by Ronald J. Lutz
p. cm.
Includes index.
ISBN 0-87006-764-8
1. Mechanical drawing. 2. Freehand technical sketching.
I. Title.
T353.L875 1991
604.2--dc20 89-17043
CIP

INTRODUCTION

APPLIED SKETCHING AND TECHNICAL DRAWING introduces you to the basic concepts and skills used in industry to communicate ideas and to produce engineering drawings. Each chapter describes and illustrates an essential portion of the knowledge and techniques you need to successfully use and apply the drafting language.

The textbook and workbook has been carefully designed and tested to enhance your learning experience. The concepts are presented from ''the simple to the complex.'' New information builds upon prior knowledge in a manner which will help you fully understand each concept. The materials presented in this text are appropriate for a wide range of teaching/learning styles including ''group instruction'' and ''independent study'' approaches. A primary aim of APPLIED SKETCHING AND TECHNICAL DRAWING is to make your learning experience both successful and enjoyable.

An overview of the seven major topics summarizes the focus of APPLIED SKETCHING AND TECHNICAL DRAWING.

LETTERING will teach you to enhance your drawings with professional lettering for improved communication.

SKETCHING will teach you to present ideas and to sketch pictorial views and multiview projections. You will learn how to ''see'' the relationship between isometric and multiview drawings.

INSTRUMENT DRAWING will teach you to successfully use common drafting equipment while developing skill in constructing a series of geometric problems.

PROJECTING IMAGES will teach you to draw isometrics, multiviews, auxiliaries, and surface developments.

DIMENSIONING will teach you to use conventional dimensioning practices to describe your drawings, as well as guide you through geometric dimensioning and tolerancing practices.

WORKING DRAWINGS will teach you to pull together all you have learned in previous chapters to allow you to produce professional-looking technical drawings. You will learn about sectioning, exploded isometrics, and first angle projection.

COMPUTER ASSISTED DRAWING AND DESIGN will introduce you to the world of CADD where drawings are developed electronically using the computer.

I personally hope you will experience great satisfaction and success as you study APPLIED SKETCHING AND TECHNICAL DRAWING to learn the knowledge, skills, and techniques of drafting.

Ronald J. Lutz

TABLE OF CONTENTS

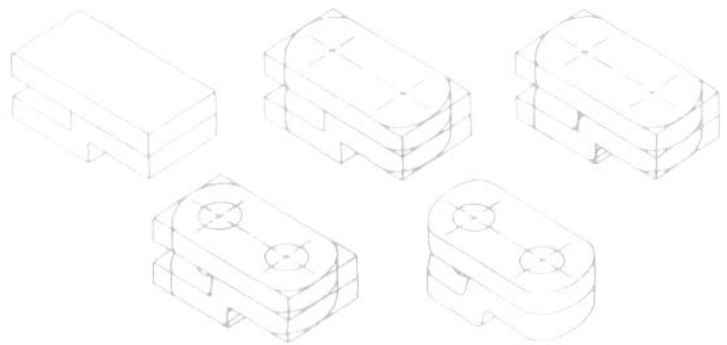

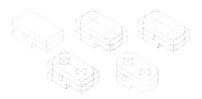

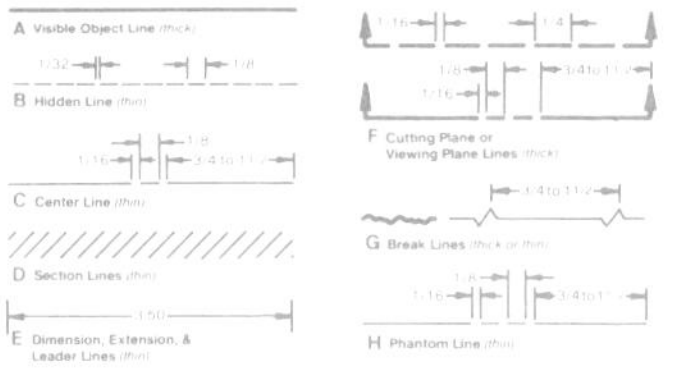
A Visible Object Line
B Hidden Line
C Center Line
D Section Lines
E Dimension, Extension, &
Leader Lines
F Cutting Plane or
Viewing Plane Lines
G Break Lines
H Phantom Line

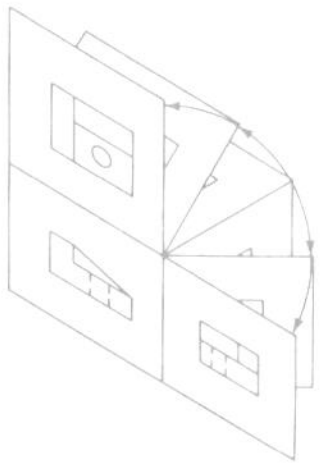

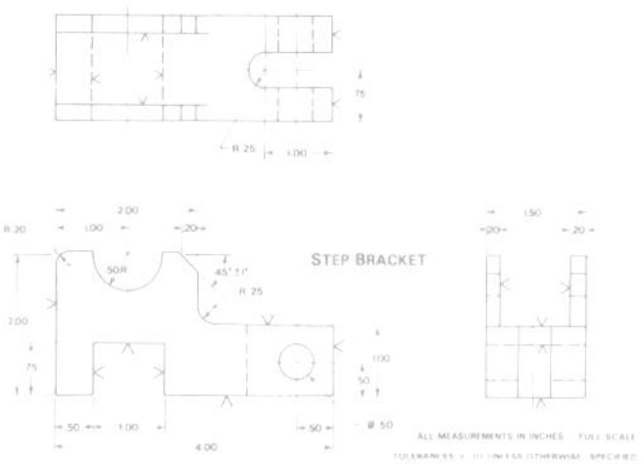
STEP BRACKET

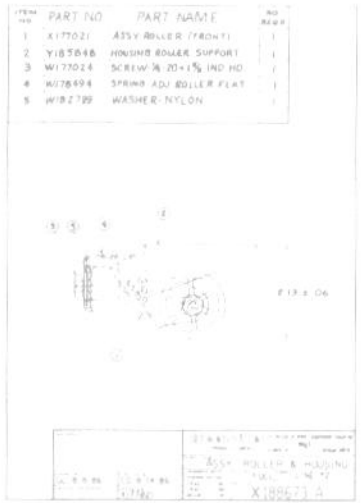

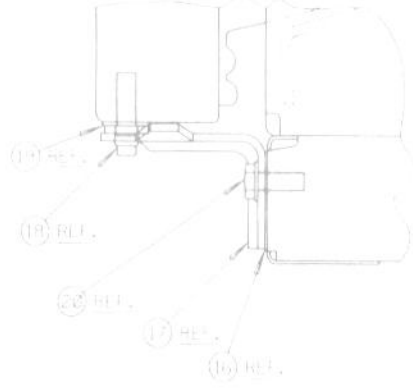

Chapter 1

LETTERING

OBJECTIVES

After completing this LETTERING chapter, you will be able to:

- ☐ *Draw guidelines for lettering.*
- ☐ *Correctly shape letters made with straight vertical, horizontal, and slanted strokes.*
- ☐ *Correctly shape letters made with straight, curved, and circular strokes.*
- ☐ *Correctly shape numerals made with straight, curved, and circular strokes.*
- ☐ *Space consistently between the letters of words and between words.*
- ☐ *Improve the quality of letters, numerals, and words such that they are professional looking.*
- ☐ *Increase your speed and accuracy in lettering.*

Lettering is an important asset to sketches and drawings. The words and phrases made with good lettering add essential details about sizes, shapes, materials, tools, processes, and specific features of a part or product. Fig. 1-1 shows a typical drawing illustrating the importance of good lettering.

These details may be created and recorded by a single individual as a project is designed. This person may, at a future date, decide to construct the project and will need plans that are easily read and understood.

Often, designers work with a team of people in preparing sketches and drawings of products. The completed drawings are then transferred to another team of people who actually manufacture the product. In this situation, good lettering is critical in help-

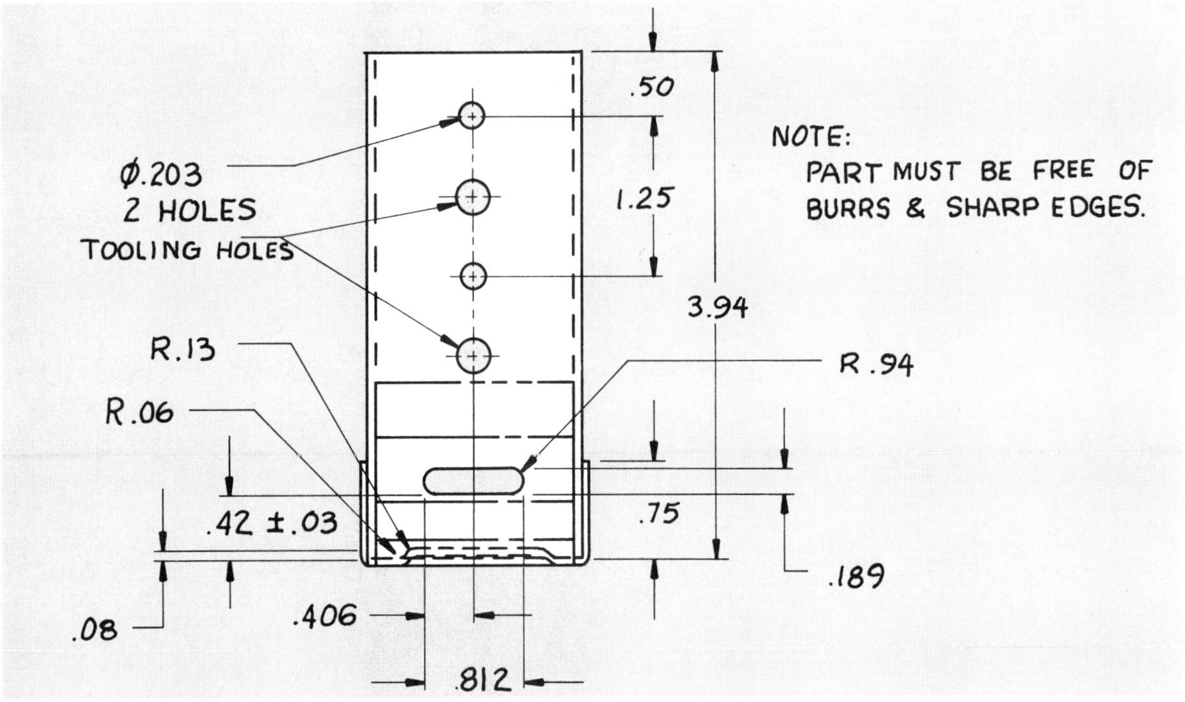

Fig. 1-1. Good lettering provides important information on a drawing or sketch.

ing others ensure accurate interpretations of the details on the drawings.

In addition to providing important accurate information, good lettering greatly improves the overall appearance of a sketch or drawing. It is worth your time to practice and concentrate on freehand lettering skills to give your drawings a professional look.

FUNDAMENTALS

Good freehand lettering is dependent upon two basic factors. First, each letter, numeral, and symbol (character) needs to be shaped accurately. The relationship between the length and width of each element should be studied carefully in the illustrations and examples. Good letters consist of straight lines, slanted lines, and curved or circular lines. Practice in making and combining these lines accurately assures good letter formation.

Secondly, the spacing should be consistent between letters, words, numerals, and fractions. In most cases, the spacing between letters and numerals should be as close as possible without having them touching each other. Spacing between words should be approximately equal to the height of the letters. A more detailed explanation of spacing between letters and numerals is included later in this chapter.

There are many different styles of letters used in our society. Some of these styles include Old English, Roman, and Gothic. In an attempt to clarify and simplify the letters and numerals used on sketches and engineering drawings, standardized lettering is used, Fig. 1-2. Referred to as single-stroke Gothic lettering, this style was standardized in the mid-1930s by the American National Standards Institute (ANSI).

The ANSI standards include upper case letters (capitals) and lower case letters as illustrated. The capitals are used almost exclusively on drawings. Vertical or inclined letters are permissible, but the vertical letters are usually preferred because they are easier to make consistently.

Minor adaptations in the shape of letters and numerals may be approved by engineering departments. Additionally, a department or company may decide that readability is improved by making the first letter of each word taller than the rest of the word. Major changes in stylizing lettering may be made by designers for architectural and structural drawings.

Whenever lettering is modified from established standards, careful thought should be given to maintaining or improving legibility. The basic requirement of all lettering is that copies or prints made from the original drawings are fully legible.

COMMON PRACTICES

As you begin lettering, concentrate on making the shapes as perfect as possible. While learning the shapes, some of the letters and numerals may not look good enough. Do not bother erasing or reform-

Fig. 1-2. Standardized letters and numerals are easily read and understood. The letters and numerals in this example meet ANSI standards.

ing them, just continue to practice until they are made correctly.

Your lettering skill will be expected to improve in both speed and accuracy as you practice. As a beginner, your letters will be made slowly. As you practice and become more comfortable with lettering, set your goal as: ''Speed — 30 letters per minute'' and ''Accuracy — 9 out of 10 letters correct.'' After learning this skill your accuracy level should improve such that all lettering is close to professional results.

MAKING LETTERS AND NUMERALS

When freehand lettering, the hardness of the lead in a mechanical holder or in a pencil determines the type of lines drawn. Refer to Fig. 1-3 to learn about the range of leads available. The first step in freehand lettering is to draw very light guidelines, with a sharp pencil, to control the height and direction of the letters and numerals. A very sharp H or 2H pencil may be used for guidelines, if only a slight amount of pressure is applied to the pencil. A harder pencil such as a 4H-9H may be used instead to draw the lines.

In contrast, the lettering should be very dark and intense. An H, 2H, or HB pencil is soft enough to make your lettering very black and distinctive. Practice with different pencils until you find the one that makes your lettering look the best.

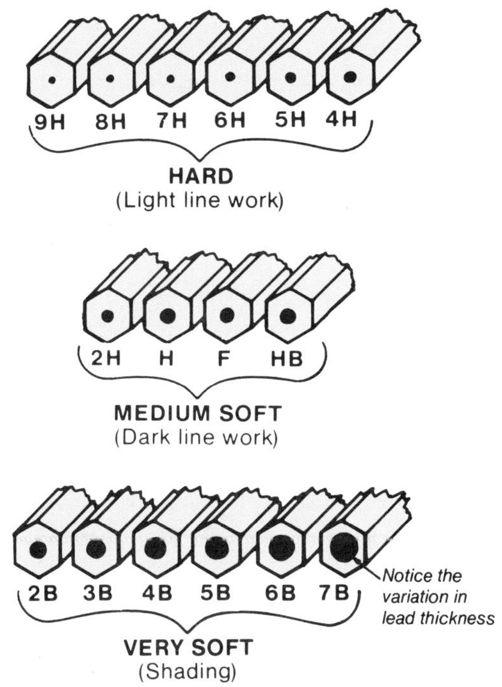

Fig. 1-3. Selection of leads available for sketching, drawing, and lettering. Hard leads are used to make guidelines. Soft leads work best for lettering.

GUIDELINES

Guidelines control the height of the letters and numerals. They assure all lettering is consistent in size. The dot pattern is used to control the width of the letters and numerals. The dot pattern also allows you to create the specific features with consistency. Refer to Fig. 1-4 as an example of a typical guideline for use in lettering. Each of the characters is 5 units tall, but they vary in width from a single stroke in the I to 5 units wide in the W. The dots used to indicate the units of height and width also locate specific features of individual letters such as upper arms and lower legs. The ratio of height to width of each character should be studied and practiced until their proportion looks correct.

Fig. 1-4. Guidelines and the dot pattern control the height and direction of the letters and numerals you create.

The space between the upper and lower guidelines varies and depends upon where the lettering appears, Fig. 1-5. Most of the details appear around the views on the body of a drawing as notes, dimensions, subtitles, tables, etc. The recommended minimum letter height is 1/8 in. for these details. Larger letters and numerals appear in other locations such as in the title block. The recommended minimum letter height for subheadings in the title block is 3/16 in. For the drawing title and number, it is 1/4 in.

LETTERS FORMED WITH VERTICAL AND HORIZONTAL LINES

While studying this section, refer to Fig. 1-6.

I. The I is made with a single stroke from the inside of the top guideline to the inside of the bottom guideline. As with all other characters, an I touches both guidelines. Note, the I has no top or bottom bar.

L. The vertical stem of the L is followed by a horizontal bar. As with all of the following examples,

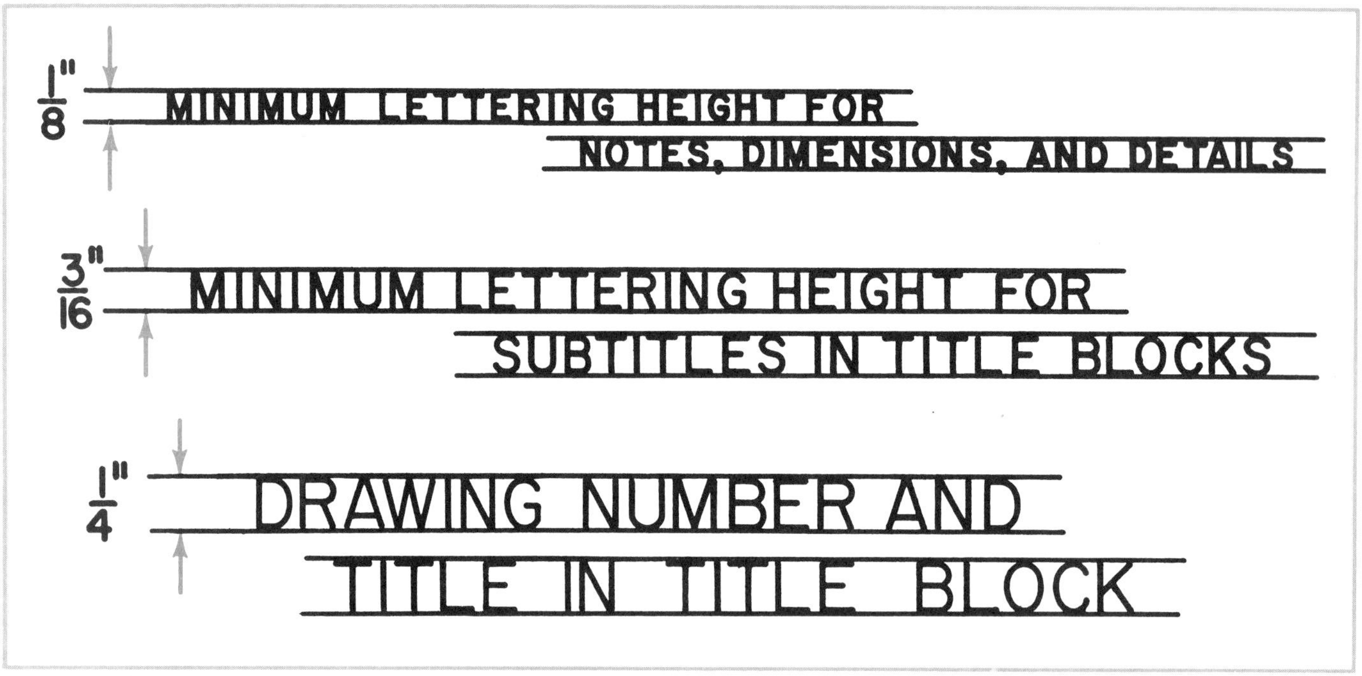

Fig. 1-5. Depending upon usage, the height of your lettering will vary from 1/8 inch to 1/4 inch on small drawings.

the L is 5 units tall. The bottom bar of the L is 3 units long.

T. For the first stroke of the T, make the top bar 3 1/2 units long. The vertical stem is added from the center of the top bar to the bottom guideline.

H. The left and right vertical stems of the H are 3 1/2 units apart. The horizontal bar is midway between the upper and lower guidelines.

F. Make the vertical stem of the F, followed by the top horizontal bar 3 units long. The middle bar is 2 units long and is slightly above the midpoint between the upper and lower guidelines.

E. The vertical stem of the E is followed by a bottom horizontal bar 3 units long. The top bar is also 3 units long followed by the 2 unit middle bar that is located slightly above the midpoint between the quidelines.

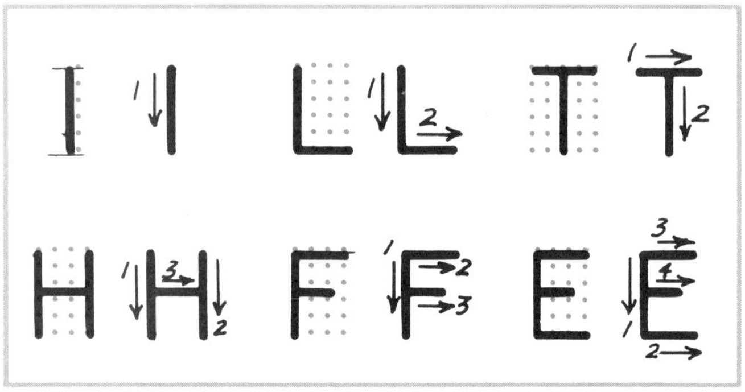

Fig. 1-6. Letters made with vertical and horizontal strokes.

LETTERS FORMED WITH VERTICAL, HORIZONTAL, AND SLANTED LINES

While studying this section, refer to Fig. 1-7.

V. The V is 3 1/2 units wide. The first stroke slants from the upper left side to the middle of the bottom and the second stroke slants from the upper right to the middle of the bottom.

X. Make the first stroke of the X slant from the upper left to the lower right corner. The second stroke slants from the upper right to the lower left and intersects midway between the upper and lower guidelines. It is 3 units wide.

Y. The top of the Y is identical to the top of the X. The two slanted lines begin at the top 3 units apart and intersect with the vertical stem in the middle of the letter.

N. The N, like the H, is 3 1/2 units wide and begins with two vertical stems. The third line slants from the upper left to the lower right.

A. An A is 4 units wide and begins at its midpoint on the top guideline with a slanted line to the lower left. The opposite side slants to the lower right. The crossbar connects the two sides 2 units above the bottom guideline.

Z. The Z is started with two horizontal lines 3 units long. The first is under the top guideline and the other is over the lower guideline. The slanted line connects the upper right and lower left corners.

K. After completing the vertical stem, the upper arm of the K begins 3 units to the right of the stem on the upper guideline and slants back to a point on the stem, 3 units below the top. The lower leg

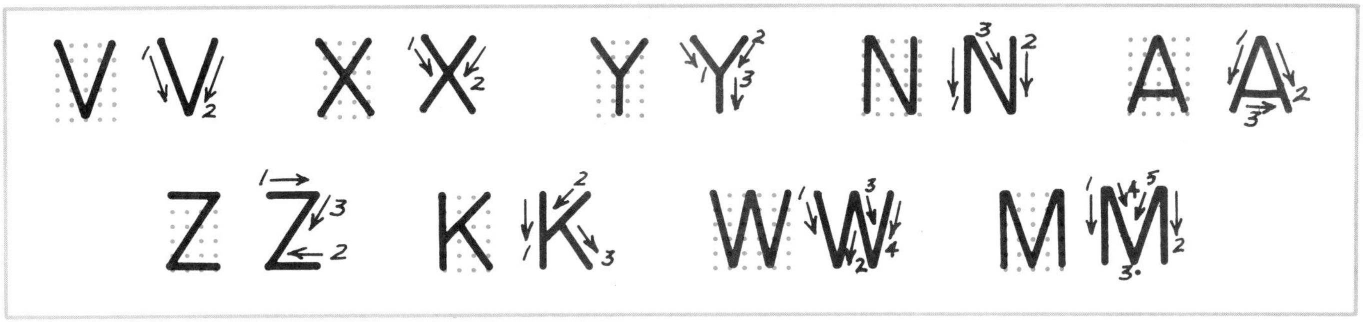

Fig. 1-7. Letters made with slanted strokes.

slants down from the upper arm. The direction of the slant is determined by an imaginary line connecting the top of the stem with a point 3 1/2 units to the right on the bottom guideline.

W. The W is formed by two slightly condensed V's that consume 5 units of width along the top guideline. The slant of sides 1 and 3 are parallel, as are sides 2 and 4.

M. Similar to the H and N, the M has two vertical stems that are made first, and are 4 units apart. Next, a point for the bottom of the V shape is located midway between the two stems and touches the bottom guideline. Connect the top of the stems and the point with two V strokes.

LETTERS FORMED WITH VERTICAL, HORIZONTAL, AND CURVED LINES

While studying this section refer to Fig. 1-8.

J. The J begins at the top and as the downward stroke approaches the bottom guideline it curves smoothly down to the left, touches the guideline, and moves back upward. The curve is 3 units wide and 1 unit high. The J has no top bar.

U. Begin a U at the top with a downward stroke that begins a smooth curve to the right as it approaches the bottom guideline, similar to a backward J shape. The second downward stroke is 3 units to the right and smoothly joins the first stroke on the bottom guideline.

D. The downward stroke of the D is followed by a short horizontal bar on the bottom guideline. The next stroke starts from the top in a horizontal direction, curves smoothly downward to the right until the letter is 3 units wide, and continues to curve until it flows into the bottom bar.

P. After making the vertical stem of the P, a short bar is made slightly below the midpoint between the top and bottom guidelines. The final stroke moves horizontally from the top of the stem, curves downward until the letter is 3 units wide, and continues to curve back to the left until it intersects with the bar and stem.

R. The R begins with a vertical stem, has a short horizontal bar added in the middle, and continues with a smooth upper loop similar to a P. The lower leg connects the loop and the lower guideline. The direction of the leg is determined by an imaginary line between the upper left corner of the letter and a point on the lower guideline, directly below the right side of the loop.

B. Several letters are included within the letter B. The downward stem (I), is followed by the bottom horizontal bar (L), and the top and middle bars (E and F). The upper loop curves smoothly down to the right 3 units wide, continues to curve downward to the left, and flows into the horizontal bar. The lower loop curves down smoothly to the right 3 1/2

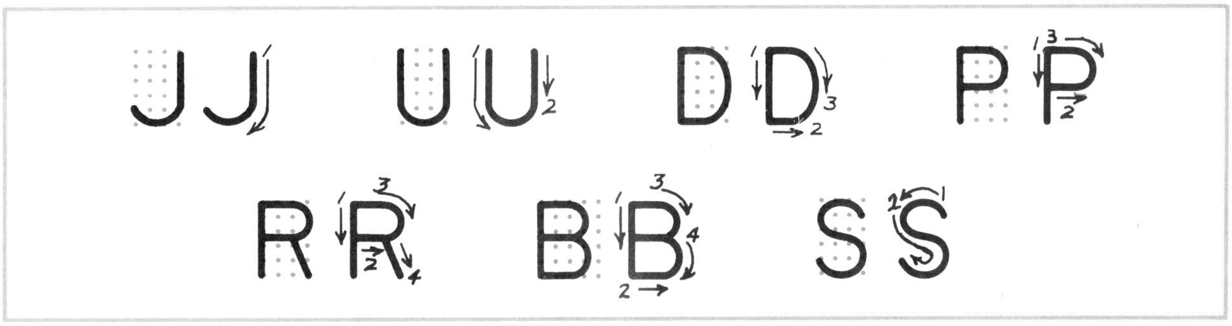

Fig. 1-8. Letters made with curved strokes.

units wide, continues to curve downward to the left, and flows into the horizontal bar on the bottom guideline.

S. The S begins 1 unit below the upper guideline. It curves up and to the left until it touches the upper guideline. Then it curves down to the left 2 1/2 units wide, loops smoothly back towards the center of the letter, swings down to the lower right, loops back toward the lower guideline, and swoops back up forming a letter 3 1/2 units wide.

LETTERS FORMED WITH A CIRCULAR SHAPE

While studying this section, refer to Fig. 1-9.

C. The C begins 1 unit from the top and 3 1/2 units over from where the left side of the letter will be formed. This circular shape curves upward to the left, touches the upper guideline. Then it swings down to the middle of the letter on its left side and back to the lower right, touches the bottom guideline, and swoops back up 1 unit high to form the letter 4 units wide.

G. Make a C for the first part of the G. The center bar is midway between the upper and lower guidelines and is 1 1/2 units long. A downward stroke from the right end of the bar touches the end of the C.

O. Make a C for the first part of the O. Connect the upper right part of the C with a gradual swooping curve down to the right and down to the left until it flows into the C.

Q. Make an O for the first part of the Q. Add a 2 unit long straight line from inside the O, down through the O at the 5 o'clock position, to the lower guideline.

&. The first stroke of the ampersand starts at the top, 2 units to the right. It curves down to the right, swings back to the center 2 units from the top, continues down to the lower left, swoops back to the center at the bottom guideline, and stops 3 1/2 units wide. The second stroke starts at the top, curves down to the left and crosses the first stroke. It continues as a slanted line until it crosses the first stroke again at the 5 o'clock position, and curves to the guideline.

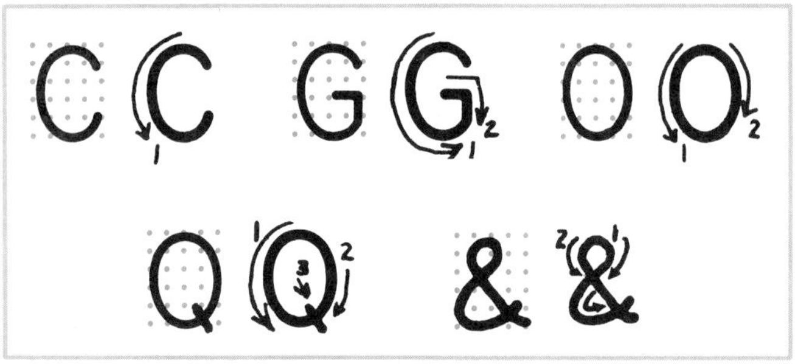

Fig. 1-9. Letters made with circular strokes.

NUMERALS FORMED WITH STRAIGHT LINES

While studying this section, refer to Fig. 1-10.

1. The 1 and the I are both made with a single downward stroke from the inside of the top guideline to the inside of the lower guideline. No top or bottom bars are used.

4. The downward stroke of the 4 begins 3 units in from the left side. The slanted line angles to the left and down 3 1/2 units. The horizontal bar is 1 1/2 units above the bottom guideline and 4 units long.

Fig. 1-10. Numerals made with straight line strokes.

NUMERALS FORMED WITH STRAIGHT AND CURVED LINES

While studying this section, refer to Fig. 1-11.

7. The horizontal bar of the 7 is 3 units long. The stem slants down to the left and then curves down to the center of the numeral on the bottom guideline.

2. The top of the 2 is shaped like the top of an S. It begins 1 unit below the upper guideline, curves up to the right, touches the upper guideline, curves back down, and swings down to the lower guideline somewhat like a question mark. The horizontal base is 3 units long.

5. The first stroke of the numeral 5 is a horizontal line 2 1/2 units long from right to left followed by a nearly vertical stem 2 units down. A smoothly rounded bottom stroke 3 units tall and 3 units wide completes it.

NUMERALS FORMED WITH A CIRCULAR SHAPE

While studying this section, refer to Fig. 1-12.

3. The upper curved shape of the numerical 3 begins one unit below the top, curves up to the right, touches the upper guideline, swings back down and around, and stops 2 units below and 1 unit to the right of the starting point. The lower curved shape swings down to the right, down to the left, touches the bottom guideline, and curves up to the left forming a loop 3 1/2 units wide and 3 units high.

6. The first stroke of the numeral 6 starts with the letter C. The second stroke begins in the mid-

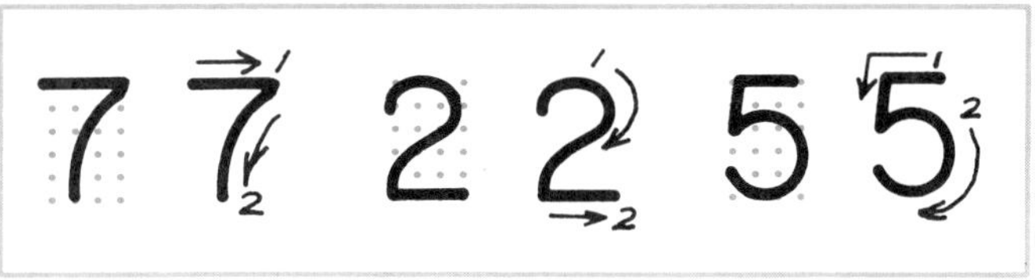

Fig. 1-11. Numerals using curved line strokes.

dle of the C, arcs up to the right, 3 units high, down to the right, and down to the left until it flows into a C.

9. The first stoke of the numeral 9 starts with a backward C. The second stroke begins on the top end of the backward C, arcs down to the right, 3 units from the top, and up to the right until it connects with the middle of the backward C.

8. Start the numeral 8 at the top with an ellipse that is 3 units wide and 2 units tall. This stroke curves down to the left, down to the right, up to the right, and finishes up to the left. Start the lower ellipse at the lower middle point of the upper ellipse. It is 3 1/2 units wide and 3 units tall. This stroke is similar to the first one except it is larger.

0. The 0 is made with a letter C, 3 units wide for the first stroke. The second stroke begins on the top end of the C, curves down to the right and back to the left, and flows into the bottom end of the C.

FRACTIONS

The numerals in whole numbers and numerals in fractions are the same height, Fig. 1-13. The line separating the numerator and denominator of a fraction should go the same direction as the guidelines for the numerals. The length of this line should be the same as the widest part of the fraction. A space must be left between the fraction numerals and the line separating them.

SPACING LETTERS INTO WORDS AND NUMERALS INTO NUMBERS

After having become familiar with the basic shape of each character, the next step to good lettering technique is spacing the letters into words and the numerals into numbers.

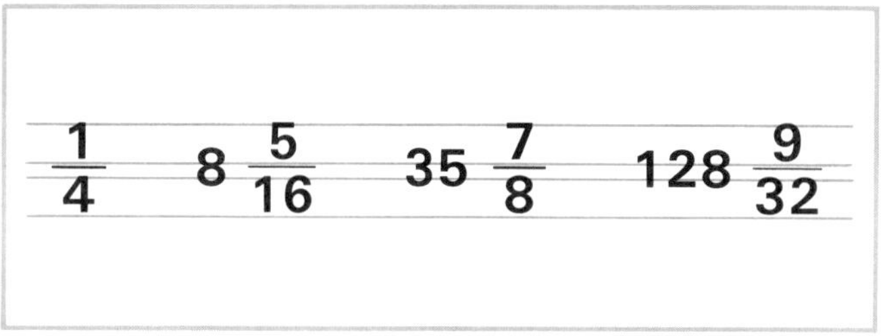

Fig. 1-13. Numerals used as fractions. Note that lettering fractions requires two pairs of guidelines.

In general, the characters within words and numbers should "look equally spaced" and be positioned as close to one another as possible without coming in contact. The space between words should be the same as the letter height. These general rules group words and numbers together to improve the speed and accuracy of their interpretation, Fig. 1-14.

The shapes of the individual characters has an effect on how closely they are placed together. Characters may be "closed" (H), "circular" (O), or "open" (T). The following discussion will help you to fine tune the spacing between letters in words and numerals in numbers.

SPACING BETWEEN CHARACTERS THAT ARE CLOSED

A rectangular open space is left between characters that are closed. In a word such as HIM, the distance between the letters is the same from the top to the bottom. To make the word easy to read, a distance of 1 1/2 units is needed between the letters H, I, and M as shown in Fig. 1-15. This same amount of open space should appear to exist between all characters of all words and numbers. The distance between numerals in a number such as 111 is also 1 1/2 units. Remember — place 1 1/2 units between closed characters.

SPACING BETWEEN CHARACTERS THAT ARE CIRCULAR

In comparison, a variable amount of open space is left between characters with circular shapes. In

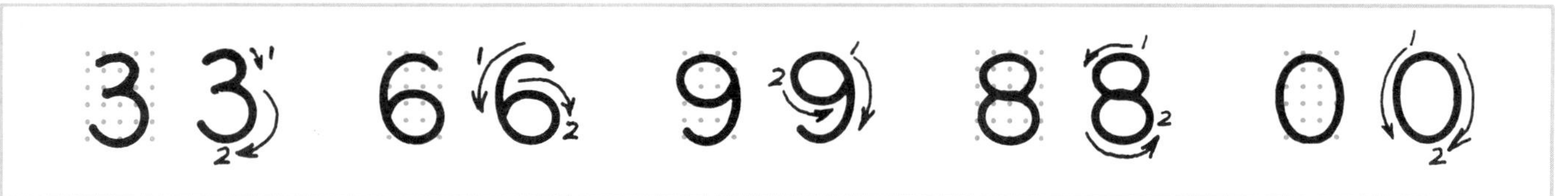

Fig. 1-12. Numerals using circular line strokes.

Fig. 1-14. Space letters so they appear as words.

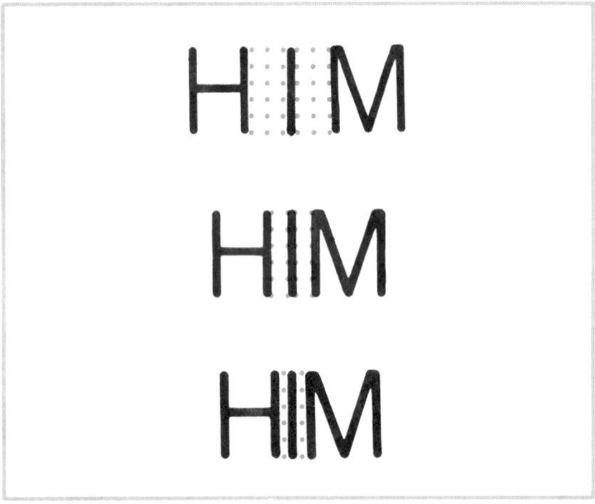

Fig. 1-15. The middle example of the word HIM is spaced best by using 1 1/2 units between letters.

a word, such as DOG, the distance between the letters is several units apart at the top, less than one unit apart in the middle, and several units apart again at the bottom, Fig. 1-16. The amount of open space between the letters of the words HIM and DOG should look the same. In a number such as 906, the amount of open space between the numerals should look the same as the amount of open space between the letters in the word DOG. Remember — place less than one unit between the middle of circular characters.

SPACING BETWEEN CHARACTERS THAT ARE OPEN

Open characters differ in many ways. For example, some are open at the top (A), some at the bottom (T), some in the middle (X), and others on one side (L). In a word such as LAVA, the L and the A must be very close to minimize the amount of open space between them, Fig. 1-17. Since the open spaces between the A, V, and A are parallel, the letters may slightly overlap each other to look equally spaced. The A and T in the word AT may also overlap to make the spacing look equal. Remember — the spacing for open characters is dependent upon your ability to compensate for the shape of the letter.

SPACING IN GENERAL

The key to spacing is to make the letters "look" as equally spaced as possible, Fig. 1-18. Practice lettering your name until each letter appears to be equally spaced. A space equal to the height of the letters will separate your first, middle, and last names. You may also want to practice lettering the name of your school or other information that will appear frequently on your drawing assignments. The vertical space between lines of lettering should be from 1/2 the height to full height of the lettering.

Professional looking lettering has a positive affect on all of your sketching and drawing activities.

PROBLEMS AND GRADING CRITERIA

The quality of your lettering has an impact on the professional appearance of your drawings. By completing the first three lettering practice sheets, you

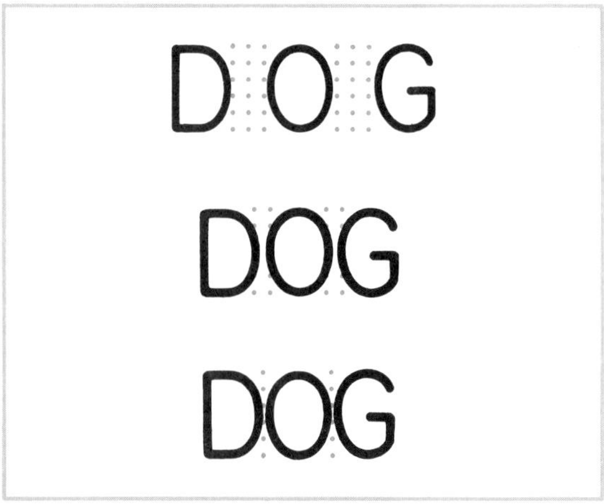

Fig. 1-16. The middle example of the word DOG is spaced best by using 1 unit between the middle of the letters.

Fig. 1-17. The middle example of the word LAVA is spaced best.

will learn the shapes of each character and begin to repeat them consistently. Refer to the illustrations and descriptions of each character so the proportions are accurate. After making letters accurately, practice spacing the letters into professional looking words.

Periodically, you may decide to repeat these practice sheets to improve your accuracy, consistency, and speed. As was mentioned earlier, your lettering accuracy should improve from about 1 letter in 4, to as many as 9 out of 10, or even better. Your ability to consistently space letters will also improve with practice until it becomes almost automatic. In addition, your speed should be expected to improve to about 30 letters per minute.

Practice lettering the words in your favorite songs, sayings, slogans, or poetry. The more you practice, the better your lettering becomes. After lettering for a few minutes your hand and arm may become tired. While resting, review your work and identify each of your best letters or words with a small dot. These dots above your letters and words may help your instructor to see your best work as it is evaluated.

Your work is evaluated on the following criteria:

1. Guidelines are light and accurately spaced.
2. Letters and words fit consistently between the guidelines.
3. Each letter and numeral is shaped with the proper strokes.
4. Letters and numerals are proportioned as in the illustrations and descriptions.
5. Letters and numbers are spaced so the words and numerals are grouped in a professional manner.
6. The accuracy and speed of your lettering technique is improved.

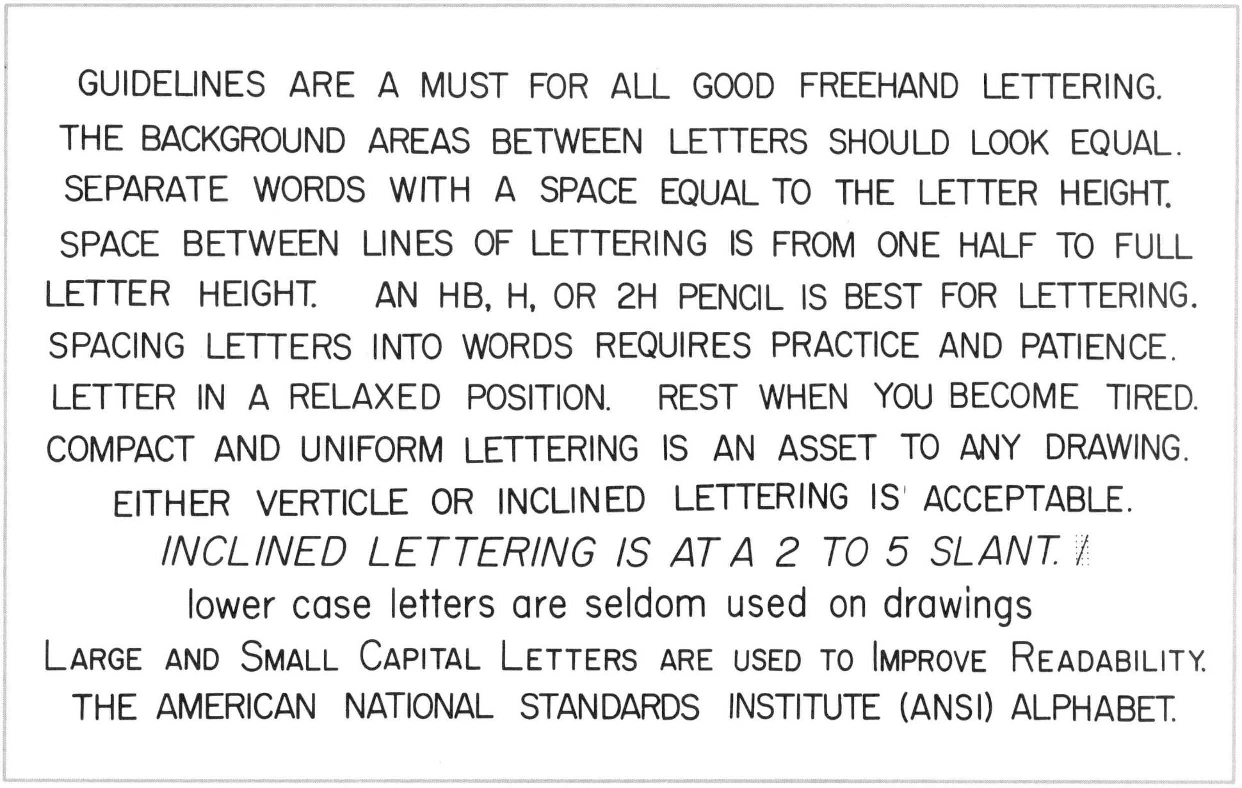

GUIDELINES ARE A MUST FOR ALL GOOD FREEHAND LETTERING.
THE BACKGROUND AREAS BETWEEN LETTERS SHOULD LOOK EQUAL.
SEPARATE WORDS WITH A SPACE EQUAL TO THE LETTER HEIGHT.
SPACE BETWEEN LINES OF LETTERING IS FROM ONE HALF TO FULL
LETTER HEIGHT. AN HB, H, OR 2H PENCIL IS BEST FOR LETTERING.
SPACING LETTERS INTO WORDS REQUIRES PRACTICE AND PATIENCE.
LETTER IN A RELAXED POSITION. REST WHEN YOU BECOME TIRED.
COMPACT AND UNIFORM LETTERING IS AN ASSET TO ANY DRAWING.
EITHER VERTICLE OR INCLINED LETTERING IS ACCEPTABLE.
INCLINED LETTERING IS AT A 2 TO 5 SLANT.
lower case letters are seldom used on drawings
LARGE AND SMALL CAPITAL LETTERS ARE USED TO IMPROVE READABILITY.
THE AMERICAN NATIONAL STANDARDS INSTITUTE (ANSI) ALPHABET.

Fig. 1-18. Clear and concise lettering used with accurate spacing between letters and words produces very professional looking drawings.

Chapter 1—LETTERING
Review What You Have Learned

Write your answers on a separate sheet of paper. Do not write in this textbook.

Essay:

1. Write a short, concise statement describing why good lettering is important on a drawing.

Multiple Choice: Carefully study each group of letters displayed below and select the letter made incorrectly. Mark the (a.b.c.d.e.) choice for the incorrect letter.

2. a. A b. D c. E d. K e. O
3. a. R b. I c. T d. S e. U
4. a. B b. C c. X d. Y e. J
5. a. G b. H c. V d. N e. P
6. a. Z b. L c. M d. W e. Q
7. a. E b. R c. K d. I e. B
8. a. J b. C c. Y d. G e. N
9. a. M b. S c. A d. W e. D

Carefully study each group of numbers displayed below and select the numeral made incorrectly. Mark the (a.b.c.d.e.) choice for the incorrect letter.

10. a. 2 b. 4 c. 5 d. 8 e. 1
11. a. 3 b. 7 c. 0 d. 9 e. 6
12. a. 7 b. 2 c. 8 d. 3 e. 0
13. a. 4 b. 6 c. 9 d. 5 e. 1

True or False: Carefully read the statements below. Write a "T" on your answer sheet for the statements which are true. For the statements which are false, write a "F." Rewrite each false statement so it becomes true.

14. Good lettering gives a drawing a professional appearance. True or False?
15. Good lettering is dependent upon accurate letters and appropriate spacing. True or False?
16. Guidelines are optional for good lettering. True or False?
17. When pencil lettering is not dark, use a harder pencil. True or False?
18. A mixed number has numerals of all the same height. True or False?
19. Letters in a word should look equally spaced. True or False?

Completion: After studying this chapter, read the incomplete sentences below. Write the missing word or words on your answer sheet.

20. ________ is always left between lines of lettering.
21. Professional looking lettering is done with a/an ________ hardness pencil.
22. ________ lead is used for guidelines and ________ lead is used for lettering.
23. Lettering speed and accuracy is improved with ________.
24. Most lettering on a drawing is ________ high.
25. The narrowest letter is the ________ and the widest is the ________.

Practice What You Have Learned: On a 8 1/2 x 11 inch sheet of paper with 1/8 inch guidelines, carefully letter the following statements from this text for developing good lettering techniques.

"APPLIED SKETCHING AND DRAFTING introduces you to the basic concepts and skills used in industry to communicate ideas and to produce engineering drawings." (Introduction to the textbook.)

"New information builds upon prior knowledge to simplify learning and to help you fully understand each concept." (Introduction to the textbook.)

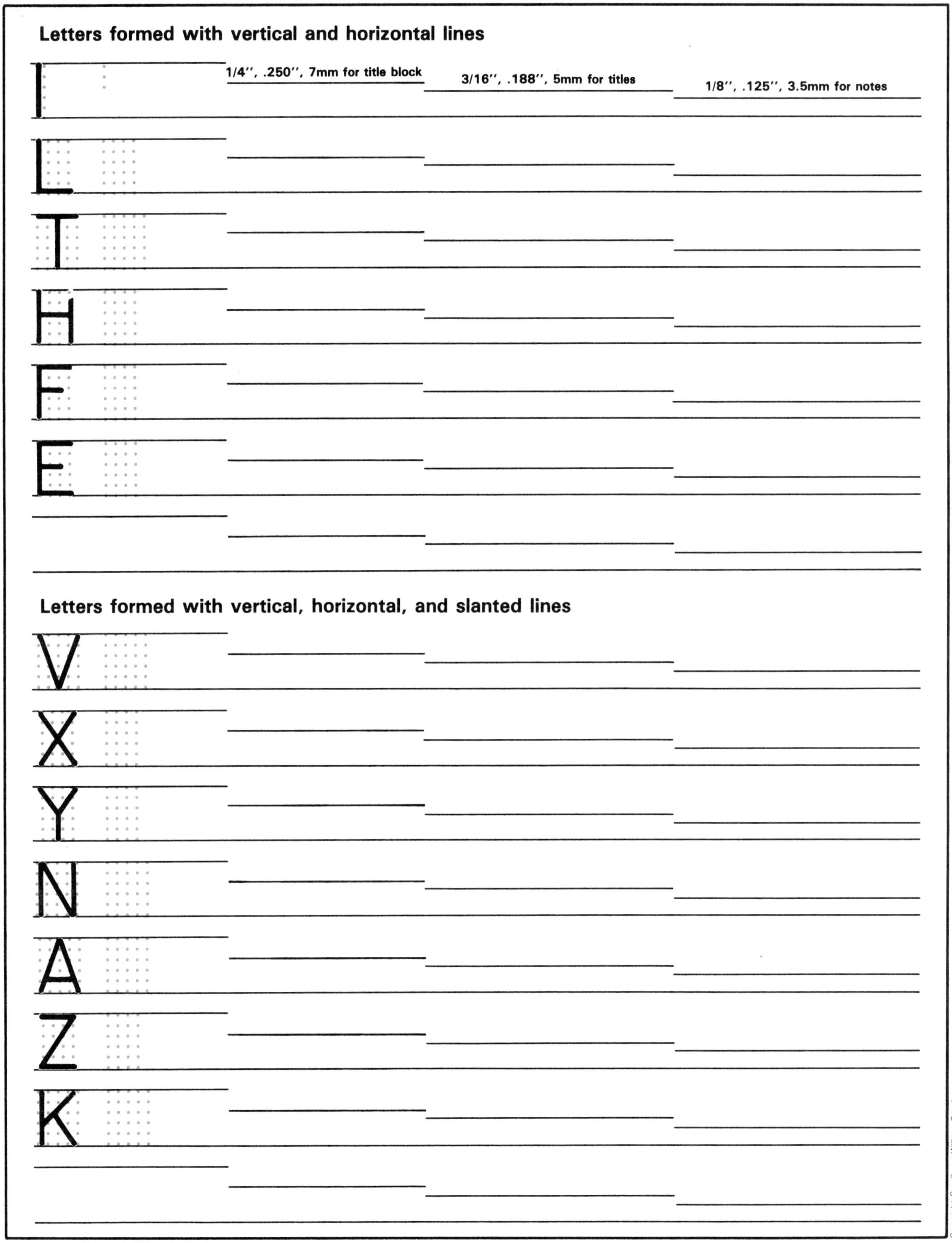

1-1 FORMING LETTERS. Study the examples of each of the letters provided for your practice. The dots indicate each letters' width and proportion. Carefully repeat each letter several times on a separate sheet of paper until you are accurate. Using narrower guidelines, practice making smaller letters. Strive for consistency.

W

M

Letters formed with vertical, horizontal, and curved lines

J

U

D

P

R

B

S

Letters formed with a circular shape

C

G

O

Q

&

1-2 FORMING LETTERS. Study the examples in this exercise. The dots indicate the proper width and proportion for each of the letters. On a separate sheet of paper, copy these guidelines and carefully practice forming each of these letters. Shape each letter with accuracy and consistency.

Numerals formed with straight lines

1

4

Numerals formed with straight and curved lines

7

2

5

Numerals formed with a circular shape

3

6

9

8

0

FRACTIONS: The numerals used for whole numbers and fractions are the same size. The horizontal line separating the numerals in a fraction is the same length as the widest number in the fraction.

$2\frac{3}{4}$ $10\frac{7}{8}$ $5\frac{9}{16}$

1-3 SKETCHING NUMERALS. The dots have been added to show you the proper width and proportion of the numerals. Repeat making each of the numeals several times to gain accuracy. Practice forming the numerals between the guidelines provided.

1-4 LETTERING PRACTICE. On an 8 1/2 x 11 sheet of paper, add the guidelines shown in this exercise and practice lettering the information in Fig. 1-18 of this text. Concentrate on shaping the letters accurately and spacing the letters and words consistently.

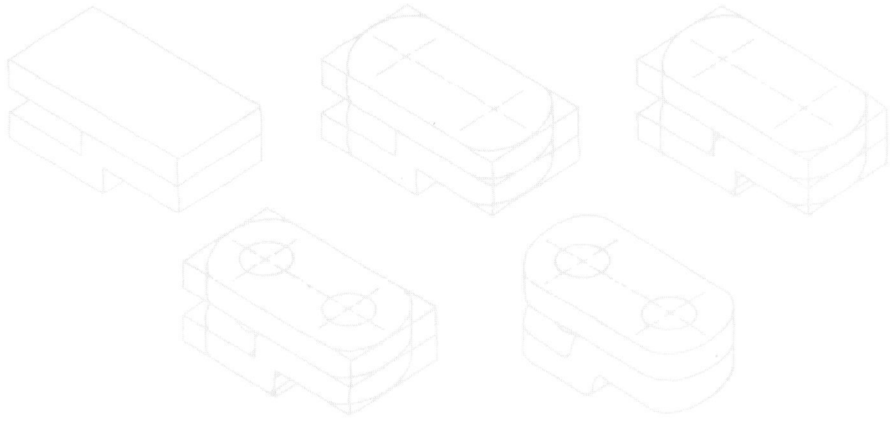

Chapter 2

SKETCHING

OBJECTIVES

After completing this SKETCHING chapter, you will be able to:

- ☐ *Sketch straight lines of uniform width.*
- ☐ *Sketch curved lines consistently and smoothly.*
- ☐ *Estimate distances so that you can sketch proportions which look right on paper.*
- ☐ *Maintain parallel relationships between lines.*
- ☐ *Sketch pictorial views.*
- ☐ *Sketch multiview projections.*
- ☐ *Sketch solutions to pictorial and multiview projection problems.*

One of the most valuable skills you will develop in drafting is the ability to sketch parts and products. A sketch is a drawing made freehand. Being able to sketch with confidence and competence, you will be able to communicate your ideas clearly. Just as you would express ideas to a friend in a conversation or a letter, you are going to learn to express product ideas or concepts by sketching a ''picture'' of it. Sketching is a graphic language which allows you to create, develop, and communicate ideas so they can be discussed, changed, and approved, Fig. 2-1. Architects, engineers, and designers rely upon sketching to communicate their ideas as they create buildings, bridges, automobiles, and millions of other industrial parts and products, Fig. 2-2.

As your sketching skills develop, you will be using this tool to communicate your design ideas. As your sketching skills improve, you will find sketching product ideas much easier than trying to communicate them in words.

Fig. 2-1. Most drawings start out as sketches of ideas.

FUNDAMENTALS OF SKETCHING

Sketching industrial objects requires several important skills and techniques. Four basic skills you will learn in this chapter include the following:

1. *Neatness* leaves a positive impression on those with whom you are communicating. Neat and organized sketches will communicate directly, with a minimum of clutter.
2. *Straight lines* need to be sketched with accuracy and with consistency. The value of good line work cannot be overemphasized.
3. *Curved lines* need to be sketched so they appear smooth and blend into an accurate portrait of the object being described.
4. *Proportion* allows you to communicate the size relationship of the object. It is very important that your sketching ability include the skill to make your drawings represent the true length, width, or height.

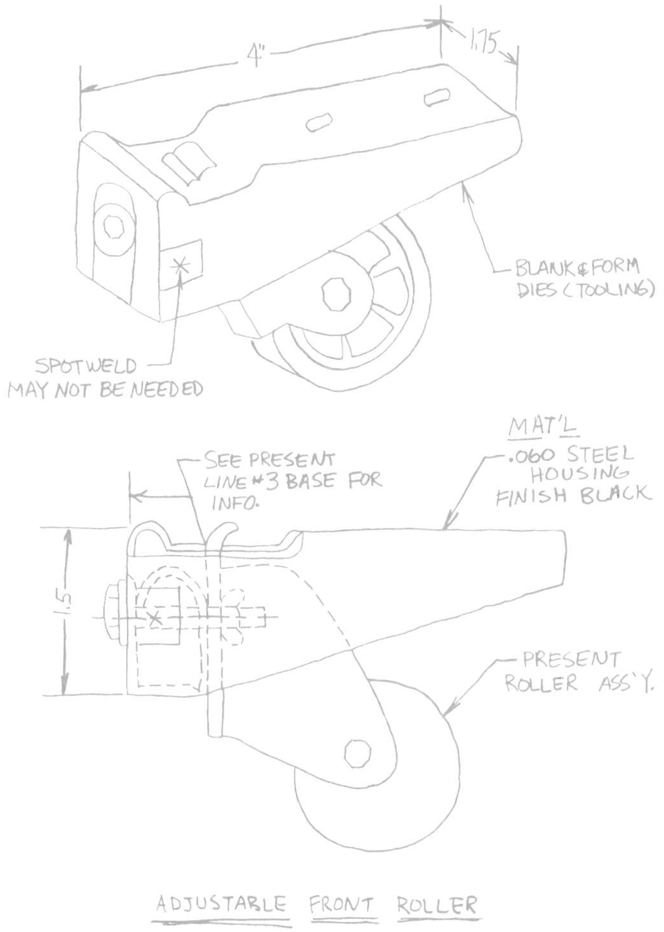

Fig. 2-2. Products such as this design for an adjustable front roller are created from sketches.

This fourth skill includes the locating and arranging of lines and curves to create an accurate image of an object. For example, rectangular objects may be divided into cubes to estimate distances and maintain relative proportions, Fig. 2-3.

A three dimensional object has length, height, and depth. The object can be represented as three flat views or as one pictorial view. It is usually easier to start sketching with a pictorial view since this is the way we see real objects. A variety of pictorial views may be used. One of the best is the isometric. **Isometric** sketches position the object with a front corner toward you. Upright edges are sketched as vertical lines. All of the horizontal lines are sketched at 30 degree angles. Refer to Fig. 2-4. It looks good and is relatively easy to complete.

After sketching a rough isometric view of an object, it will become simpler to visualize and sketch its individual surfaces. The front view, top view, and side view illustrate every flat surface seen in the pictorial. A complete sketch of the flat surfaces of an object normally includes the front view, the top view (which appears directly above the front view) and the side view placed either to the right or left of the front view). Fig. 2-5. This arrangement of the three views is called a **multiview sketch.**

Drawings are often made in this multiview arrangement. This method is commonly known as orthographic projection. **Orthographic projection** refers to the process of extending the lines of the object outward to show the exact size and shape of the surfaces of the object. This technique allows

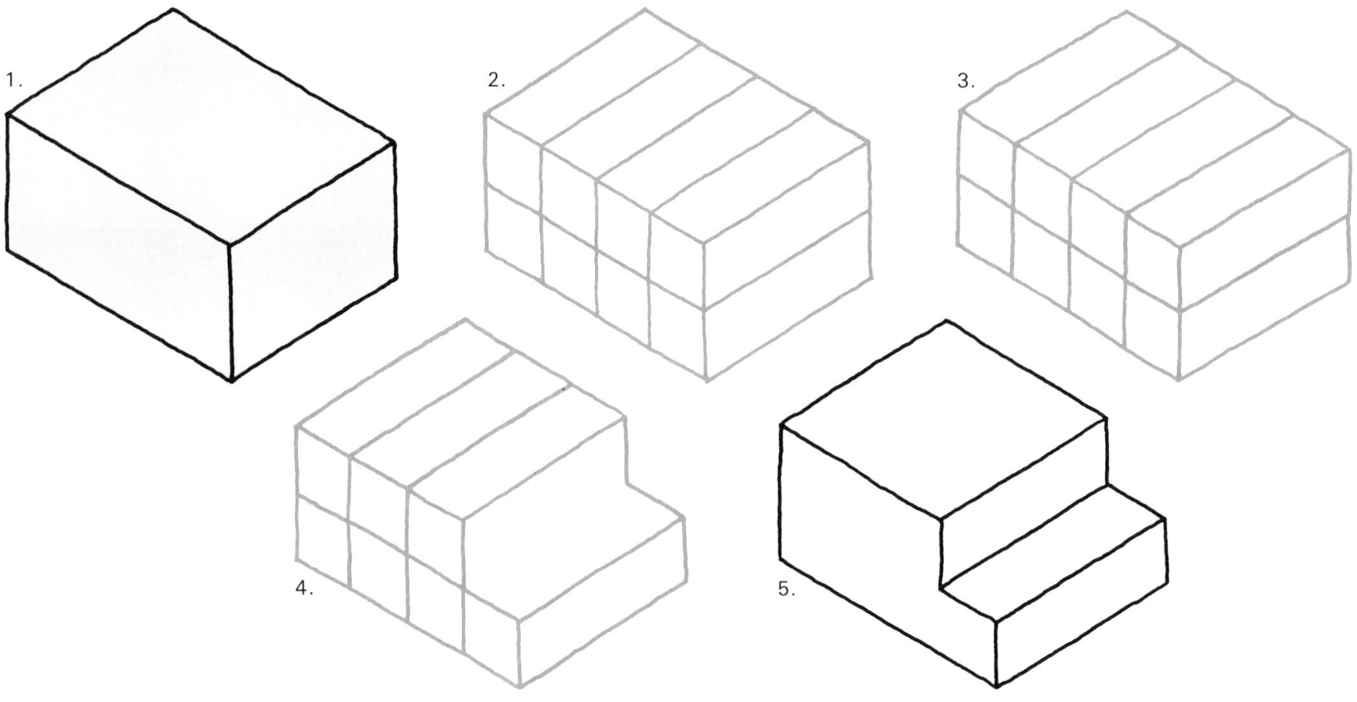

Fig. 2-3. Begin sketching pictorials with a rectangular cube.

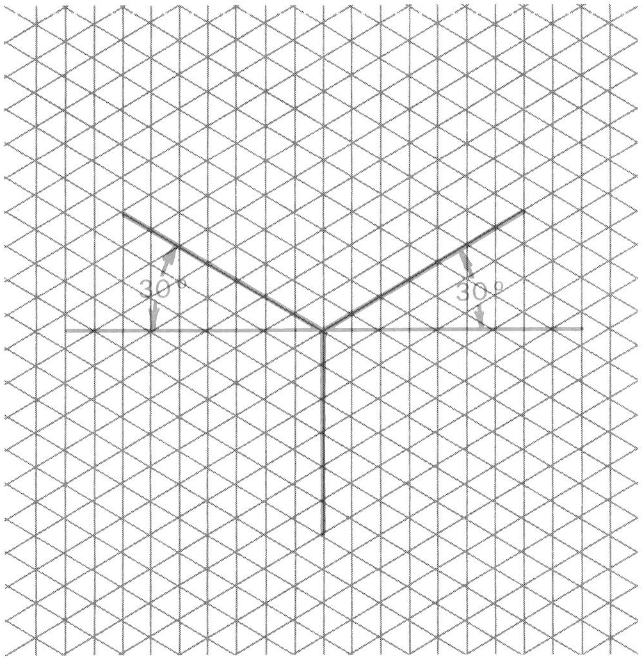

Fig. 2-4. Visualize the isometric axis to develop pictorial sketches.

you to look at the object from six different directions: front, top, right side, left side, bottom, and back. To clearly visualize an object in three dimensions, an isometric sketch may be necessary. Even though sketching it may take a few minutes, it will probably save you time overall and help you avoid mistakes. The more you sketch, the more you will improve. As you improve you can expect people to begin to admire your work.

Family of Lines

Lines vary in width and may be solid or broken to provide a special meaning, Fig. 2-6. Whether sketched or drawn, lines go through a light layout stage and a final stage where the lines are made sharp, crisp, and distinctive.

Object lines are the most commonly used. These lines make up the edges of objects. They are the same width as lines made with a standard ball point pen. **Border lines** are solid lines, thicker than object lines and used to frame your drawing. **Cutting-plane** and **reference lines** are broken in a ''long-short-short-long'' sequence. These lines are also thicker than object lines.

Other lines are thinner than object lines. Included in this group are the following:

1. **Centerlines** are broken in a ''long-short-long'' sequence. They are used to indicate the center or balance of an object.
2. **Hidden lines** are dashed and are used to indicate surfaces not seen in a straight-on view.
3. **Extension, dimension,** and **leader lines** are used in dimensioning.
4. **Section lines** are used to represent different materials.
5. **Guidelines** assist the drafter in placing lettering on a drawing. They are always made very lightly — just dark enough to see for lettering.

SKETCHING STRAIGHT LINES

Straight lines are used in laying out the basic shape of an object being sketched pictorially. Sloping straight lines may represent other planes of the pictorial sketch.

Straight lines are also used for object lines, border lines, centerlines, extension lines, dimension lines, leaders, cutting-plane lines, section-lining lines, reference lines, guidelines for lettering, and lines to divide a drawing up into different zones, etc. It is important to make these lines accurately and quickly.

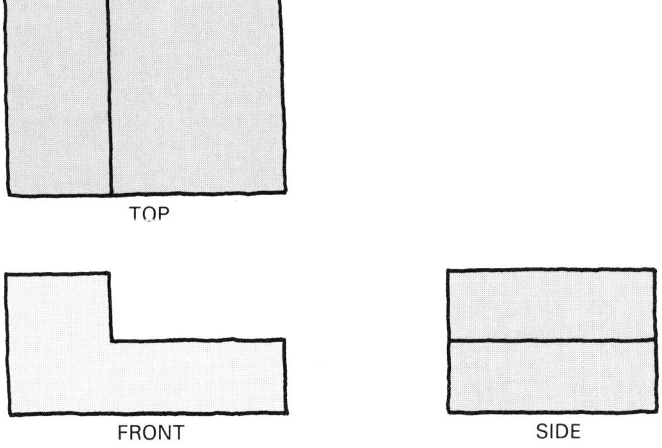

Fig. 2-5. Position the top, front, and side views of a multiview sketch as shown.

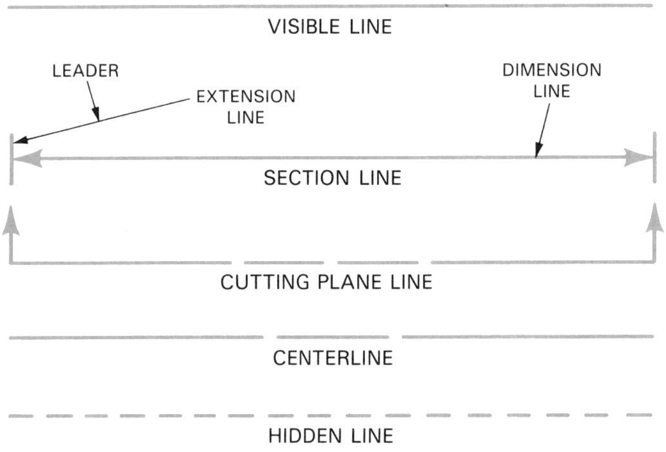

Fig. 2-6. Lines vary in width and spacing to provide special meaning. This is also known as the family of lines or the alphabet of lines.

Straight lines are also used when laying out multiview projections of an object. Using straight horizontal and vertical lines keeps the views arranged properly.

Practice making straight lines. Your work will be slow at first, as you need to concentrate on neatness and accuracy. As your eye-hand coordination improves, your speed should increase. The three elements of neatness, accuracy, and speed are very important in sketching.

Sketching Along a Straight Edge

Adding a border line makes a sketch look professional. Only a few seconds are needed to complete it. A pencil, paper, flat surface, and a straightedge (clip board, counter top, desk, or drawing board) are needed.

Hold the edge of the paper securely to the flat surface parallel to the straightedge, Fig. 2-7. With the other hand, hold the pencil firmly between the thumb, pointer, and middle finger.

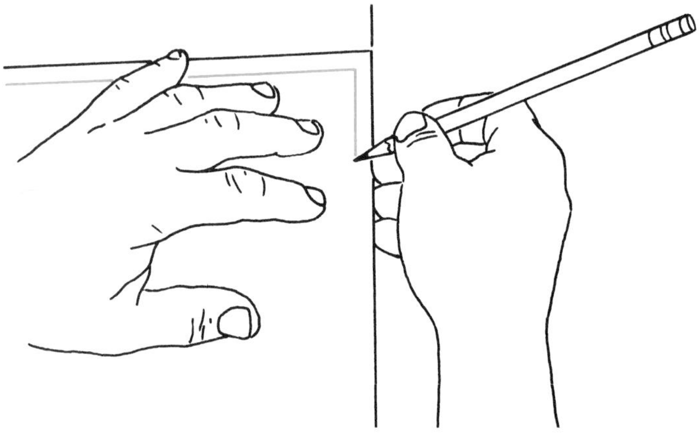

Fig. 2-7. Border lines may be sketched using the edge of a table as an aid.

Place the end of your middle finger against the straightedge with the inside of your hand facing upward as shown. Adjust the length of the pencil over the paper until you have the desired margin. Using the middle finger as a guide, pull the pencil down the paper. Turn the paper and repeat the procedure for the second, third, and fourth border lines. Uniform line width may be achieved by repeating the process.

Sketching Long Lines Between Two Points

To sketch long lines, use the following procedure for consistent straight lines:

1. Estimate where the line will start and finish.
2. Indicate the starting and finishing points with dots.

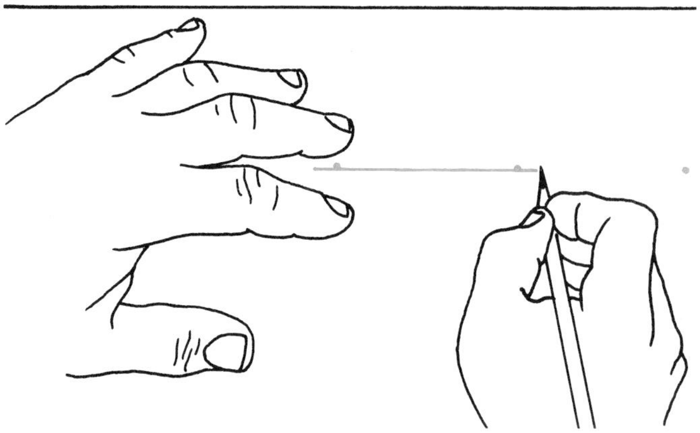

Fig. 2-8. Long, straight lines may be sketched by using the dot to dot technique.

3. Visualize the path of the line and place additional dots between the starting and finishing points. The width of about three fingers is a good distance to space additional dots.
4. Place your pencil at the starting point. Look at the next dot and sketch a line to this second dot without looking at your pencil. Repeat this process, as in Fig. 2-8, until you reach the end of the line.

Improve the line as needed by erasing the poorest sections and reconnecting the dots. Again, use short overlapping strokes to make the line look professional.

Sketching with Short Overlapping Strokes

First, sketch a short straight line about as long as the nail of your little finger. Then, return to the middle of the first line and make a similar second short, straight line. Repeat this overlapping of short line segments until the line is as long as needed, Fig. 2-9.

You will soon be able to make these short, overlapping strokes at a rate of two or three per second. Most good sketchers use this technique.

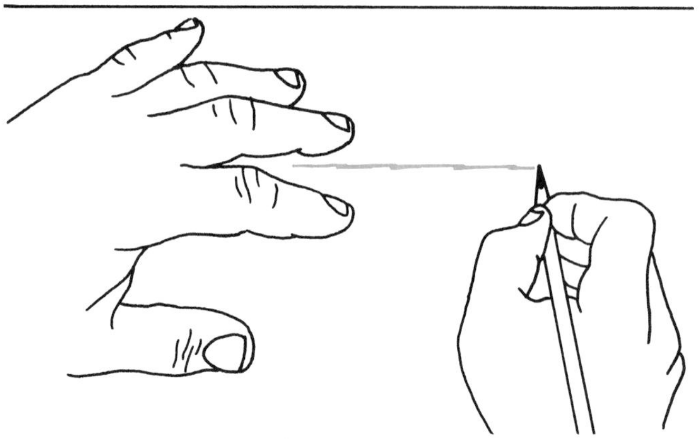

Fig. 2-9. Sketching lines with short, overlapping strokes.

Remember, sketch lightly at first so you can erase and resketch crooked lines.

Sketching Parallel Lines

Parallel line relationships must be maintained when sketching isometric and multiview drawings.

Horizontal and vertical parallel lines are commonly used in multiview projections to position the top and side views. Two other sets of parallel lines are needed in sketching pictorial views in isometric. One set of parallel lines slopes upward 30 degrees to the right. The other set of parallel lines slopes upward 30 degrees to the left. Refer back to Fig. 2-4.

Here is a useful hint for sketching isometric guidelines. You can estimate 30 degrees from horizontal by visualizing the hands on a clock. When one hand points toward the ''2,'' it forms a plane that slants approximately 30 degrees upward to the right. When the hand points to the ''10,'' it forms a line slanting upward about 30 degrees to the left.

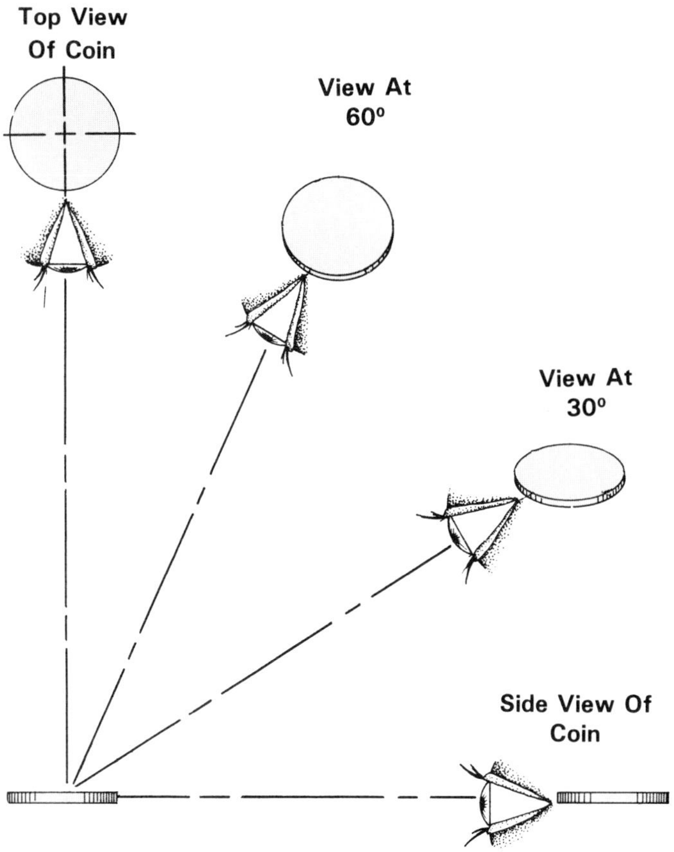

Fig. 2-10. A round surface may appear as a line, an ellipse, or a circle depending on your point of view.

SKETCHING CURVED LINES

Circular and elliptical shapes are often more difficult to sketch than straight lines. Circular shapes illustrate holes and cylinders in industrial parts and products when they are viewed ''straight on.'' However, when holes and cylinders are viewed from a position other than ''straight on,'' they appear elliptical (egg shaped).

For example, a silver dollar lying at your feet would appear round. If you walked away from the silver dollar at your feet and viewed it from an angle, its appearance would change from a circle shape to an elliptical shape. A ''bug's-eye'' view of the same coin would appear as a rectangle or a straight line. Refer to Fig. 2-10.

Sketching Circles

A circle is a series of points placed all the way around a center point. Each point is the same distance from the center point. This distance from the center point to the circle is known as the radius.

To sketch a circle, first locate the center point. Then, add vertical and horizontal centerlines. Estimate a distance from the center point and mark the radius along each side of the centerlines (left, right, top, and bottom). Refer to Fig. 2-11.

Place your pencil on the first mark. Look at the second mark and sketch the arc without looking at your pencil. Continue the same procedure around the circle. It is helpful to use your small finger as a pivot during this procedure.

Remember to keep all of your lines light at first so they can be easily erased. Resketch to improve the shape of the circle. For larger circles, place additional radius marks around the center point.

Sketching Ellipses

An ellipse has a center point, the same as a circle. The centerlines of an ellipse are not at right angles.

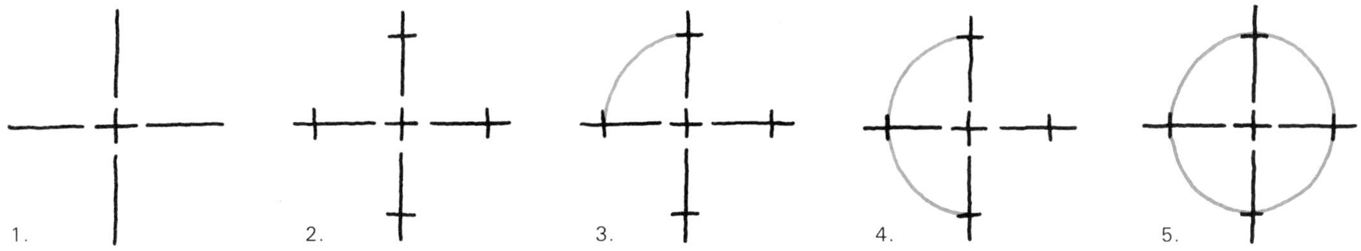

Fig. 2-11. Circles have four equally shaped arcs.

Just as you viewed the silver dollar on the floor from an angle, the centerlines of an ellipse are at an angle. Instead of having one round shape as a circle, an ellipse has two curved shapes smoothly connected between the centerlines.

To help you visualize an ellipse, think of a perfect circle made of stiff wire. This wire circle has horizontal and vertical rods connected to the circle and running through the center point. These rods have a fixed length which is the radius and which can slide along the outside of the stiff wire circle. Now, slide these right angle centerlines representing the radius into an angles position.

Next, keeping the upright centerlines in place, slide the horizontal radius into an angled position. Drop the horizontal radius from the 3 o'clock position to the 4 o'clock position. On the other side of the shape, the radius moves from the 9 o'clock position to the 10 o'clock spot. Moving the centerline into an ellipse orientation causes the wire to bulge outward around the 5 o'clock and 11 o'clock positions and pull inward around the 2 o'clock and 8 o'clock positions. This will help you visualize the formation of an ellipse.

Prepare to sketch an ellipse by locating and marking a center point. Add two centerlines as shown in Fig. 2-12. Isometric ellipses have one vertical centerline and one centerline either slanted 4 o'clock — 10 o'clock or slanted 8 o'clock — 2 o'clock. Estimate and mark equal distances away from the center point in all four directions. Sketch bulged curved shapes in the quadrants where the centerlines are close together. Sketch straighter curved shapes where the centerlines have been stretched apart. Darken the elliptical shape with short, overlapping strokes so all four shapes flow together smoothly.

SKETCHING PICTORIAL VIEWS

There are many different types of pictorial views. One of the quickest to sketch and easiest to visualize is an isometric view. Isometric means ''equal measure'' and the equal measure relates to the equal angle between the three principal axes. One axis is vertical, the second is inclined 30 degrees to the right, and the third is inclined 30 degrees to the left. Refer back to Fig. 2-4.

Pictorial views are much like photographs of objects seen in real life. The primary advantage of sketching pictorial views is they are easier to visualize and understand. The primary disadvantage is they may be difficult to sketch until some basic procedures are learned and practiced.

An isometric sketch has lines in only three directions. To learn how to sketch pictorial views, follow the discussion below. First, locate a starting point. This point is slightly below and a little to the right of the center of the drawing space, Fig. 2-13. From this point, drop a line vertically down 2 units long. Estimate a unit as the width of the nail on your little finger. Next, sketch a line 3 units long from the starting point inclined 30 degrees to the right. Now, sketch a line 4 units long from the starting point inclined 30 degrees to the left. These three lines represent the isometric axes and will be used repeatedly. Mark the unit lengths on each line for future reference.

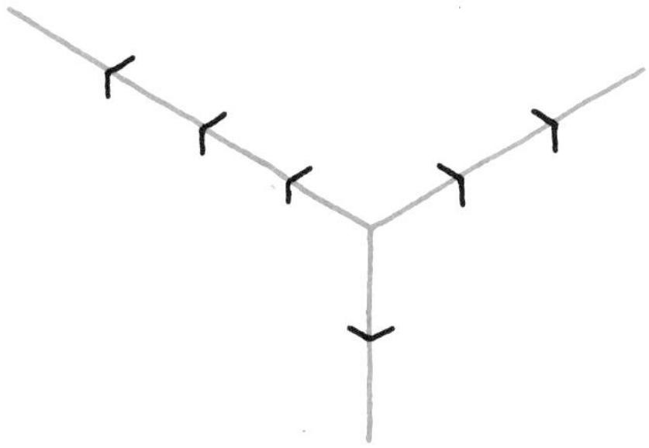

Fig. 2-13. An isometric corner has three sets of lines sketched in three directions to show length, height, and depth.

Sketching a Basic Isometric Cube

To sketch a cube, drop a vertical line from the end of each inclined line, 2 units long. Refer to Fig. 2-14. Then, sketch two lines inclined 30 degrees to the right, 2 units long. Finally, add two lines inclined 30 degrees to the left, 2 units long.

You should have three sets of parallel sides and each set should be the same length. If it looks like a cube, darken the cube with short, overlapping

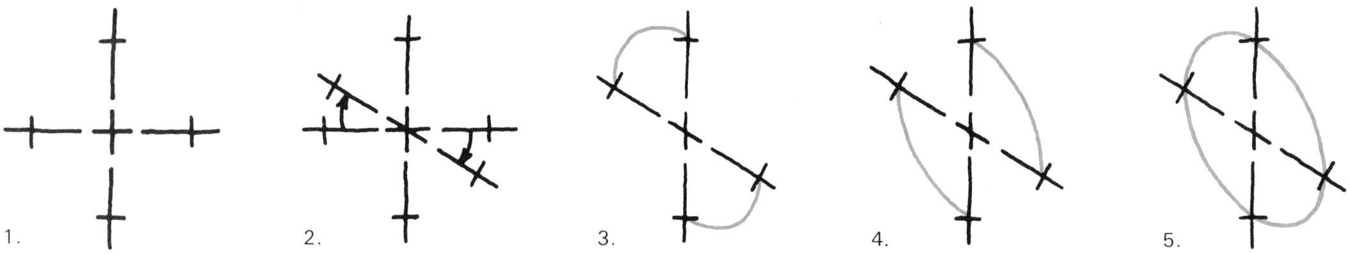

Fig. 2-12. Ellipses have pairs of stretched and bulged arcs.

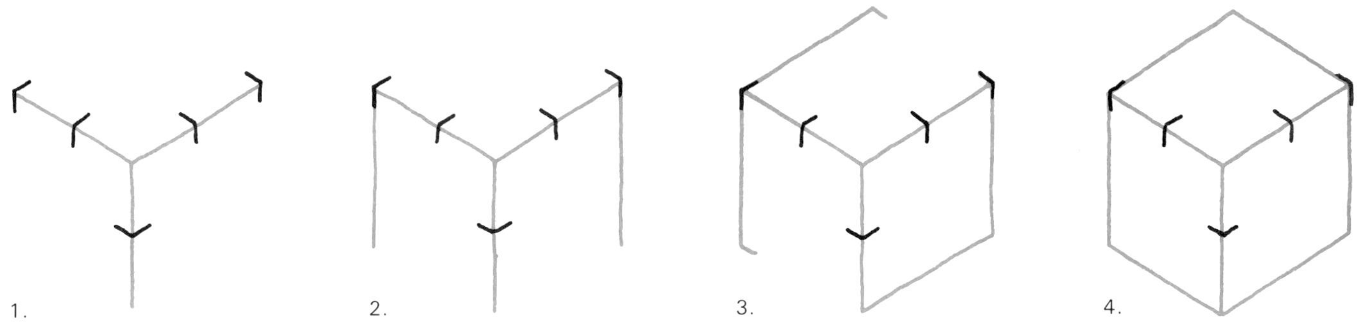

Fig. 2-14. An isometric cube has three sets of equal length lines sketched on the isometric axes.

strokes. If something looks wrong, try sliding a pencil across the page parallel to each of the three axes to check for parallel line relationships. Erase inaccurate lines. Then correct your sketch and darken the lines.

Sketching a Basic Rectangular Solid

Sketching the basic isometric solid is an initial step used in sketching more complex shapes. With a little practice, the basic solid can be sketched lightly in a few seconds and helps to keep objects symmetrical. Refer to Fig. 2-15 and follow the procedure to sketch a rectangle 2 units high, 3 units deep, and 4 units long.

A popular procedure to sketch rectangular objects is to first lightly sketch a basic isometric rectangle. Secondly, divide it up into smaller cubes. Thirdly, darken slightly the parts of the object that appear on the outside surfaces of the rectangle. Fourth, erase the parts of the rectangle that are not used. Fifth, add lines in the three basic directions to complete the shape of the object. Sixth, darken the finished object with short, overlapping strokes when it looks right.

Sketching a Rectangular Solid with Spaces Removed

Sketching a basic isometric rectangular solid is a useful first step in creating more complex shapes. This process provides a general outline of an object from which spaces can be added or removed, Fig. 2-16.

After visualizing the object, lightly sketch an isometric solid with the right proportions of length, height, and width. Sketch additional lines that outline areas to be removed. Keep these lines parallel to the outside of the solid. It may be helpful, at first, to divide the solid into unit sized blocks to improve parallel line relationships and proportions.

Next, erase all the unnecessary lines and add lines that outline the removed areas. After checking each set of parallel lines, darken the lines of the object with short, overlapping strokes for a finishing operation.

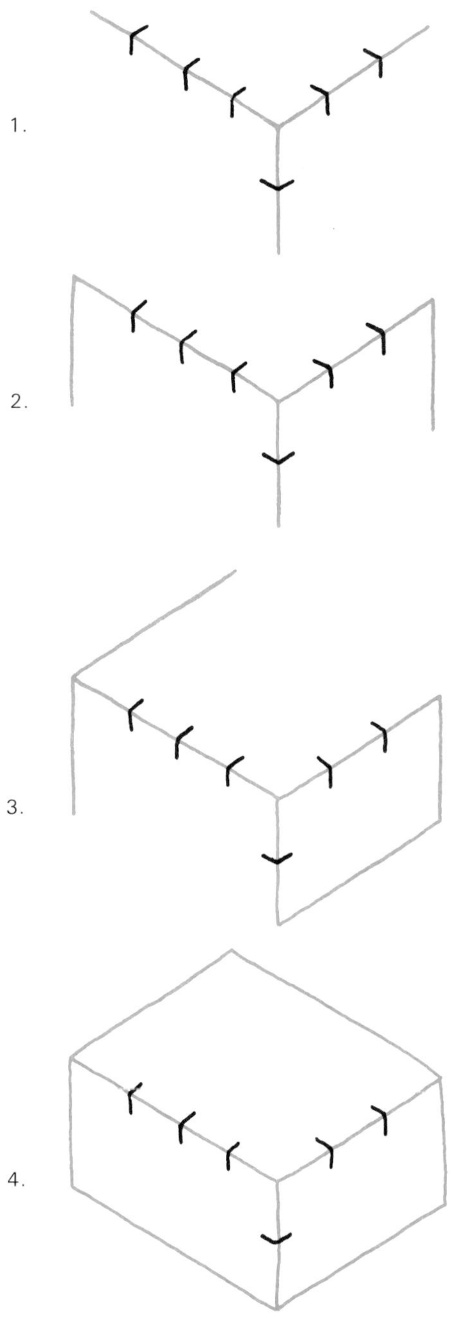

Fig. 2-15. An isometric rectangle has three sets of unequal length lines sketched on the isometric axes.

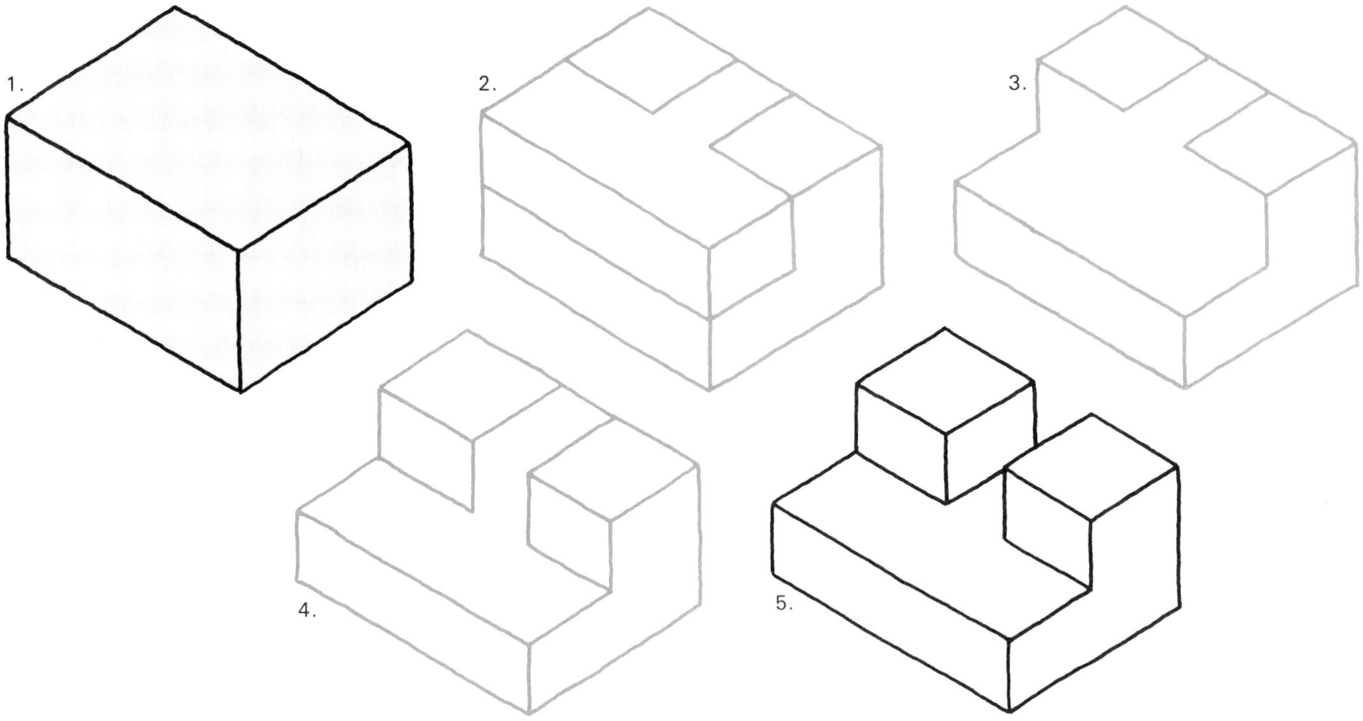

Fig. 2-16. An isometric rectangle provides the framework for sketching more complex objects by adding or subtracting lines.

Sketching Objects with Areas Removed or Added

Some objects are easiest to sketch by removing areas from an isometric solid representing the outside shape of the finished object. Others are best sketched by adding isometric solids together like building blocks. A combination of removing and adding areas is also quite common. Fig. 2-17 shows the sketching of an object using both procedures.

The important skill to develop is keeping the lines of rectangular solids going in one of three basic directions. As you add lines, some may look ''off.'' They are probably straying away from their original vertical, inclined to the right, or inclined to the left direction. As mentioned earlier, there is a good

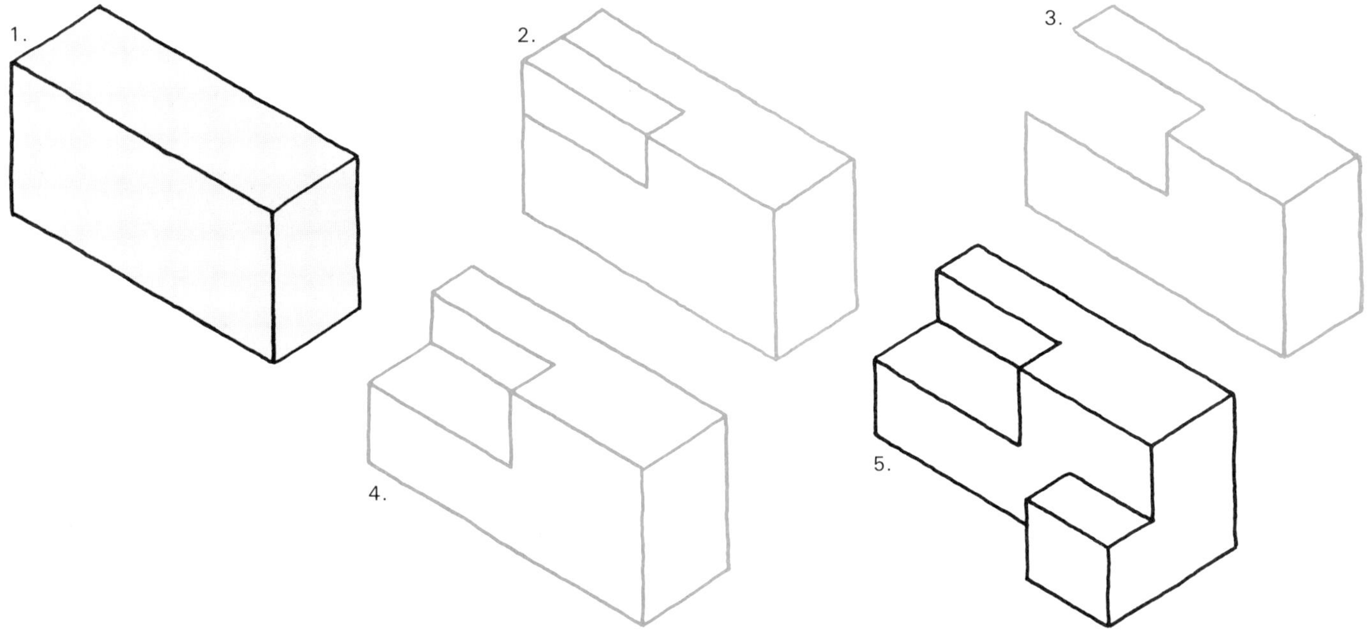

Fig. 2-17. When adding or removing isometric lines, keep the parallel relationship for accurate sketches.

technique for checking the direction of each family of parallel lines. Lay a pencil down on the sketch parallel to one of the basic directions. Slide the pencil across the sketch and compare each line with the direction of the pencil.

Erase and resketch any stray lines. Finally, straighten and darken each line of the sketch with overlapping strokes.

Sketching Objects with Slanted Surfaces

Objects often have slanted surfaces that are not parallel to the standard surfaces of an isometric rectangular solid. First, sketch the solid. This establishes the overall size and shape of the rectangular part of the object. It also provides a skeleton for locating and outlining the slanted surfaces in the right proportions.

Each object must be analyzed for the best beginning shape. Some may start with a large, lightly sketched, isometric cube that is dissected. Others may combine a series of smaller rectangular solids added together. A combination of a dissected large cube with smaller cubes added is also possible.

After having completed the basic rectangular shape of the object, estimate points where the slanted lines begin and end. Follow the steps in Fig. 2-18. Connect the points. Erase original lines that do not appear on the object. Make any straight line or parallel line corrections by erasing and resketching. Finally, resketch the object with overlapping strokes for sharp, consistent lines.

SKETCHING PICTORIAL VIEWS OF CIRCULAR OBJECTS

In a pictorial or isometric view, circular shapes appear elliptical. The isometric rectangular solid is again recommended as a starting layout technique. The solid helps to locate center points and centerlines for the elliptical shapes, Fig. 2-19. An isometric cube equal in height, width, and depth provides three locations for sketching ellipses.

The top surface may be used to sketch an elliptical shape for circular objects that stand up, like the rim of a drinking glass. The surfaces to the left and right may be used to sketch the elliptical shape for objects lie down such as a roll of paper towels or a length of pipe. Take time to estimate distances

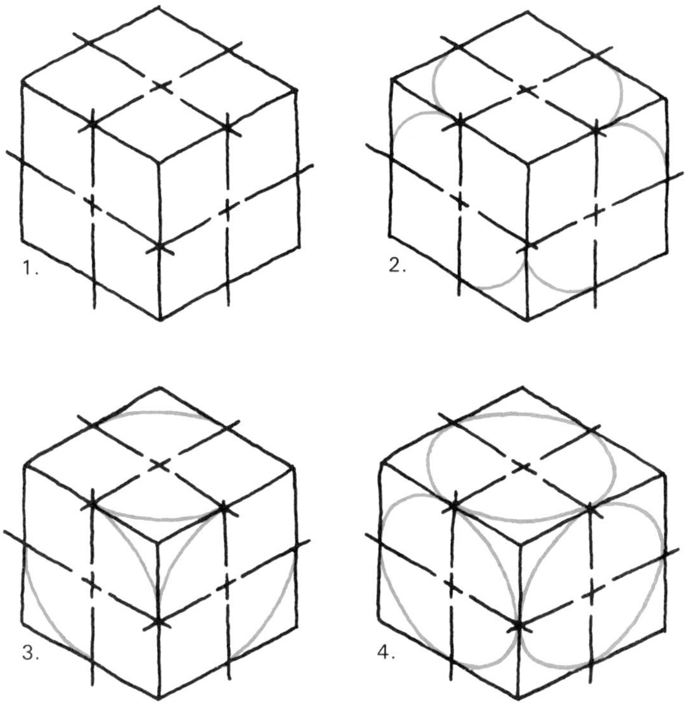

Fig. 2-19. An isometric cube is the framework for laying out and sketching an ellipse.

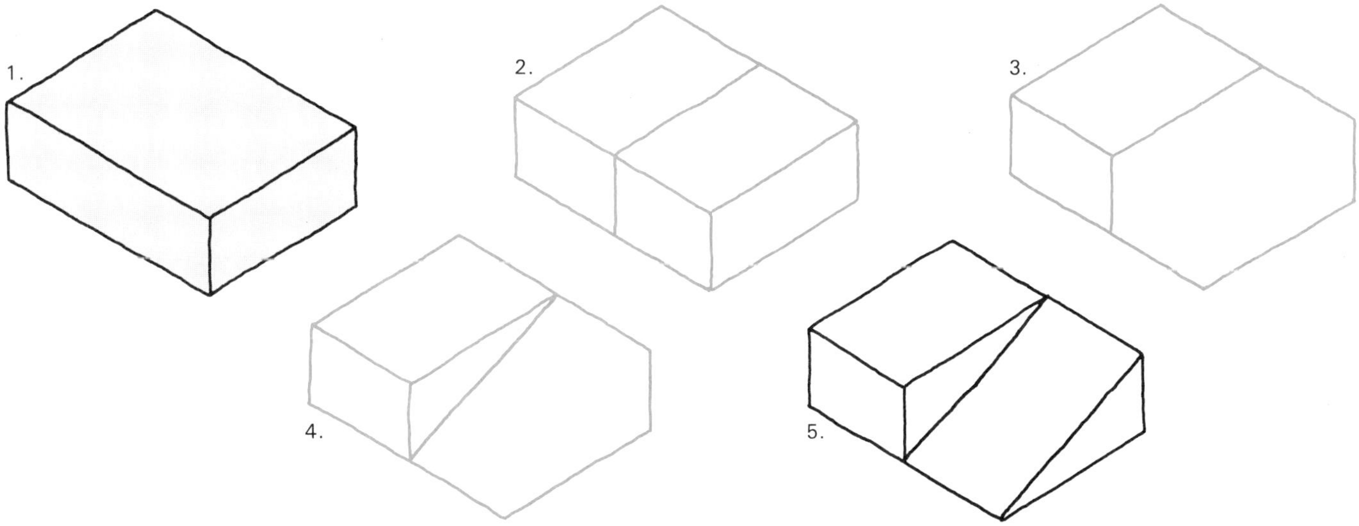

Fig. 2-18. Slanted surfaces can be sketched by connecting points on the isometric rectangle.

accurately and sketch centerlines parallel to the original cube. These procedures help to shape the ellipses consistently.

Sketching Circular Objects from the Top

When sketching a cylindrical object standing up like a metal soup can on a low shelf, two sets of centerlines are needed, Fig. 2-20. One set is used to shape the top of the can and the other is for the bottom of the can. The bottom set of centerlines are parallel to the lines on top of the isometric cube and intersect in the middle of the cube's surface. As compared to the hands on the clock face, the centerlines are at the 2 and 8 o'clock and the 4 and 10 o'clock positions.

Next, for the top of the can, add the bulged elliptical shapes at the 3 o'clock and 9 o'clock positions. Then add the stretched elliptical shapes at the 6 o'clock and 12 o'clock positions. Add the bottom of the can by sketching the stretched shape at the 6 o'clock position and one-half of the bulged shape at each end. Drop two vertical lines down from the extreme left and right sides of the newly formed ellipse.

Erase all construction lines except the centerlines. Finally, make all elliptical shapes flow together with smooth lines by using short, overlapping strokes.

Sketching Circular Objects from the Front

A circular object, like a roll of paper towels on a countertop, may be sketched lying on its side. As you walk around the object, it can be seen in two positions for isometric sketching. One position has a circular end at your lower left with a tubular shape going from 8 o'clock to the 2 o'clock position at the other circular end.

An isometric rectangular solid is a useful first step in sketching this object, Fig. 2-21. The solid establishes the proportions and helps maintain parallel line relationships. Sketch it very lightly because it will eventually be erased. The end of the rectangle has lines of equal length. Two are vertical and two slanted back to the left.

The three lines slanting back to the right complete the cube and establish the depth of the object. The ends of the cube have two centerlines for establishing the elliptical shapes.

Sketch the elliptical shape on the lower left end of the rectangular solid. Next, sketch the stretched elliptical shape and add half of the bulged shape on the other end. Connect the lower left and upper right curved shapes with lines to show the sides of the object. Erase unneeded lines. Complete the sketch by darkening lines with short, overlapping strokes.

Sketching Circular Objects from the Side

Another desirable position for sketching the circular object is shown in Fig. 2-22. The tubular shape aligns with the 4 o'clock to 10 o'clock position. Again, the isometric rectangular solid is useful as part of a layout process.

The circular shaped ends are formed by sketching two centerlines and two sets of elliptical shapes. One centerline should be vertical and the other should slant back in the 2 o'clock to 8 o'clock position. Sketch the bulged and stretched elliptical shapes in the lower right end of the isometric solid. Continue with identical elliptical shapes in the upper

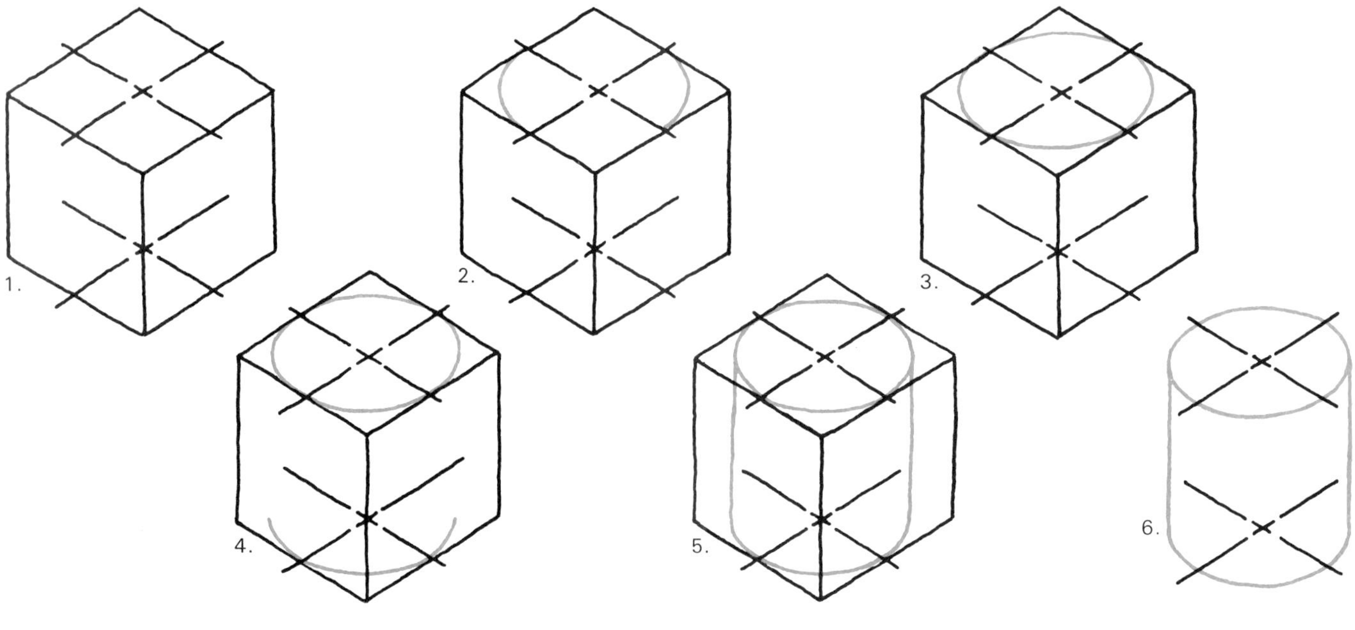

Fig. 2-20. Sketching circular objects from the top requires centerlines to be placed in the 2 o'clock and the 4 o'clock positions.

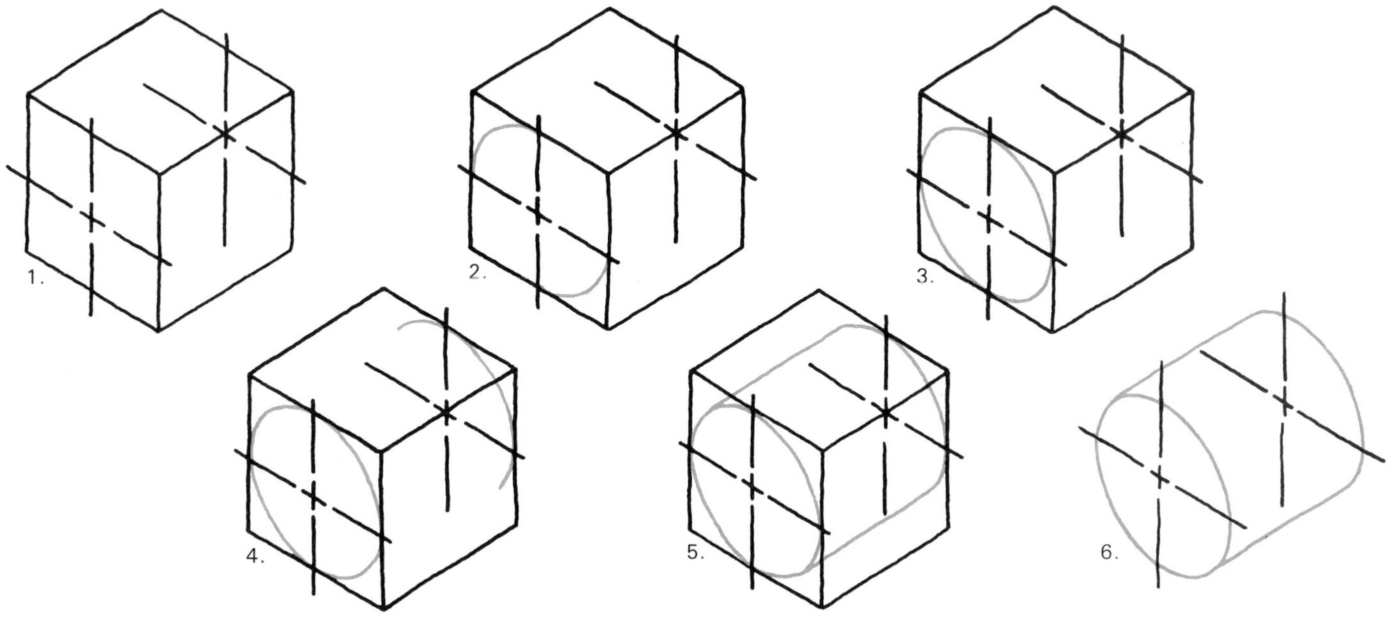

Fig. 2-21. Sketching circular objects from the front calls for the centerlines to be placed in the veritcal and the 4 o'clock positions.

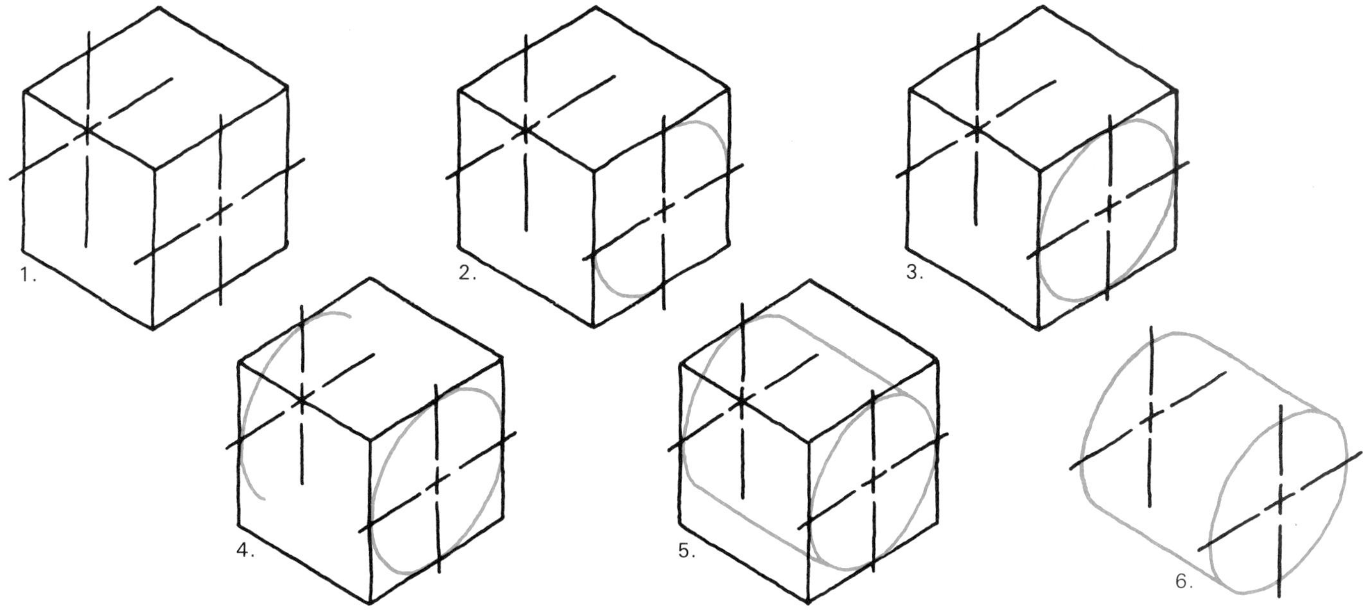

Fig. 2-22. Sketching circular objects from the side so the tube slants to the left requires the centerlines to be vertical and in the 2 o'clock position.

left end. Sketch two parallel lines between the upper and lower ellipses.

Erase all construction lines. Resketch the centerlines. Complete the object by making the elliptical shapes and straight lines flow together with short, overlapping strokes.

Sketching a Hole in the Top of an Object

A simple product to illustrate a hole in the top of an object is a nut or flat washer.

Sketch an isometric rectangular solid 1 unit high, 4 units long, and 4 units deep. See Fig. 2-23. Locate the center points on the top and bottom surfaces. Add two sets of centerlines parallel to the sides of the isometric rectangle. Estimate 1 unit outward in all four directions from the center point of the upper centerlines. Mark the points with a small dot. These are your guides for sketching elliptical shapes on the top surface.

Sketch the bulged elliptical shapes on the right

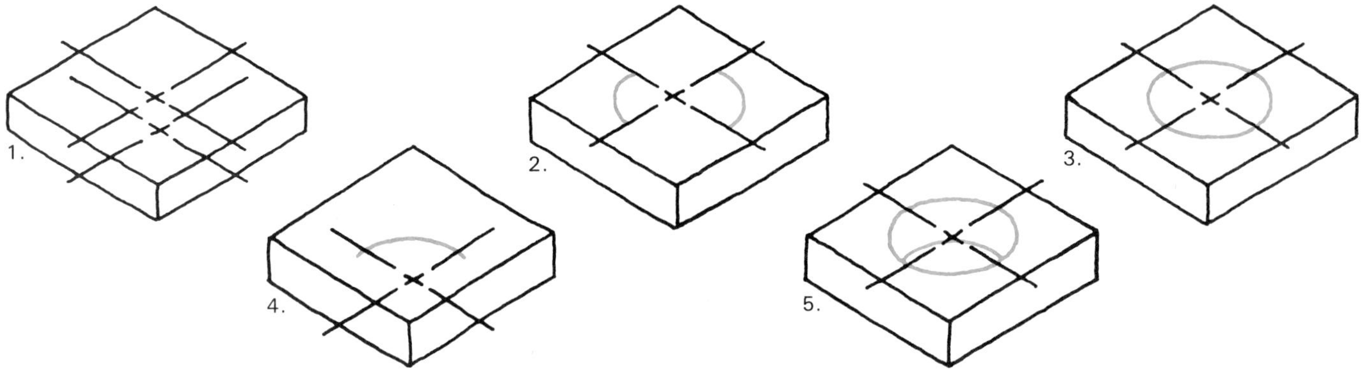

Fig. 2-23. When sketching a hole in the top of an object, the "show through" arc is the same as the arc directly above it.

and left sides of the top surface. Then, follow with the stretched elliptical shapes on the other two sides of the hole.

You may be finished with the layout of the top of the hole, but check one more detail. Will the hole "show through"? Check by estimating 1 unit out to the upper right and upper left on the lower centerlines. Sketch a stretched elliptical shape identical to the one directly above on the top surface. The distance between these two curves should look the same as the thickness of the material or 1 unit. Look at Fig. 2-23 again.

Erase all layout and construction work except for the centerlines. Resketch centerlines, ellipses, and outside cube with short overlapping strokes. For additional practice, sketch a washer.

Sketching a Hole in the Front of an Object

Using the same product, the nut, the following steps illustrate how to sketch a hole in the front of an object. Sketch an isometric rectangle 4 units high, 4 units long, and 1 unit deep, Fig. 2-24. Locate the center points and sketch the centerlines parallel to the sides of the isometric rectangle. Estimate 1 unit out from the center point in all four directions on the front surface. Mark the four points on the centerlines and sketch the bulged elliptical shapes in the upper left and lower right areas. Sketch the stretched elliptical shapes in the upper right and lower left areas.

To illustrate the hole "showing through," estimate 1 unit out from the center in the 6 and 10 o'clock directions on the back surface centerlines. Sketch the stretched elliptical shape identical to the one on the front surface, 1 unit away. Erase all unnecessary lines, resketch the centerlines, elliptical shapes, and straight object lines with short overlapping strokes.

Sketching a Hole in the Side of an Object

Again, let us use the nut as an example for sketching a hole in the side of an object, Fig. 2-25. Sketch an isometric rectangle 4 units high, 1 unit long, and 4 units deep. Locate the center points on the outside and inside surfaces. Add two sets of centerlines. Estimate 1 unit outward in all four directions on the outside surface.

Sketch the bulged elliptical shapes in the upper and lower areas and the stretched elliptical shapes in the right and left areas. The hole will "show through," so estimate 1 unit out from the center on the back surface in the 2 o'clock and 6 o'clock directions. Sketch the stretched elliptical shape identical to the one on the side surface, 1 unit away.

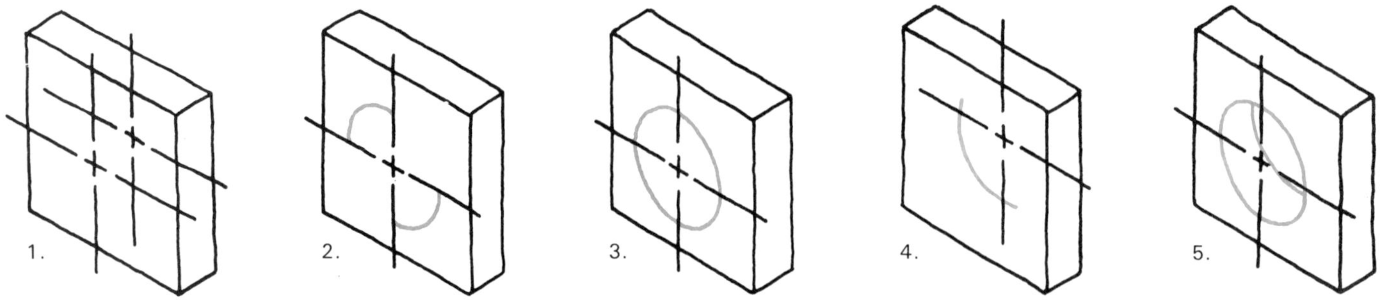

Fig. 2-24. From the front view, the "show through" arc matches the hole in the front surface.

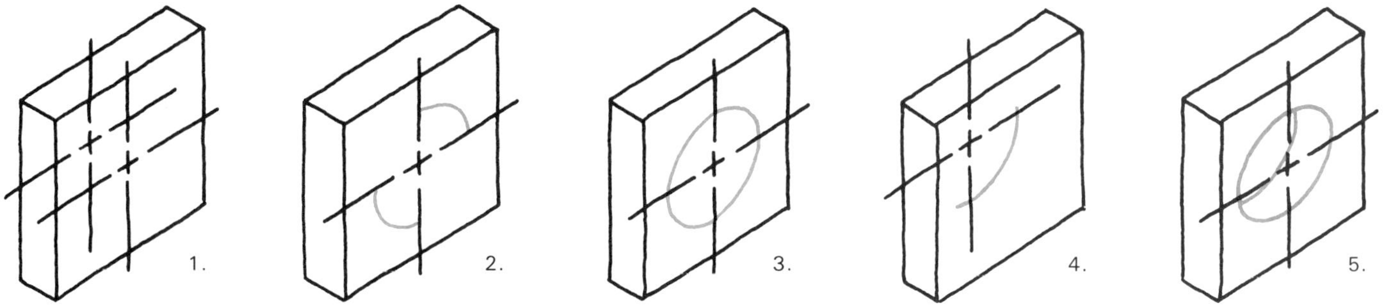

Fig. 2-25. A hole in the side is sketched so the ''show through'' arc matches the arc on the side.

Erase unnecessary layout work. Resketch the centerlines elliptical shapes, and straight object lines with short overlapping strokes.

Sketching Objects with Arc Shapes

Objects may be a combination of rectangular and circular shapes. When the circular shapes do not complete a full circle, they are called arcs. They may appear as an external (outside) or internal (inside) arc. Fig. 2-26 shows how an external arc is constructed.

An isometric rectangle is a starting point to establish proportions and to start the layout work. When sketching an arc, a center point and centerlines are necessary. An arc may be sketched similar to cylinders and holes. Once the centerlines are sketched and the radius has been marked on the centerlines, sketch the appropriate elliptical shapes.

Finalize the sketch by erasing unnecessary lines. Resketch object lines with short overlapping strokes.

COMBINING RECTANGULAR, SLANTED, AND CIRCULAR SHAPES FOR A TRICYCLE TRAILER

Parts and products often combine several basic shapes. By using the steps discussed and illustrated in this chapter, you should be able to analyze, lay out, refine,and sketch almost any object with confidence. With practice, you will develop speed in sketching objects you wish to copy or ones you visualize. More importantly, you will be able to communicate your design work in a professional manner.

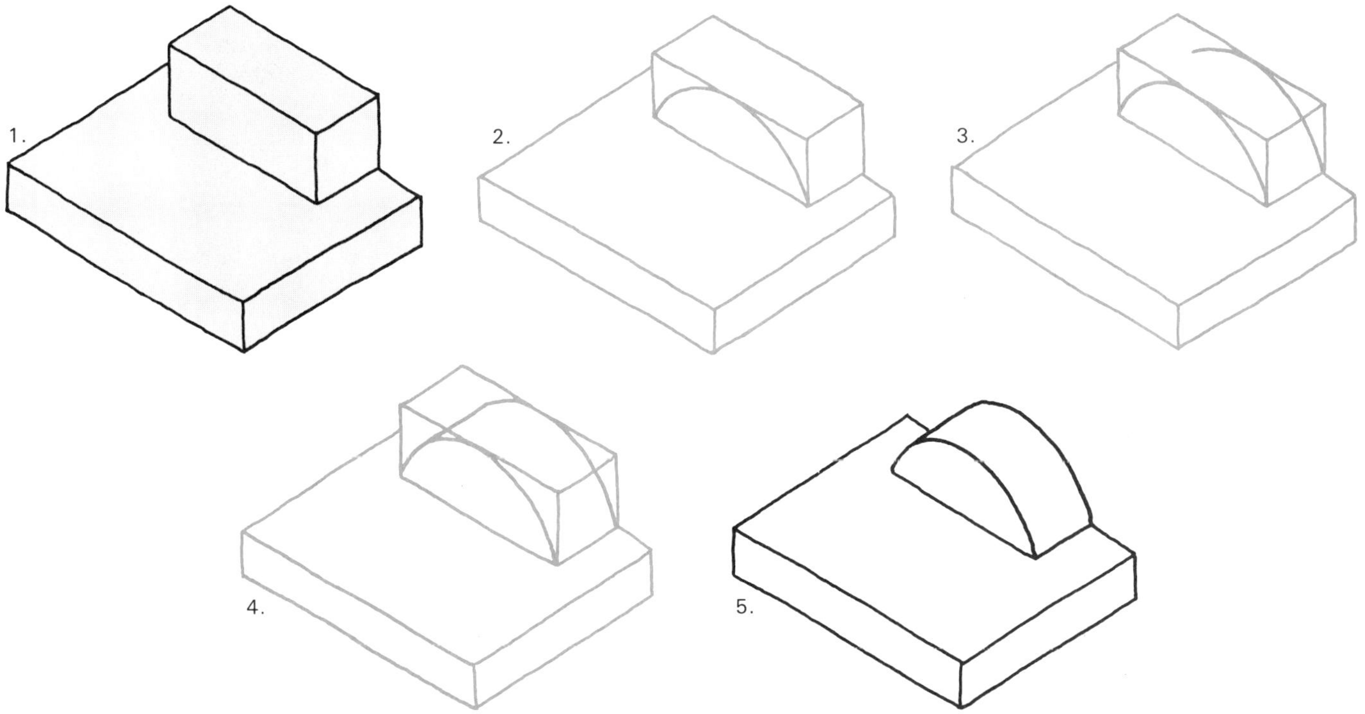

Fig. 2-26. To sketch an arc, use centerlines and sketch elliptical shapes.

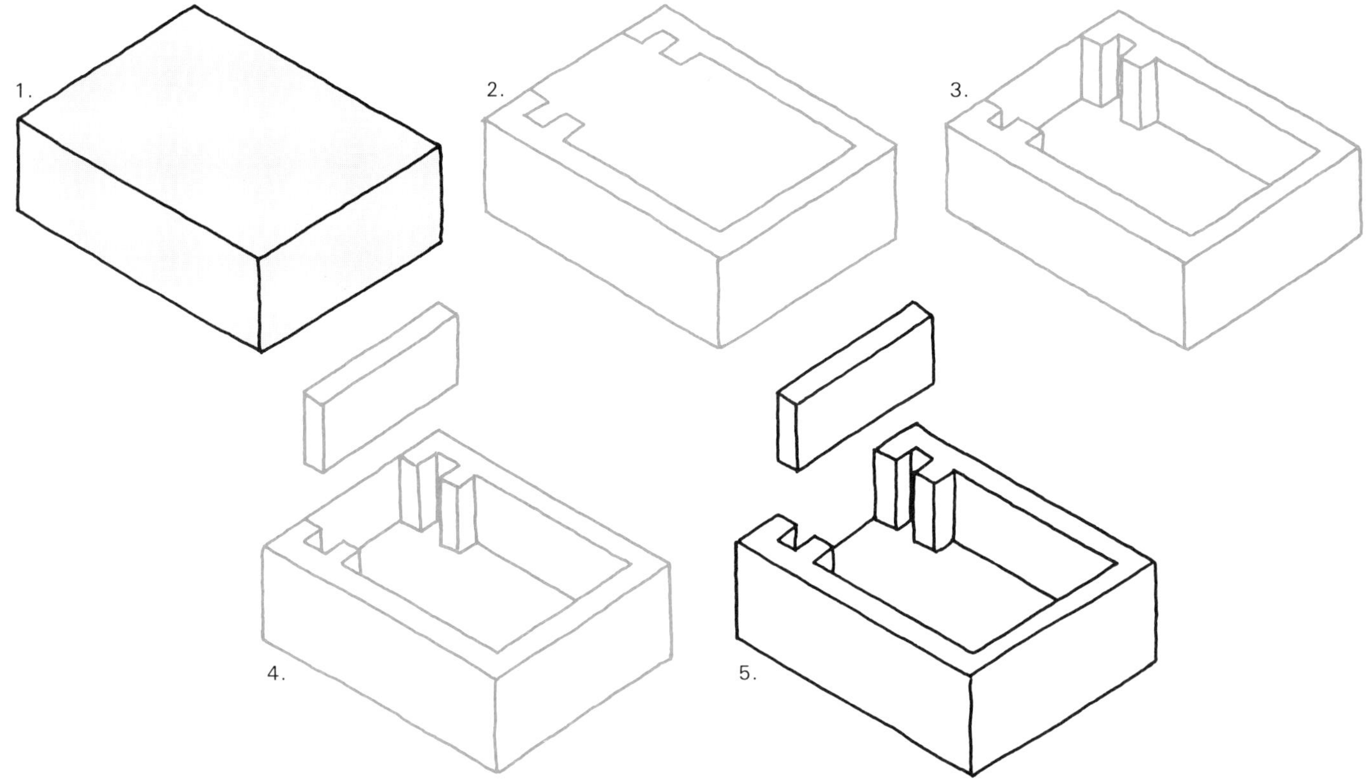

Fig. 2-27. The trailer box is based on the basic isometric rectangle.

Creative thinking may occur at anytime and anyplace. You may have an idea during a meal, as you wake up, or riding in a car. Your skill in "thinking with a pencil" and capturing ideas may become as important as your skill in writing.

As a practical design example, the following parts are sketched to satisfy a request by a 4-year-old youngster for a new tricycle trailer. You may want to picture youself designing such an item for a younger brother or sister. In an attempt to pool the

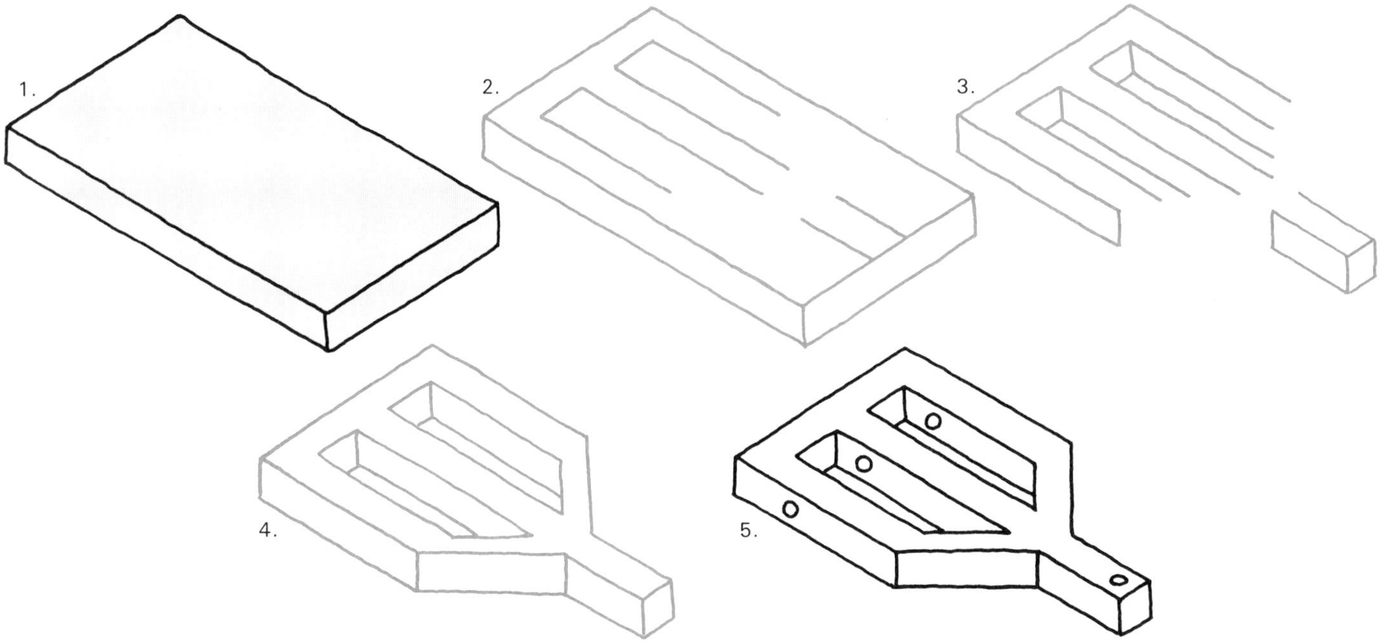

Fig. 2-28. The trailer frame starts with an isometric rectangle and uses angular parts.

ideas for the trailer box, an isometric rectangle is drawn first, Fig. 2-27. The rectangle will establish the proportions and provide the basic layout for designing the trailer box. This layout will help to solve the problems of wall thickness, end gate details, and construction features.

After completing the basic shape, add the wall thickness with lines parallel and inside the outer wall. Add the U shaped end gate brackets. Erase the unnecessary line connecting the sides. Drop vertical lines down from the corners of the end gate bracket. Add a line at the bottom of the trailer bed. Finally, sketch an end gate above the trailer box.

Now that the trailer box is designed, how will you plan to support the load? You need to sketch a frame. The frame will be attached to the under side of the box, hold the axle, and provide a connecting point with the tricycle. The initial sketch or concept may change when a material is selected for the part.

The sketch could be laid out as a series of three pieces of material running back to the end gate with an end cross member, Fig. 2-28. Two angular braces near the front would attach to a tricycle. Thickness would be added to each piece. Finally, an ellipse is sketched for hitching the trailer to the tricycle.

Next, the wheels and axle unit and tricycle hitch are designed and sketched. The basic shape of these components is primarily circular. The wheel and axle unit is laid out as two rectangular blocks for the wheels, connected by two parallel lines for the axle, Fig. 2-29. A center point and a pair of centerlines are added to the front surface of each wheel block.

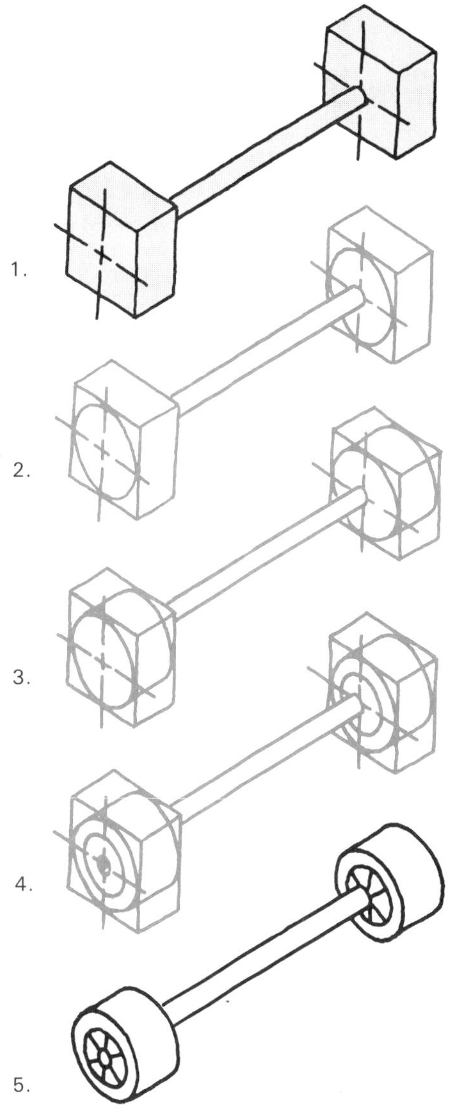

Fig. 2-29. The trailer wheels and axle start as rectangles.

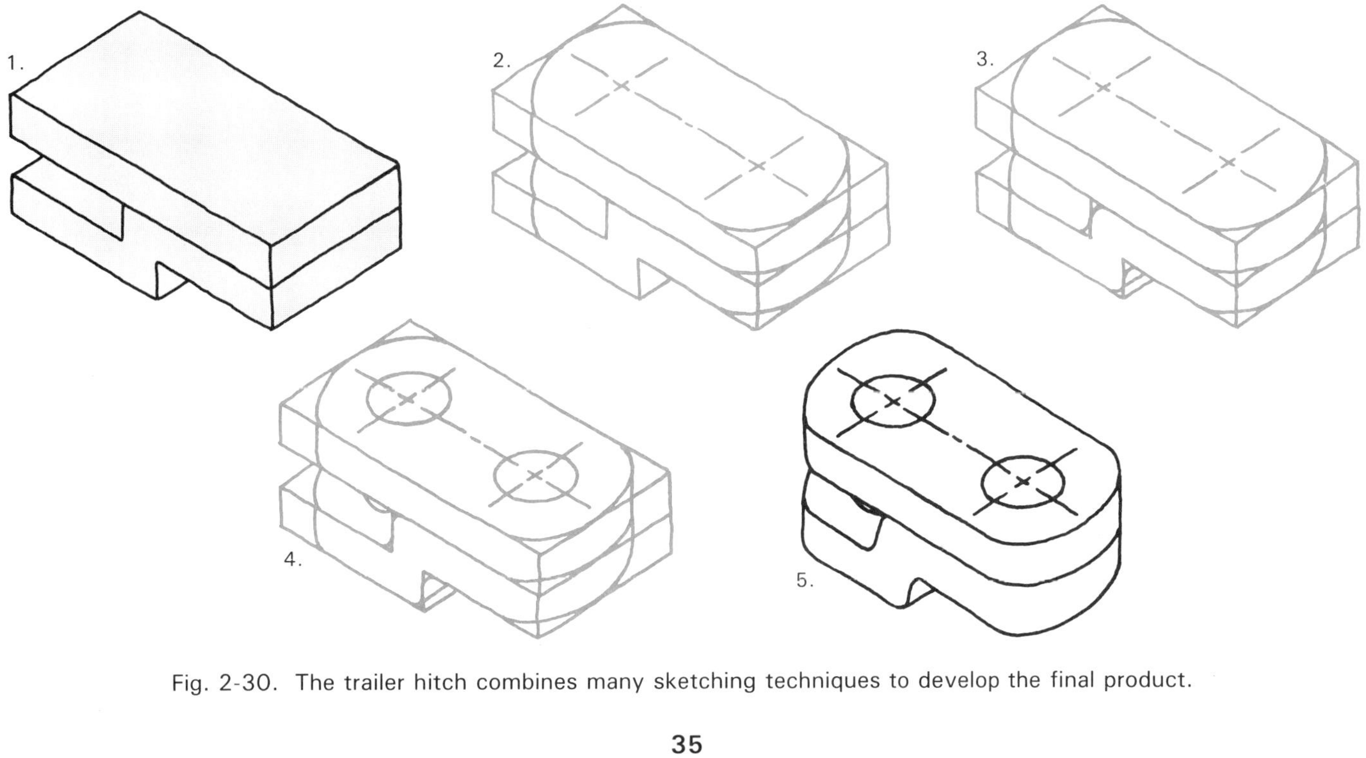

Fig. 2-30. The trailer hitch combines many sketching techniques to develop the final product.

The front elliptical shapes would be followed by identical elliptical shapes repeated to show the tire width. A straight line at the top and bottom of each of the two ellipses will finish the outside of the tire.

A smaller ellipse may be added to each tire to illustrate the thickness of the tire. Spokes can be made by darkening the centerlines and sketching additional lines through the center. The sketch of the wheels should follow the size and shape of the wheels purchased for this product.

The hitch may be sketched by laying out the top rectangle first, Fig. 2-30. Add the bottom curved piece next. Each end of the hitch needs a center point and centerlines for sketching elliptical shapes representing holes for attaching the trailer to the tricycle. The outside arcs are connected at the right and left sides with straight lines.

After sketching the holes, remember to check if the hole shows through. Finish your sketch by erasing the construction and layout lines. Resketch the centerlines, elliptical shapes, and straight lines.

SKETCHING A BRACKET WITH RECTANGULAR, SLANTED, AND CIRCULAR SHAPES

The bracket in Fig. 2-31 is an example of a fixture incorporating many basic sketching techniques. Your first step is to analyze the sketch and see that two isometric slabs can be used for the initial layout. Remember to sketch lightly so that erasing will be easy.

The horizontal slab is 1 unit high, 4 units long, and 2 units deep. The vertical slab is 5 units high, 4 units long, and 1 unit deep. The vertical slab sits directly behind the horizontal slab as shown. To complete the rough layout, add the angular wedge on the back side between the two slabs.

Next, locate the center point and sketch centerlines for the lower hole. Sketch the ellipse. To complete the base of the bracket, sketch an isometric square in the lower left and the lower right corners. Sketch a pair of lines between the lower left and lower right corners to complete the slanted base.

Now, complete the upper area of the bracket. Locate the center point and sketch centerlines for the hole. Sketch the ellipse. Use the hole vertical and horizontal centerlines to sketch the arc on the upight slab from the 2 o'clock to the 10 o'clock position. Then, add the slanted line from the lower right corner up to the left against the upright slab. Add a second slanted line identical to the first one. Add a straight line across the top of the slant at the point it attaches to the top of the bracket. Erase all initial construction work. Darken the elliptical shapes and darken the straight lines for a professional touch.

Sketching a Spindle Using Elliptical Shapes

The spindle in Fig. 2-32 is an example of a simplified part that utilizes your skill in sketching elliptical shapes. The layout of the spindle may include two isometric rectangles. The lower one would be a slab 1 unit high, 4 units long, and 4 units

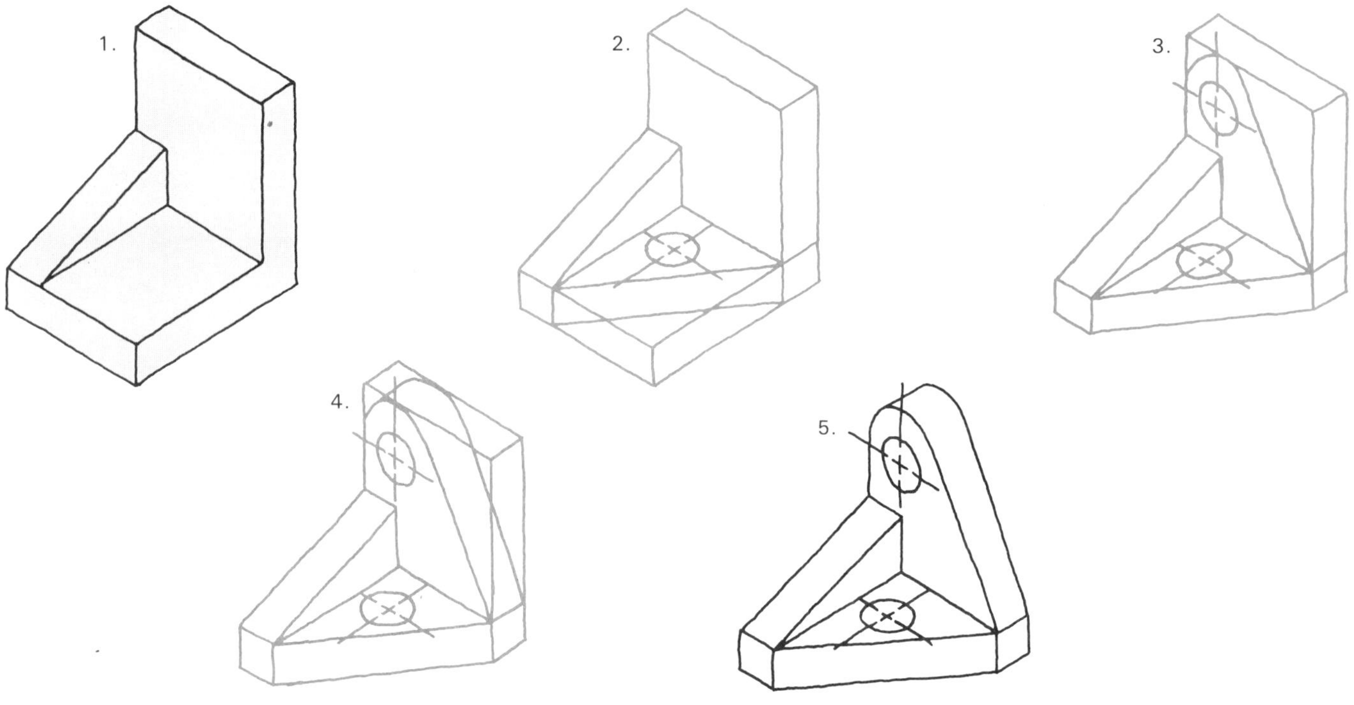

Fig. 2-31. The bracket is based on basic rectangular shapes.

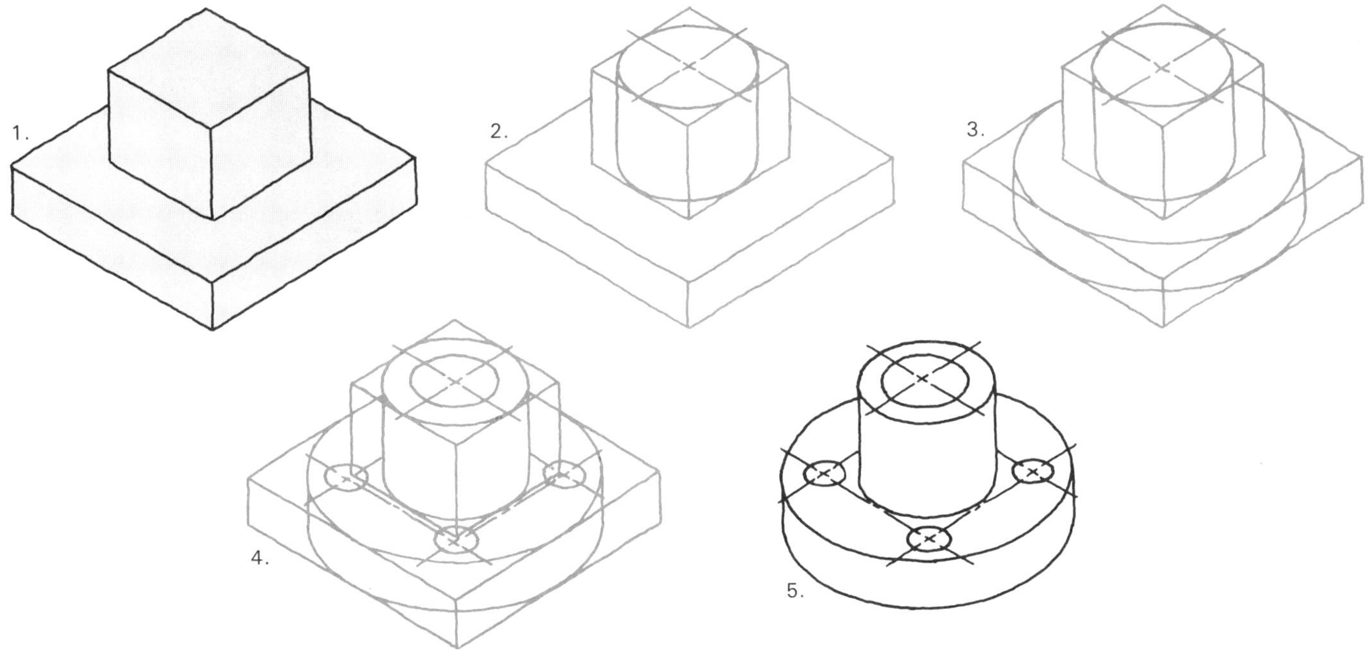

Fig. 2-32. The spindle is based on ellipses developed from rectangles.

deep. The upper one would be a cube 2 units high, 2 units long, and 2 units deep.

Starting with the top of the cube, locate a center point and sketch a pair of centerlines. Similarly, sketch centerlines on the top of the lower slab that is the same as the bottom of the cube. Sketch centerlines for the bottom surface of the lower slab. Add a pair of centerlines for three small holes on the lower slab.

Lightly sketch an ellipse on top of the cube. Repeat the lower half of the same ellipse at the base of the cube. Connect the two elliptical shapes with a pair of vertical lines forming the left and right sides.

Sketch a large ellipse on the top of the lower slab. Repeat the lower half of the same ellipse on the bottom of the slab. Connect the elliptical shapes for the base with vertical lines to define the sides.

Add the ellipse for the hole on top of the cube. Sketch three more ellipses for the three smaller holes on the bottom slab. Finally, erase all construction and layout work. Resketch the centerlines, elliptical shapes, and straight lines.

SKETCHING MULTIVIEW PROJECTIONS FROM AN ISOMETRIC SKETCH

One of the ways of analyzing a pictorial view of an object is to look at the object from different positions. This technique helps isolate and focus attention on features and details when viewed or seen from a single direction.

As a standard practice, objects are commonly viewed from the top, front, and right side. The arrangement of these views is also standardized. The right side view is projected to the right of the front view. The top view is projected above the front view. Allocate space on your paper for sketches in quadrants as follows: An isometric sketch (upper right), front view (lower left), top view (above front view), and right side view (right of front view).

As a simple illustration of these standard practices, visualize a common refrigerator. Make an isometric sketch of it with two doors and two handles on the front of a rectangular cube. Now, visualize three large sheets of glass or clear plastic. One is standing in front of the refrigerator, one is on the right side, and the other is lying on top of your refrigerator. Object lines on the sheets illustrate the shape of the refrigerator and hinges allow the glass or plastic to move. The top sheet will hinge up from the front. The right side will swing out from the front. Study the procedure in Fig. 2-33.

Visualize the front view marked on the plastic. It includes the outline of the appliance as well as the doors and handles. Make a small sketch of this front view from the plastic.

Next, visualize the right side view on the second sheet of plastic. It is a large rectangle with the doors and handles on the left edge. Hinge this sheet out until it is flat with the front sheet. The two views have a horizontal relationship and both show the same height. Sketch the right side view directly to the right of your front view.

The third sheet of plastic shows the top view. The drawing would be a square shape with handles on the bottom edge. Hinge this sheet up from the front view until it is flat. These two views have a vertical

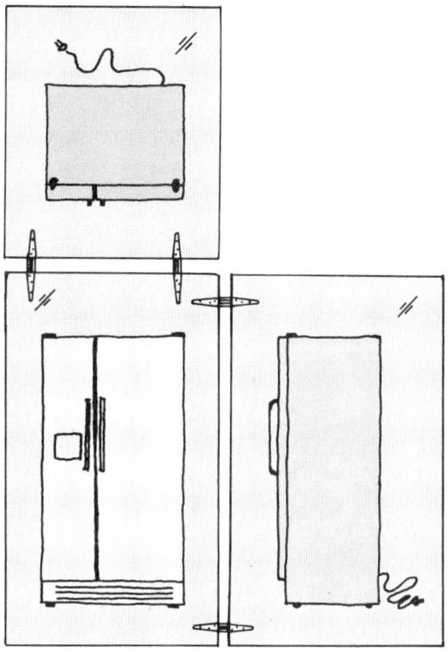

Fig. 2-33. The procedure for sketching the refrigerator used to show multiview projections.

relationship and both show the same width. Sketch the top view directly above the front view.

The depth of the refrigerator is illustrated by the top and right side views. Always check that the depth looks the same in these two views. Also, check to make sure the handles are consistent between the views. The handle should have the same vertical relationship between the front and top views, and the same horizontal relationship between the front and side views.

Sketching Multiviews of Rectangular Objects

The front, right side, and top views of the isometric sketch shown in Fig. 2-34 are required to complete this assignment. An ''L-shaped space'' is required for these three views. First sketch the front view in the lower left area. It contains a rectangle 2 units high and 4 units long. Make this rectangle ''U'' shaped by removing an area (1 unit by 2 units) from the middle of the upper half.

The right side view is sketched directly to the right of the front view. The height may be projected across from the front view. The depth is estimated as 3 units.

The top view is sketched directly above the front view. The length may be projected up from the front view (4 units) and the depth is the same as in the side view (3 units). Two additional vertical lines are added to the top view. One line is one unit in from the left edge, and the other line is 1 unit in from the right edge.

Dashed lines represent surfaces that exist, but are not directly viewed from the specific direction of sight. The side view needs to have a dashed line added horizontally through the middle. This dashed line will touch the vertical object line on the right and on the left.

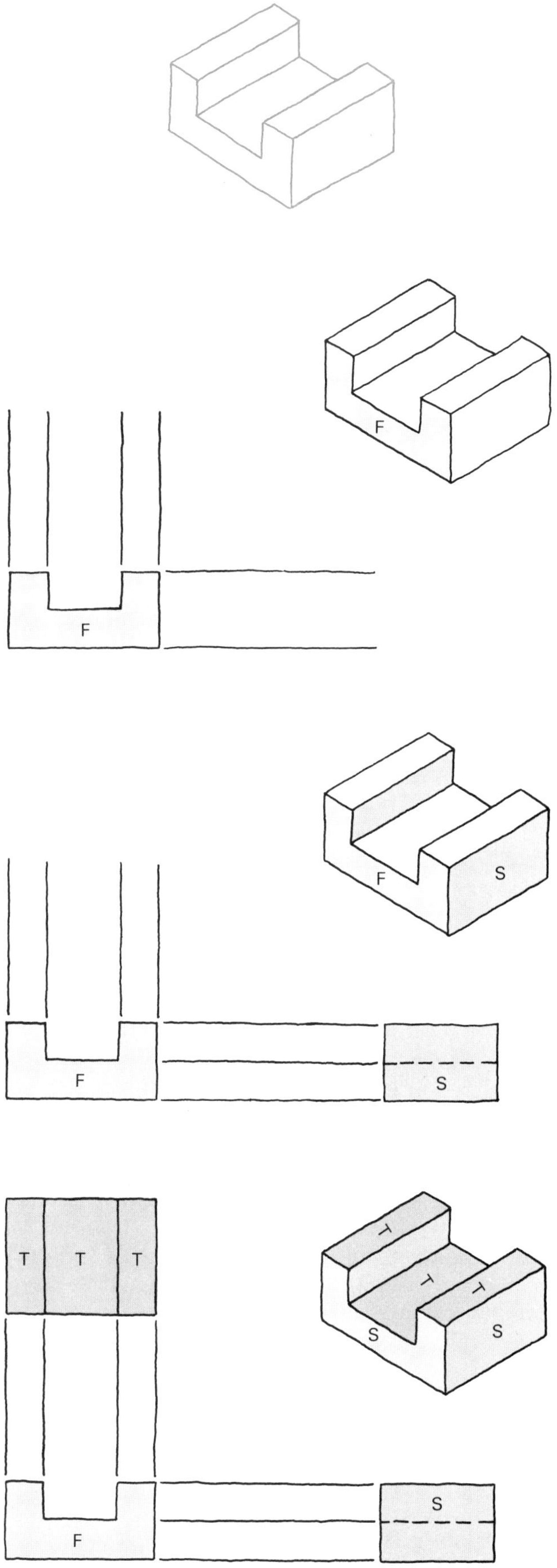

Fig. 2-34. The front and top views are in vertical alignment. The front and side views are in horizontal alignment.

Finally, erase all layout work. Resketch object lines so they are sharp, black, and consistent. You may leave the projection lines if they are light. Label each surface with F (front), S (side), or T (top) in the multiview and isometric.

Sketching Multiviews of Objects with Slanted Surfaces

The front, right, and top views will be sketched from the isometric shown in Fig. 2-35. The front view is 4 units long and 2 units high. A horizontal line 1 unit long is located in the middle of the object vertically and 1.5 units from each side. Slanted lines connect the ends of this horizontal line with the upper left and right corners.

Project the lines horizontally from the front view to the right, to determine the height of the right side view. Estimate the depth as 3 units and sketch two vertical lines to form a rectangle 2 units high and 3 units deep. Add a horizontal dashed line through the middle to represent the flat surface.

Project the lines vertically up from the front view to determine the length of the top view. Estimate the depth as 3 units and sketch two horizontal lines to form a rectangle 4 units long and 3 units deep. Add two additional vertical lines to indicate where the edges of the slat and slanted surfaces are joined.

Erase the layout work. Resketch the object lines with short, overlapping strokes to make them sharp and black. Label each surface with an F, S, or T in each view to demonstrate your understanding.

Sketching Multiviews of Objects with Circular Shapes

The object shown in Fig. 2-36 with holes and arcs is sketched from the front, right, and top. The front view combines a rectangle, 1 unit high and 3 units long, below a square 2 units high and 3 units long. Add centerlines to the square and sketch the semicircle with a radius of 1 unit and a circle with a radius of .5 unit. The slot will show a pair of dashed lines 1 unit apart and a centerline in the middle of the lower rectangle.

The right side is the same height as the front view, so project each level to the right. The depth is 5 units and the heights is 3 units in a backward "L" shape. Add a horizontal centerline and a pair of dashed lines to represent the hole. The slot will be represented by a pair of vertical centerlines 1 unit apart and a pair of dashed lines 2 units apart.

Project the lengths upward into the top view and transfer the depths from the side view. The hole is shown as a pair of vertical dashed lines and a centerline in the middle of the upper-most rectangle. The slot appears as two semicircles and two straight lines tangent to the semicircles on the lower rectangle. The two pairs of centerlines are 1 unit apart.

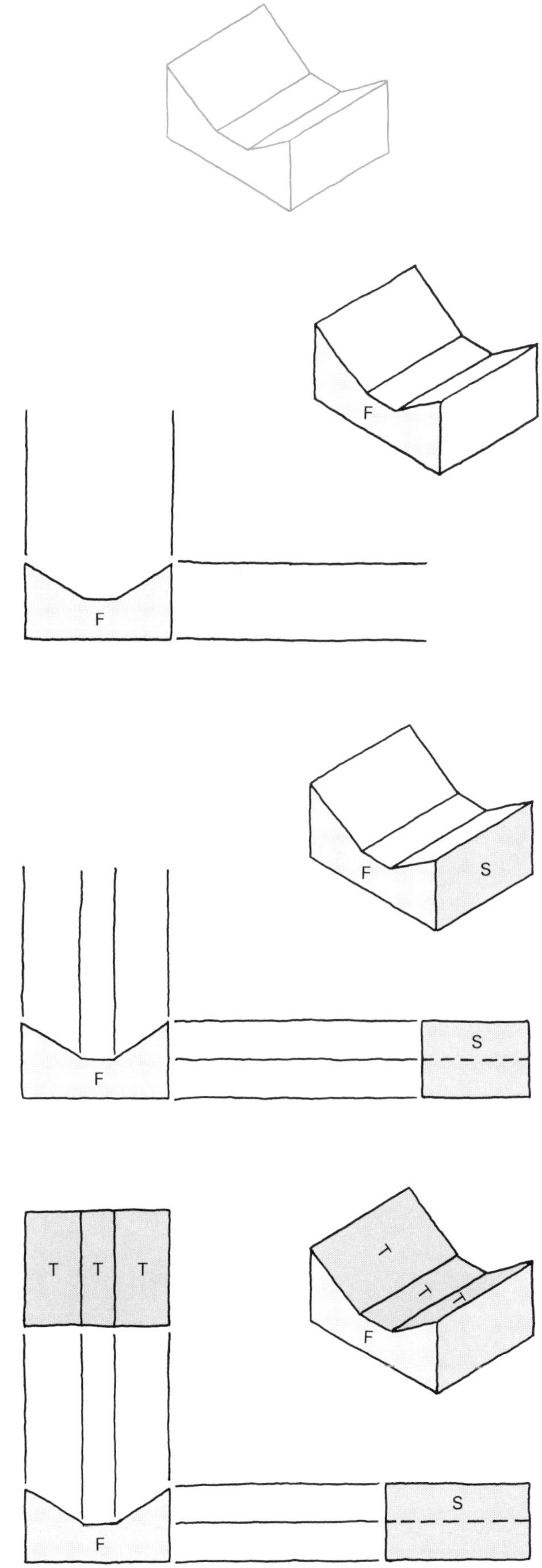

Fig. 2-35. The depth of the surface should appear the same in the top and side views.

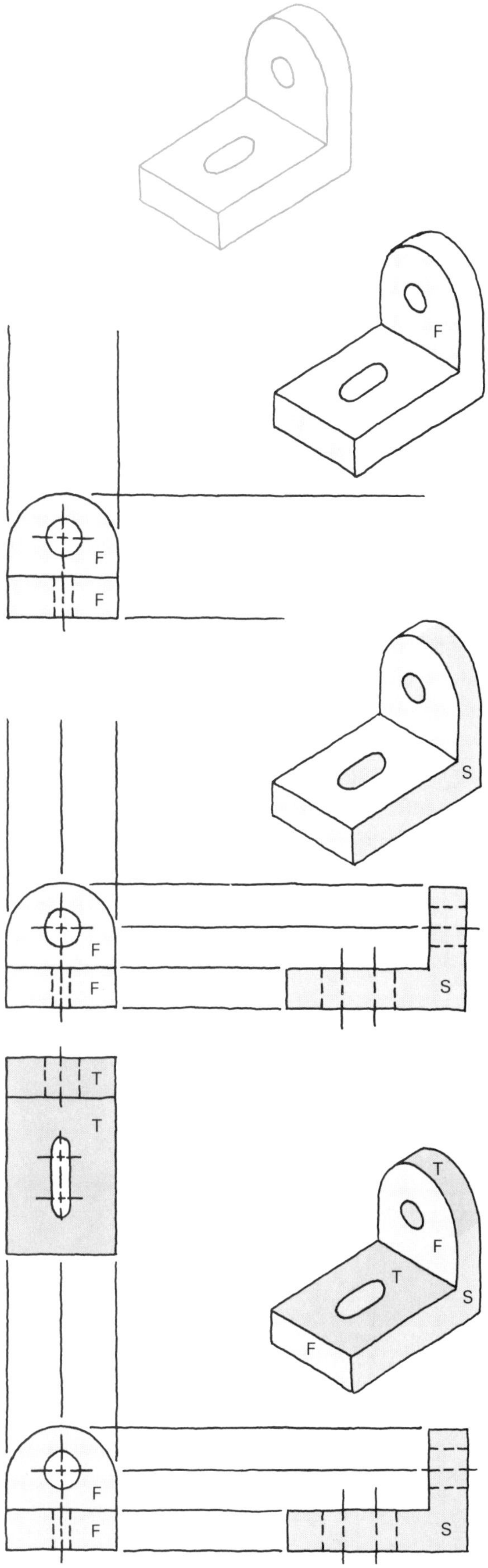

Fig. 2-36. When sketching holes in surfaces, the feature will appear as circles with pairs of hidden lines in adjacent views.

Erase all unnecessary layout work. Resketch the circles, arcs, straight lines, dashed lines, and centerlines.

CREATING ISOMETRIC SKETCHES FROM MULTIVIEW PROJECTIONS

When multiview projections are provided without an isometric view, there may tend to be uncertainty and confusion as to what the actual object looks like after manufacturing. This part of the chapter will help you to quickly and accurately discover what an object looks like by sketching an isometric view.

Isometric Sketches of Rectangular Objects

The front, top, and side views of the rectangular object are provided as shown in Fig. 2-37. Since an isometric view is desired, start with a rectangular cube. The height (2 units) and length (4 units) can be estimated from the front view, and the depth (3 units) is available from the top or side views.

Lay out the lines on the isometric cube as they appear on the front, side, and top views. Each line becomes a clue in discovering the shape of the isometric view.

The front surface is a ''U'' shape with a short horizontal line in the middle of the right side. The right side view has a horizontal line through the middle. The line is solid on the left and dashed on the right. The dashed and solid lines do not touch so they are representing the same surface. The rule here is: When a surface is represented by a solid line that continues as a dashed line, the solid and dashed lines do not touch. A vertical line connects the center of the top line and the center of the solid-dashed line. The top surface has a long rectangle on the left and a short rectangle on the right.

The front view tells us that the ''U'' shape is a trough (2 units long all the way through). The side and top views tell us that the upper right corner of the front is void.

Erase the layout lines. Resketch the object with sharp, crisp lines.

Isometric Sketches with Slanted Surfaces

The front, side, and top views shown in Fig. 2-38 provide clues about the shape of the object. Sketch an isometric rectangle with the same proportions. The height is 2 units, the length is 4 units, and the depth is 3 units.

The front view reveals a ''V'' groove cut through the middle and two vertical lines 1 unit from the sides. The top view shows the corners removed and three vertical lines. The side view verifies the discovery of the shape. The long horizontal dashed line represents the bottom of the ''V'' groove. The vertical line indicates where the corner slant begins.

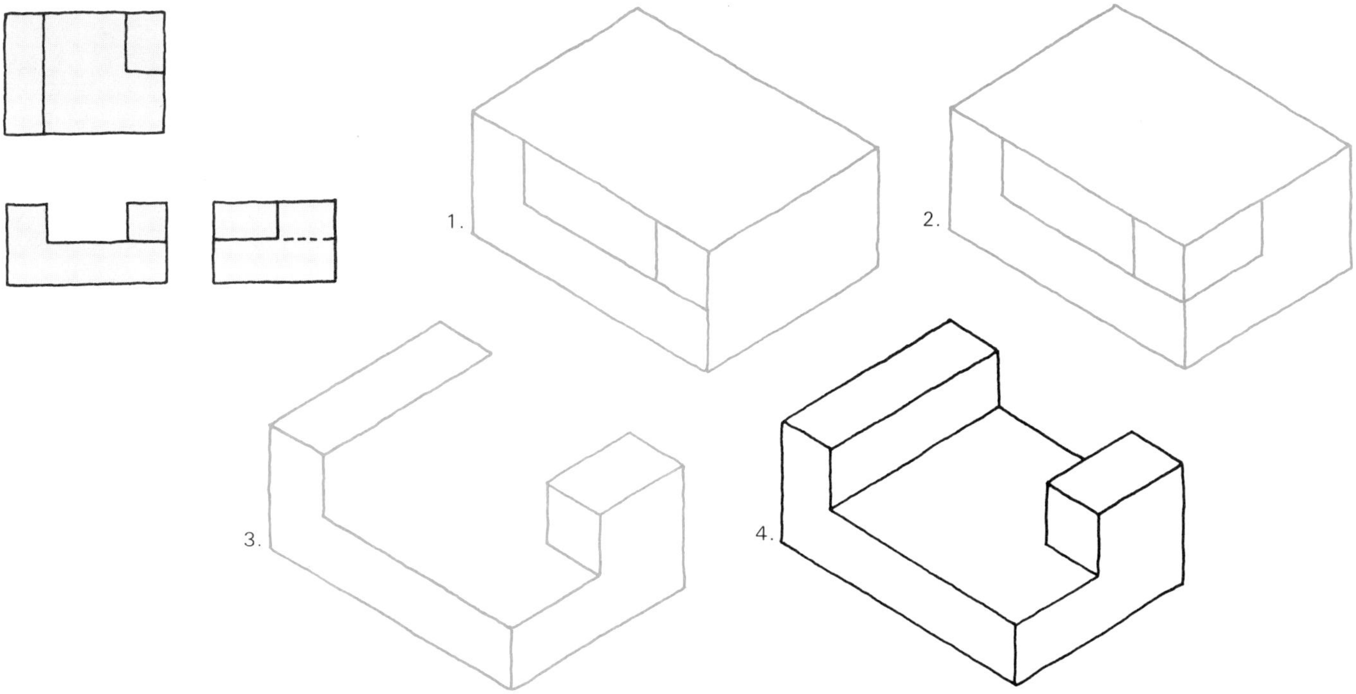

Fig. 2-37. Given the front, top, and side views, an isometric or pictorial sketch can be developed.

Concentrate on solving these isometric puzzles and enjoy the challenge. Finish the task by cleaning up your work with sharp, black lines.

Isometric Sketches with Circular Shapes

Circular shapes seen in the front, side, and top views of a multiview projection become elliptical in an isometric sketch. Study Fig. 2-39. First, sketch an isometric rectangle 2 units high, 4 units long, and 3 units deep.

Next, lay out the front surface by removing a 1 by 1 unit square from the upper right and upper left corners. Erase the corners and add vertical and slanted lines to fill in the voided areas. Divide the

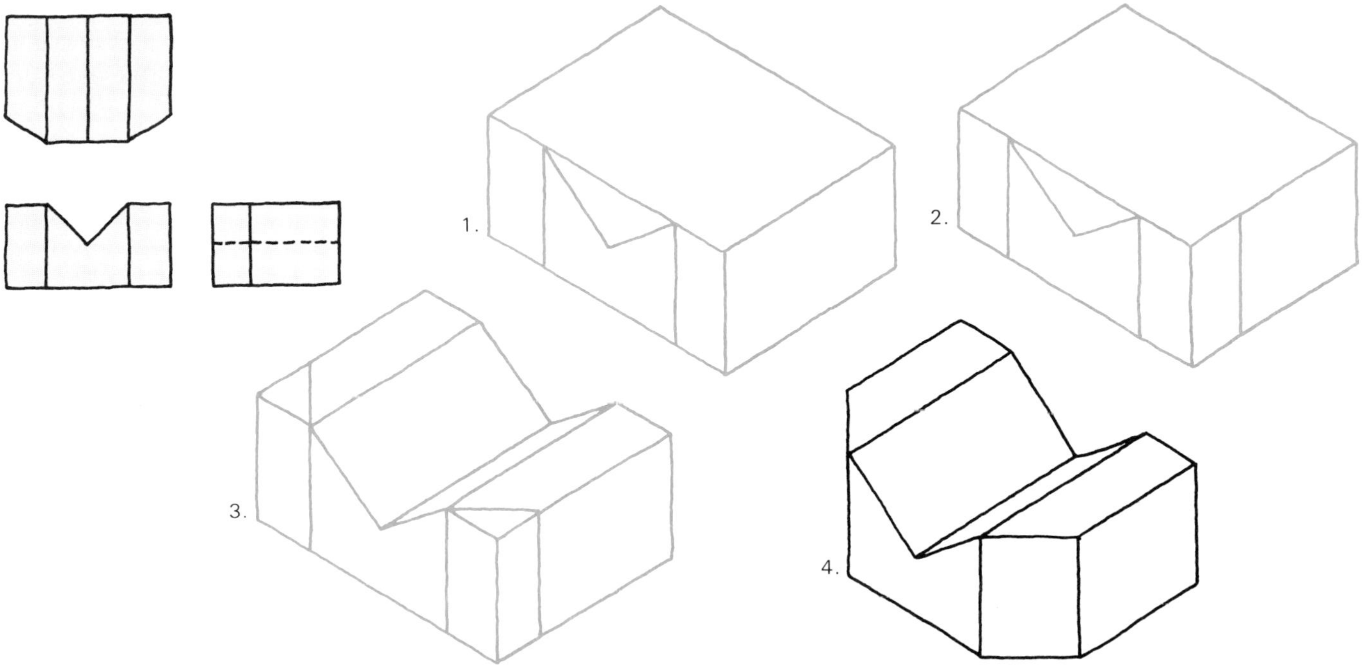

Fig. 2-38. An isometric sketch can be made from front, top, and side views including slanted surfaces.

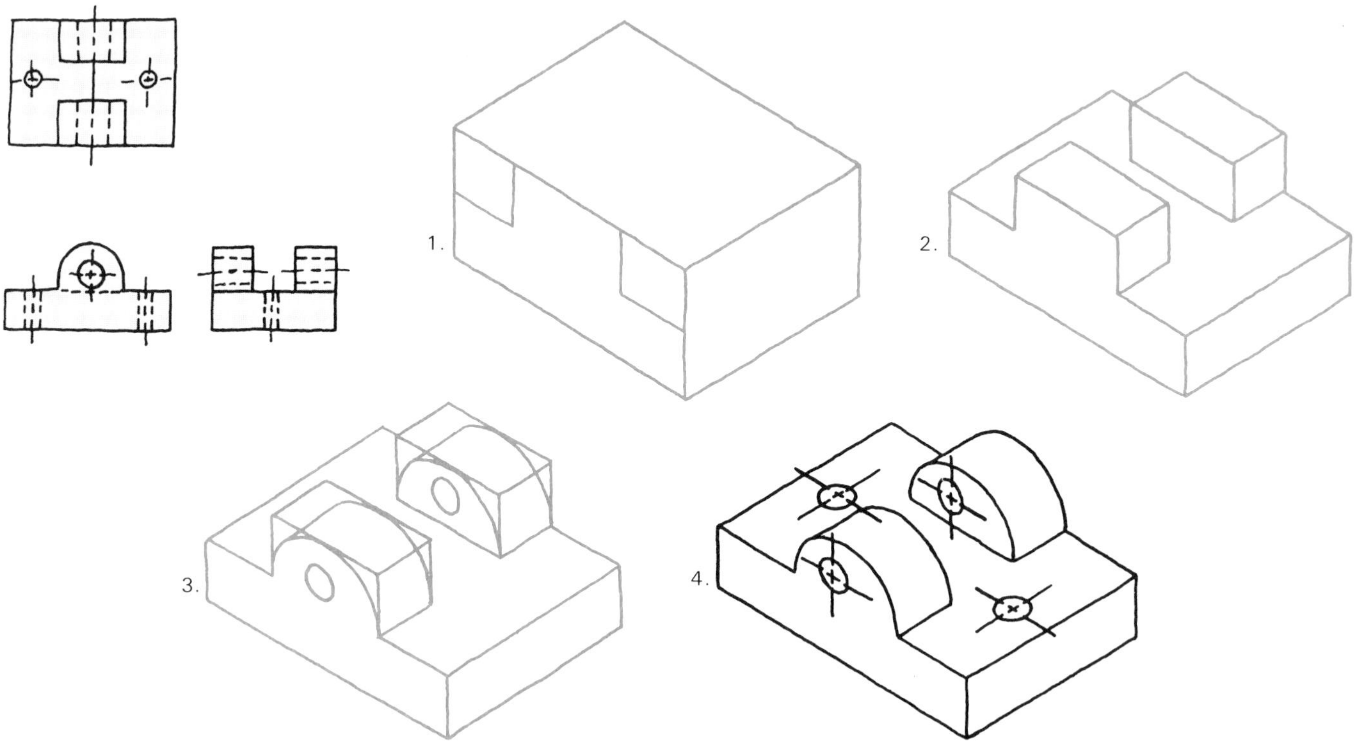

Fig. 2.39. Study the front, top,and side views to sketch an isometric view of objects with circular shapes.

top surface into thirds. Remove the center section by erasing and adding lines to the voided area.

Then, locate center points, sketch centerlines, and mark the radii on the centerlines for the elliptical shapes. Finally, sketch the elliptical shapes. Erase all unnecessary layout lines. Resketch all lines to make them consistent.

Notice the horizontal dashed line in the middle of the front view does not touch the solid horizontal line on either end. This open space indicates the ''hidden surface'' represented by the dashed line, continues on both ends as a ''visible surface'' and is represented by solid lines.

DESIGNING PRODUCTS USING MULTIVIEW AND ISOMETRIC SKETCHES

One of the most valuable outcomes of the previous series of activities is for you to become comfortable in sketching products. With practice, sketching becomes easier, more accurate, and faster. As you use sketching to design products and refine them, both multiview projections and isometric sketches will be useful. As you add advanced concepts to your sketching abilities, such as in dimensioning, you may want to develop the ideas for projects for you and others to produce.

PROBLEMS AND GRADING CRITERIA

Now that you have read and studies this chapter, you are encouraged to practice your sketching skills. The completion of the following problems will, first of all, help you to better understand sketching techniques and, secondly, improve your sketching ability. As with any skill, practice is essential. The more you practice, the better you will become. Hopefully, sketching will become a new language for you to use in communicating your ideas and the work of others graphically.

You and your teacher will need to select criteria to be used to evalute your work. The following list suggests criteria that may be applied to the various problems:

1. Sketch lines that are straight.
2. Sketch curved lines that are symmetrical.
3. Estimate the angles for an isometric cube accurately.
4. Sketch isometric cubes to the proper proportions.
5. Maintain sets of lines parallel in an isometric sketch.
6. Add to and subtract from an isometric cube.
7. Arrange the front, right side, and top views properly.
8. Project distances and features between views consistently.
9. Sketch dashed lines appropriately.
10. Make final lines straight, sharp, and consistently wide.
11. Sketch ellipses with consistent shapes and good quality centerlines.
12. Keep work neat and accurate.

Chapter 2—SKETCHING
Review What You Have Learned

Write all of your answers on a separate sheet of paper. Do not write in this textbook.

Essay:

1. Write a short, concise statement describing the professional people who sketch products.
2. Write a paragraph describing the value of sketching.

Multiple Choice: Carefully read the statements below and write the letter of the best answer for each of the items on your answer sheet.

3. Sketching is useful for recording ideas of:
   a. Hobbyists.
   b. Engineers.
   c. Architects.
   d. Designers.
   e. All of these.
4. In isometric and multiview drawings, circles may appear as:
   a. Circles.
   b. Dashed lines.
   c. Ellipses.
   d. a and c.
   e. All of these.
5. Sketching combines:
   a. Vertical/horizontal lines.
   b. Slanted lines.
   c. Arcs.
   d. Circles.
   e. All of these.
6. A hole drilled in a product may appear as what in a multiview sketch?
   a. Straight line.
   b. Circle.
   c. Dashed lines.
   d. b and c.
   e. All of these.

True or False: Carefully read the statements below. Write a "T" on your answer sheet for the statements which are true. For the statements which are false, write an "F." Rewrite each false statement so it becomes true.

7. Sketching is a quick way to create and record product ideas. True or False?
8. Circular shapes in an isometric view are round. Truc or False?
9. Making short overlapping strokes, helps to keep lines straight and consistent. True or False.?
10. Sketching dark layout lines is preferred over light layout followed by darkening lines later. True or False?
11. A dashed line represents a visible surface. True or False?
12. Good isometric sketches involve making lines straight, keeping lines parallel, and estimating distance accurately. True or False?

Completion: After studying this chapter, read the incomplete sentences below. Write the missing word or words on your answer sheet. In this chapter,some of the answers may be drawings as well as words.

13. When compared to a clock face, isometric views rely upon sets of lines that are in ________, ________, and ________ o'clock directions.
14. The number of centerlines sketched for a hole is ________ when it is circular and ________ when it is a pair of hidden lines.
15. Ellipses can be formed by sketching two circular shapes that are ________ and ________ between the centerlines.
16. Angular lines may be sketched in isometric by connecting ________ that are located on the rectangular cube.
17. A sketched ________ view of a product helps to visualize the product accurately.
18. A centerline is sketched as ________-________-________.
19. Hidden lines are sketched as ________.

Matching: Match the view of an isometric sketch in column A with the appropriate pair of centerlines from column B needed in each view to sketch an ellipse.

Column A	Column B
20. Top view.	a. Vertical and 10 o'clock directions.
21. Front view.	b. Vertical and 2 o'clock directions.
22. Side view.	c. 10 o'clock and 2 o'clock directions.
	d. Horizontal and 10 o'clock directions.
	e. Horizontal and 2 o'clock directions.

Match the views of a multiview sketch in column A with their appropriate length, width, and depth relationships from column B.

Column A	Column B
23. Top view.	a. Length- depth.
24. Front view.	b. Depth - height.
25. Side view.	c. Height - length.
	d. Height only.
	e. Depth only.

Practice What You Have Learned: On a blank sheet of 8 1/2 x 11 inch paper, carefully sketch the objects listed below to gain practice in sketching techniques.

A video cassette.

A squeeze water bottle that will clip on a bicycle.

A cabinet to hold your favorite sound/video system. Include sketches of all of the components.

SKETCHING OBJECT LINES

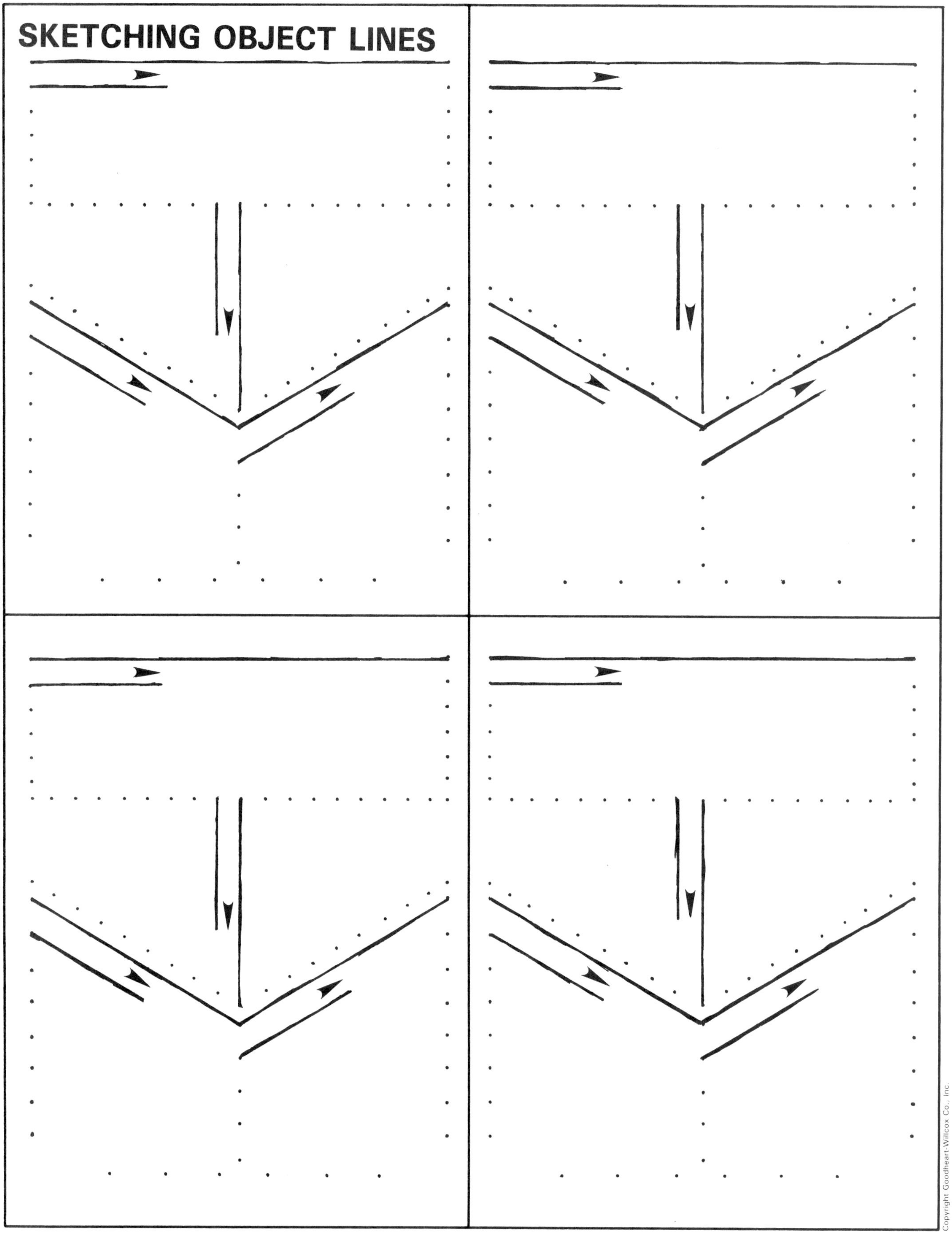

2-1 SKETCHING PRACTICE. On a separate sheet of paper, sketch this assignment. First sketch the border lines by sketching along a straight edge. Secondly, divide the sheet into four equal spaces by estimating distances and then sketching long lines between two points. Use short overlapping strokes to sketch the horizontal, vertical, and slanted lines parallel to each other between the dots.

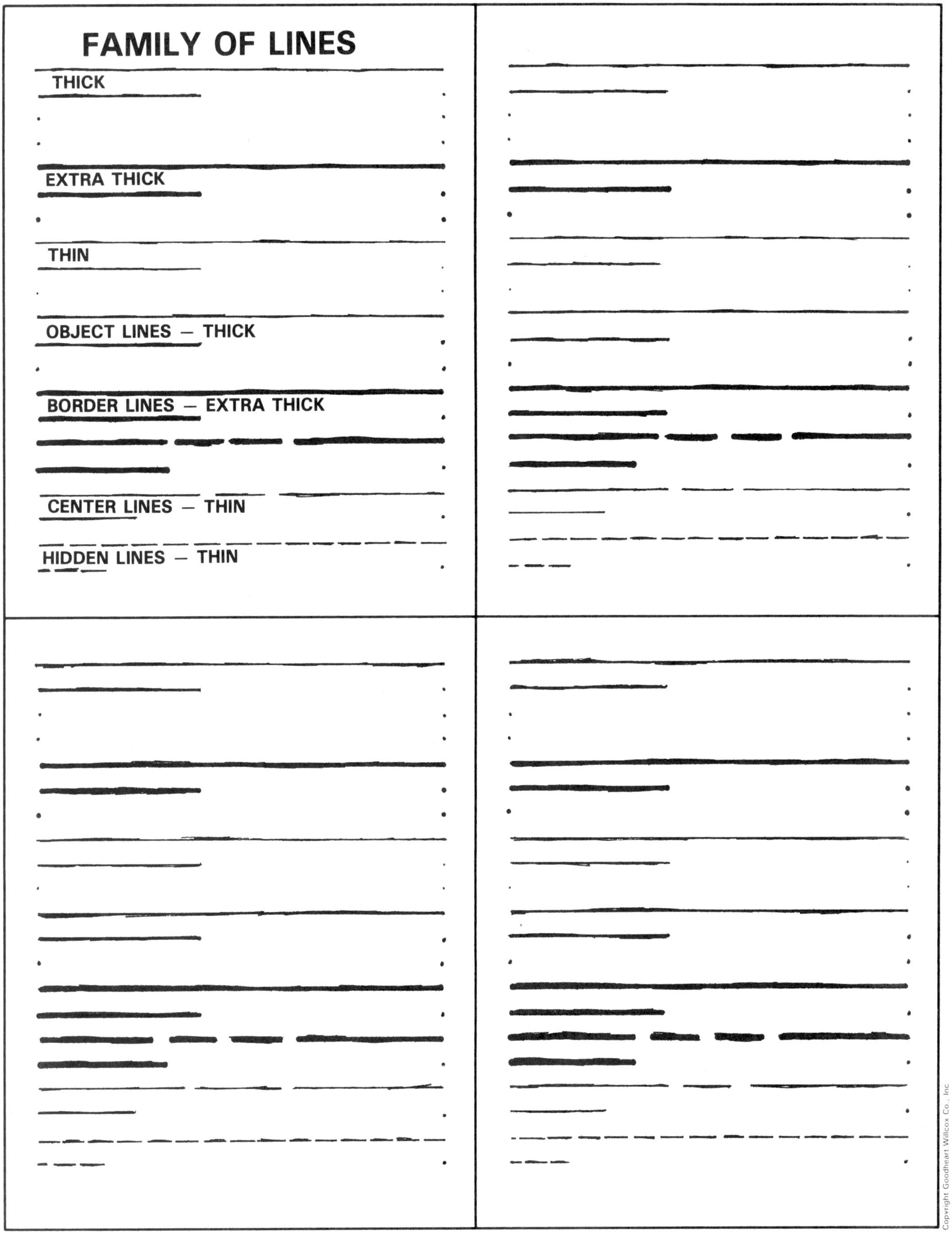

2-2 SKETCHING THE FAMILY OF LINES. On a separate sheet of paper, sketch this assignment. Sketch the border lines and divide the sheet into fourths. Sketch thick, extra thick, thin, object lines, border lines, centerlines, and hidden lines. Letter each of the panels.

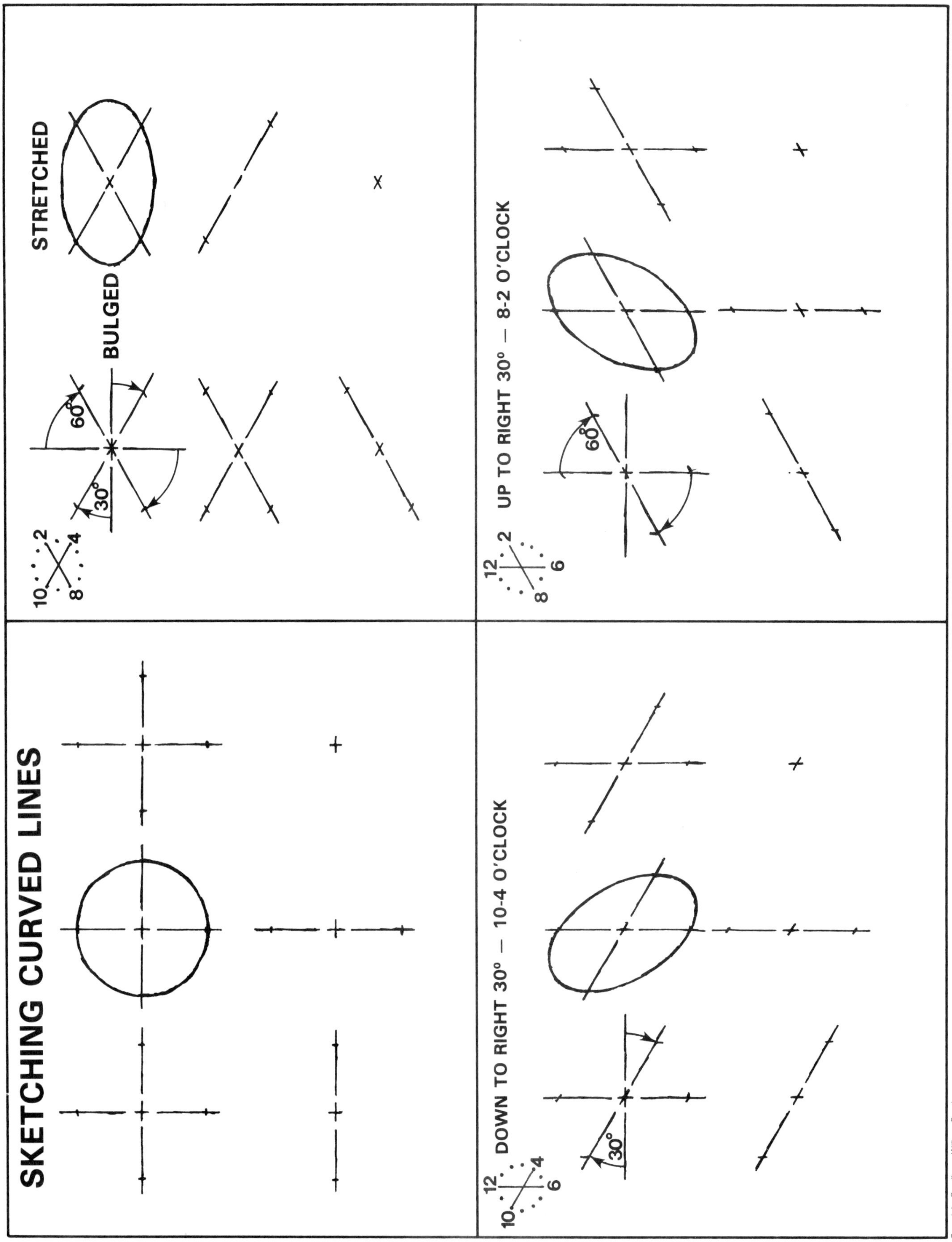

2-3 SKETCHING CURVED LINES. Practice sketching circles and ellipses on a separate sheet of paper. For circles, estimate equal distances away from the center point in all four directions. For ellipses, estimate equal distances on opposite sides of the shape. Make the curved lines sharp, black, and consistent, and smooth.

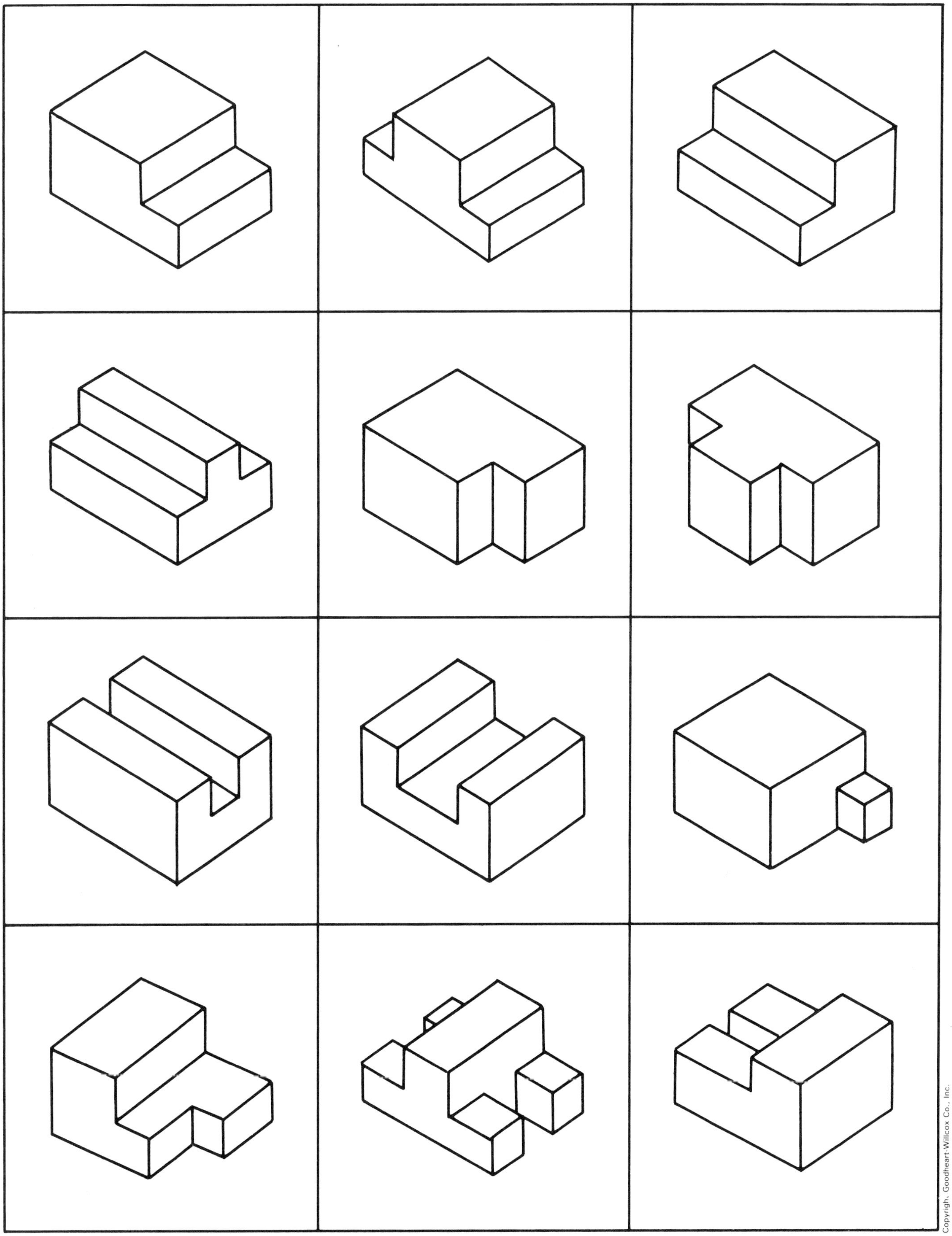

2-4 SKETCHING RECTANGULAR OBJECTS. Divide a sheet into fourths. Sketch pictorial views of the objects shown in this exercise. Start by sketching isometric cubes, then add or remove areas. Keep lines straight and parallel.

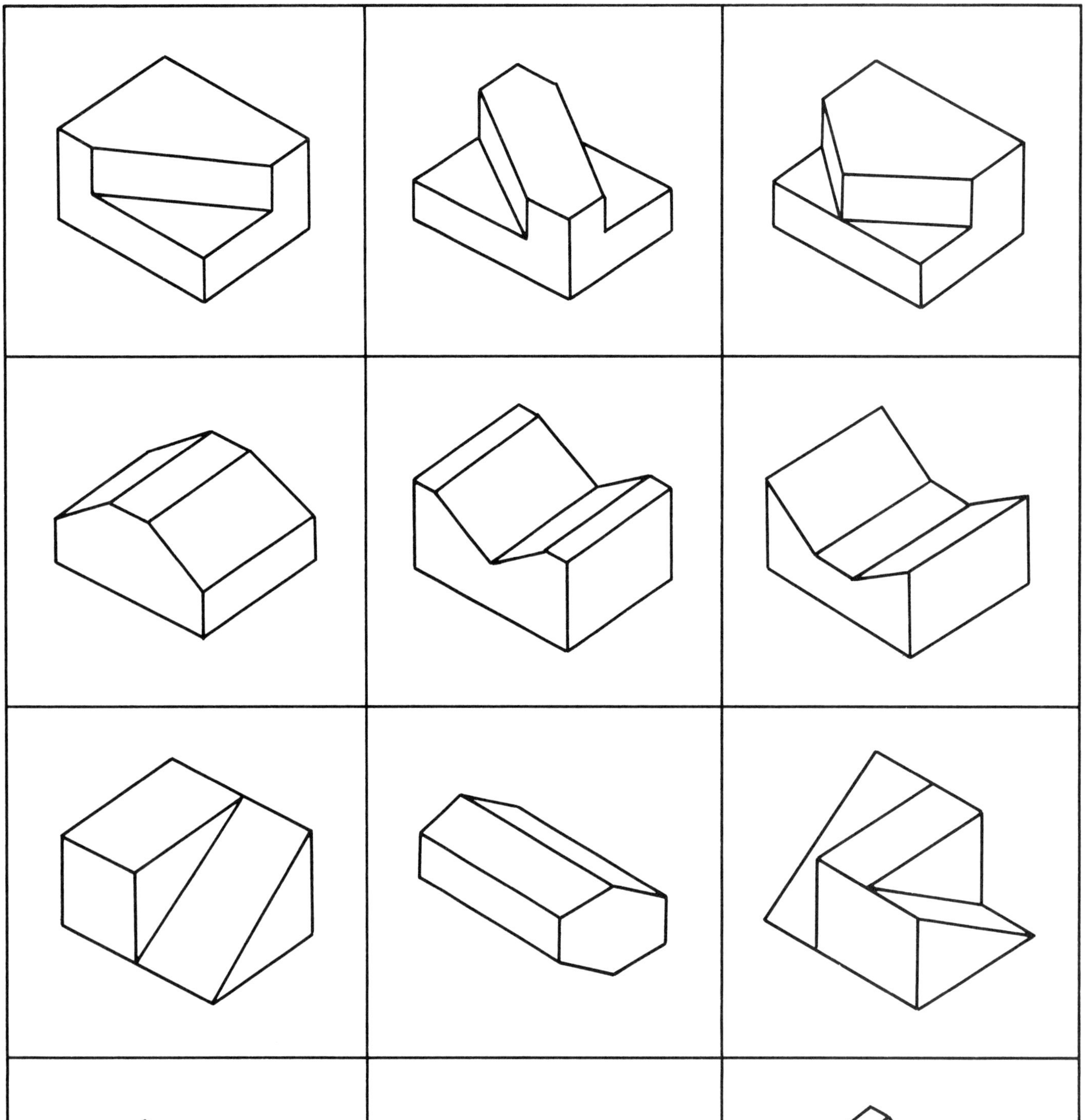

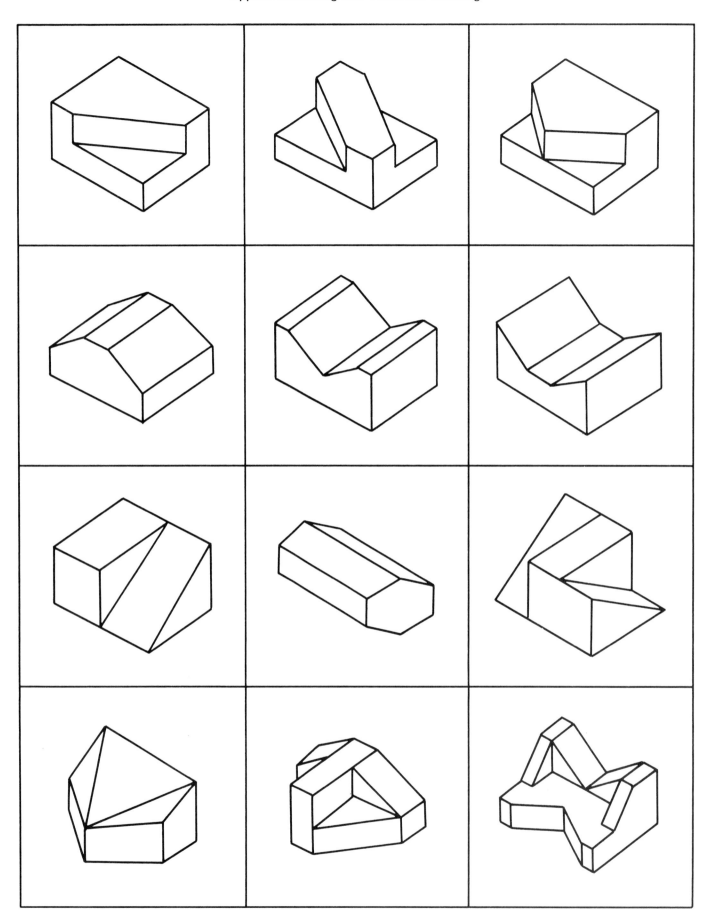

2-5 SKETCHING OBJECTS WITH SLANTED SURFACES. Select objects from this exercise and sketch the pictorial views. Start with an isometric cube and add or remove the slanted portion.

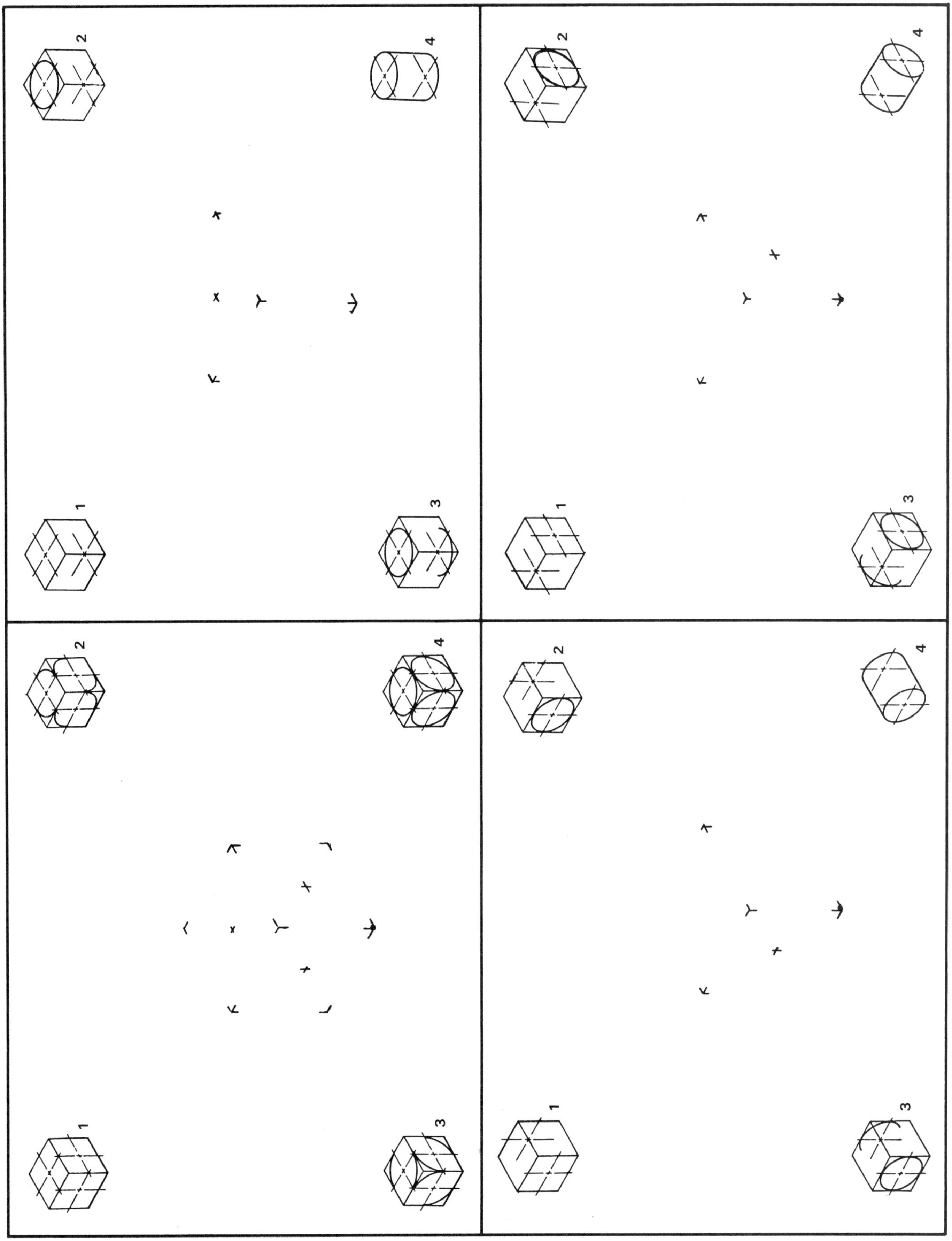

2-6 SKETCHING OBJECTS WITH CURVED SURFACES. Sketch the pictorial views of these objects in the center of the space provided. Start with an isometric cube and add centerlines. Sketch a cylinder viewed from the top, front, and side.

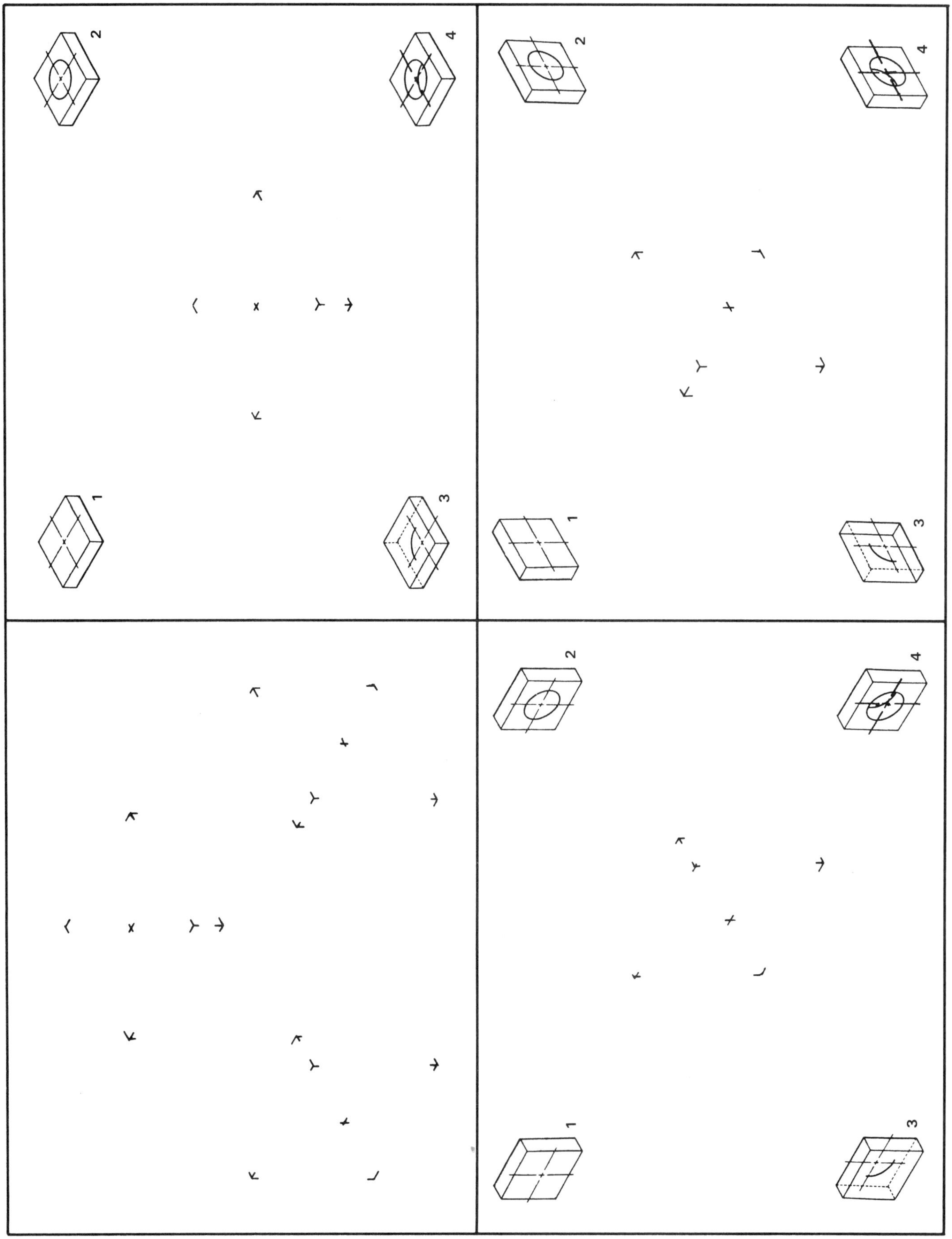

2-7 SKETCHING OBJECTS WITH HOLES. In the top left panel, sketch three rectanglar slabs 1 x 4 x 4 units in size, then add centerlines. Use the tick marks as starting points. In the remaining three panels follow the sequence to sketch a slab with a hole removed from the top, from the front, and from the side.

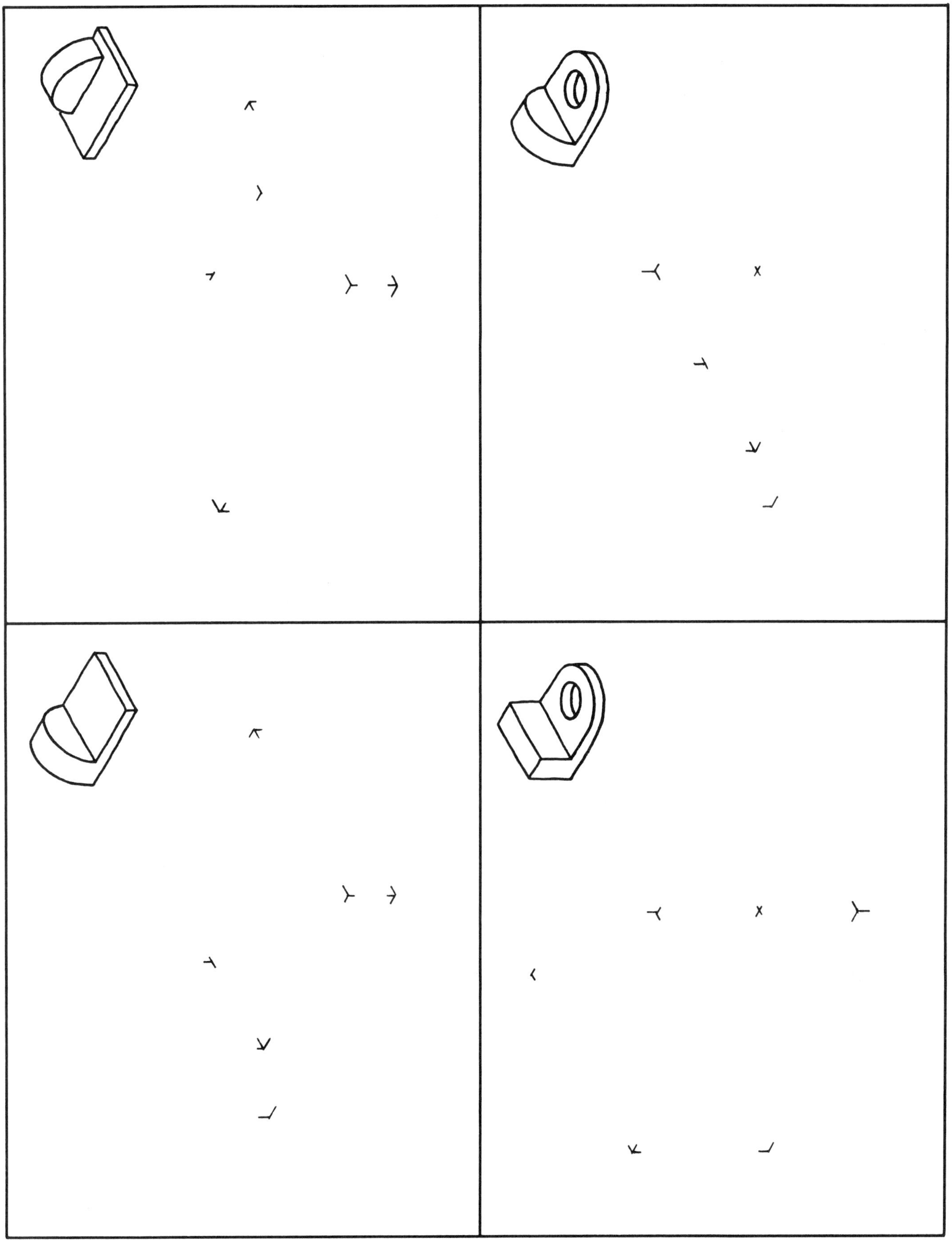

2-8 SKETCHING CIRCULAR OBJECTS. Sketch the circular objects shown. Use the tick marks to position your sketch. Refer back to any previous exercise for assistance.

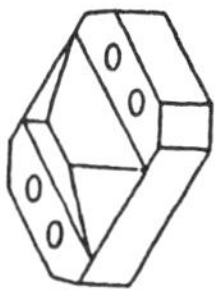

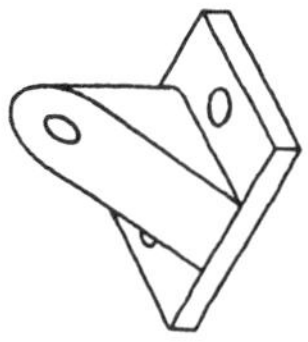

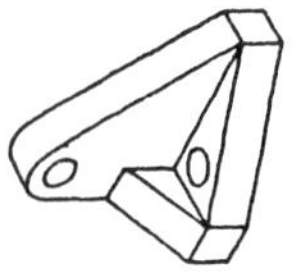

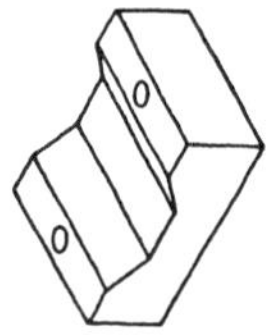

2-9 SKETCHING PICTORIAL VIEWS OF BRACKETS. On a separate sheet of paper, sketch the brackets shown in this exercise. Add centerlines.

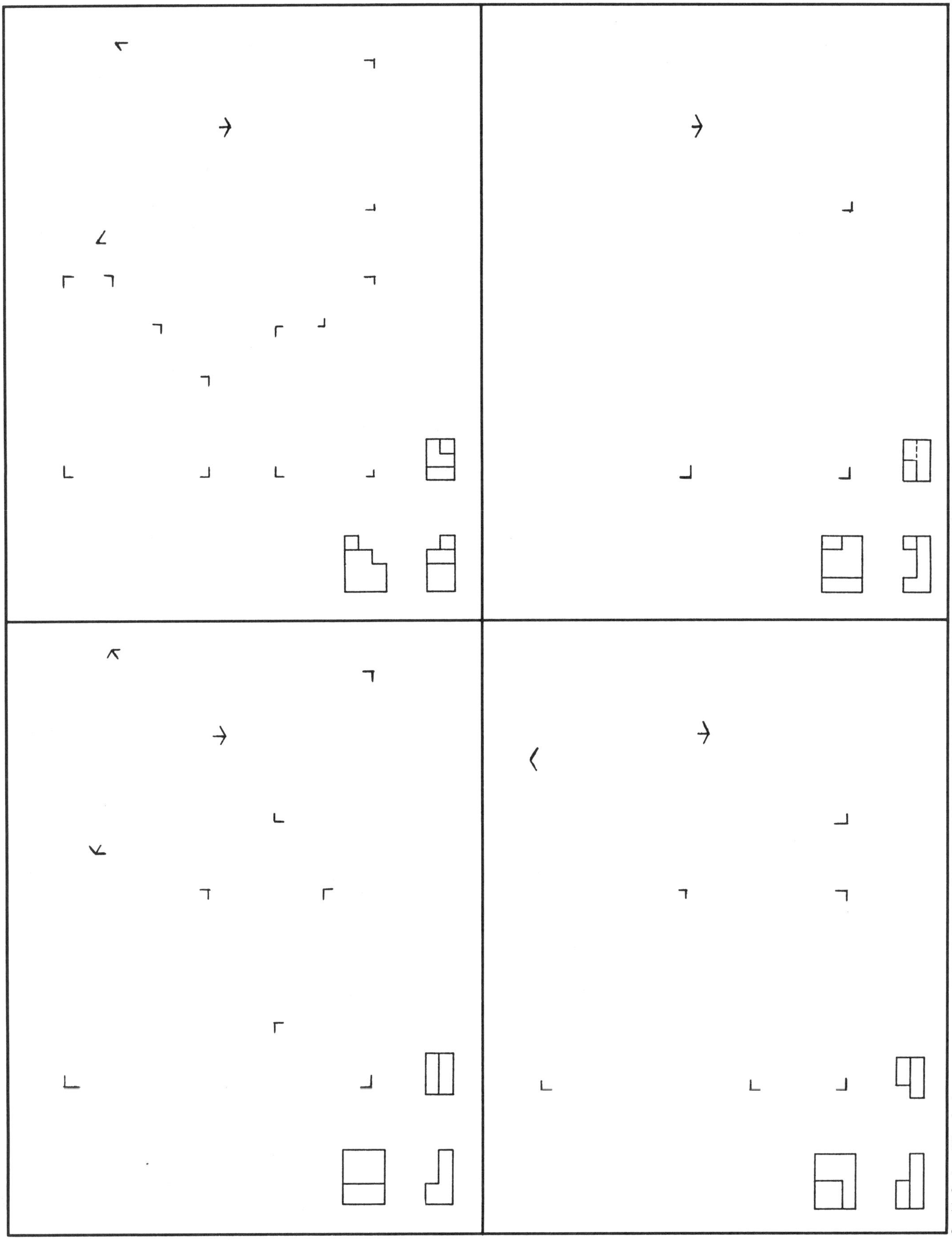

2-10 SKETCHING MULTIVIEWS AND PICTORIALS OF RECTANGULAR OBJECTS. Using the tick marks as starting points, sketch the multiview of the object shown. Next, label the surfaces as F (front), T (top), and S (side). If there is more than one top surface, for example, label the views T1, T2, etc. Sketch the pictorial view of the object and label the surfaces.

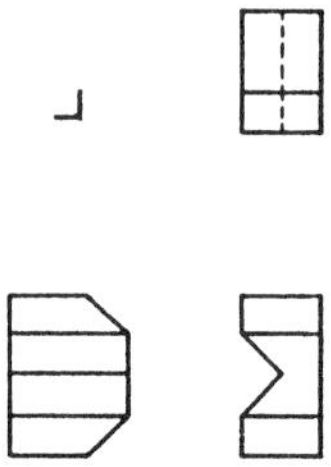

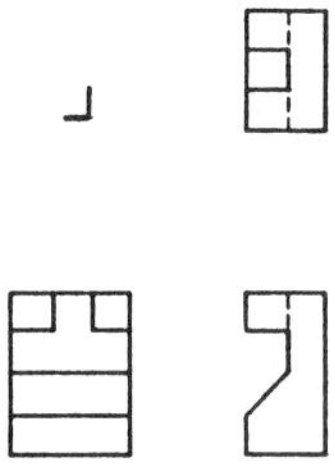

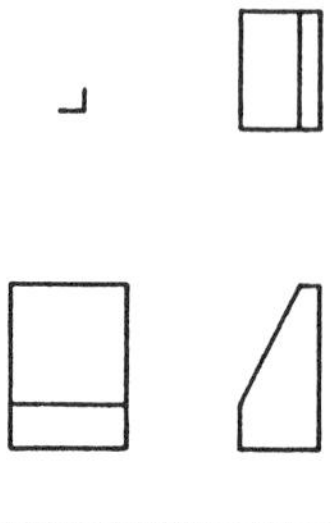

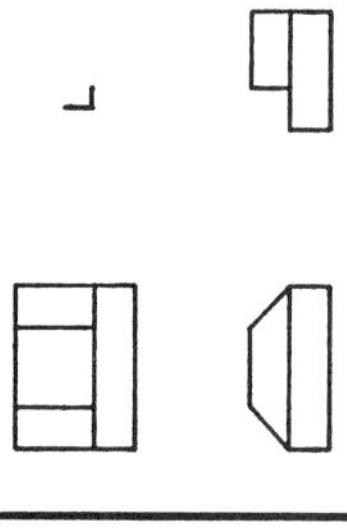

2-11 SKETCHING MULTIVIEWS AND PICTORIALS WITH SLANTED SURFACES. Sketch the multiview of the slanted surface objects shown in this exercise. Label the surfaces using F, T, and S as in problem 2-10. Sketch the pictorial view of the object and label the surfaces.

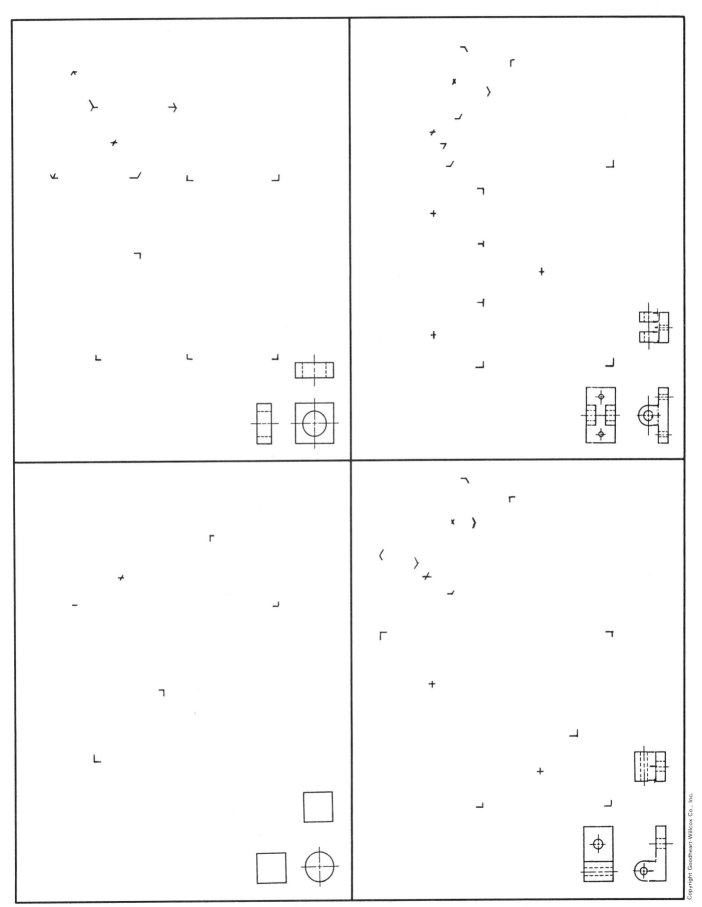

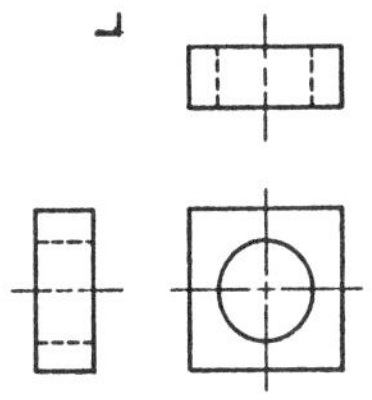

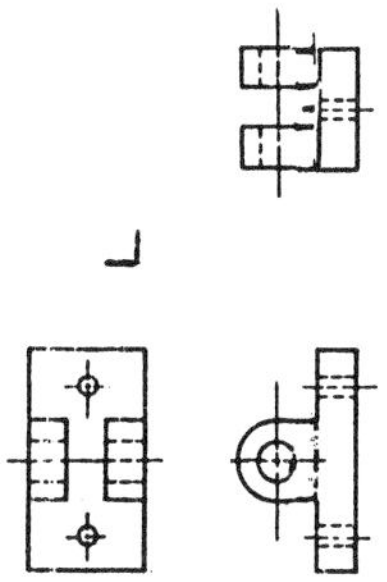

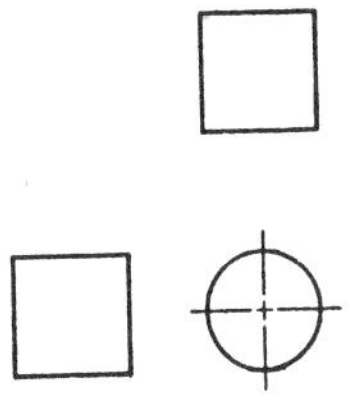

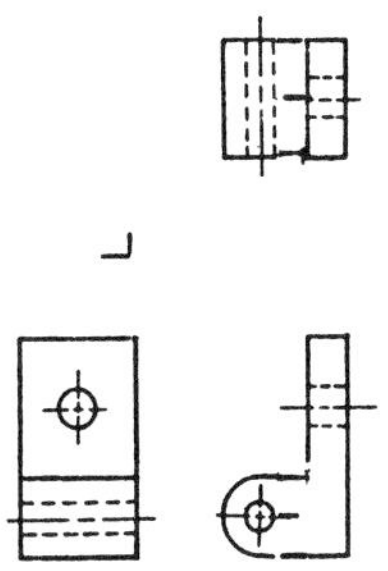

2-12 SKETCHING MULTIVIEWS AND PICTORIALS OF CIRCULAR SHAPES. Sketch the multiviews of the circular shapes shown here. Be sure to include the centerlines. Label the surfaces. Sketch the pictorial view of the object and label the surfaces.

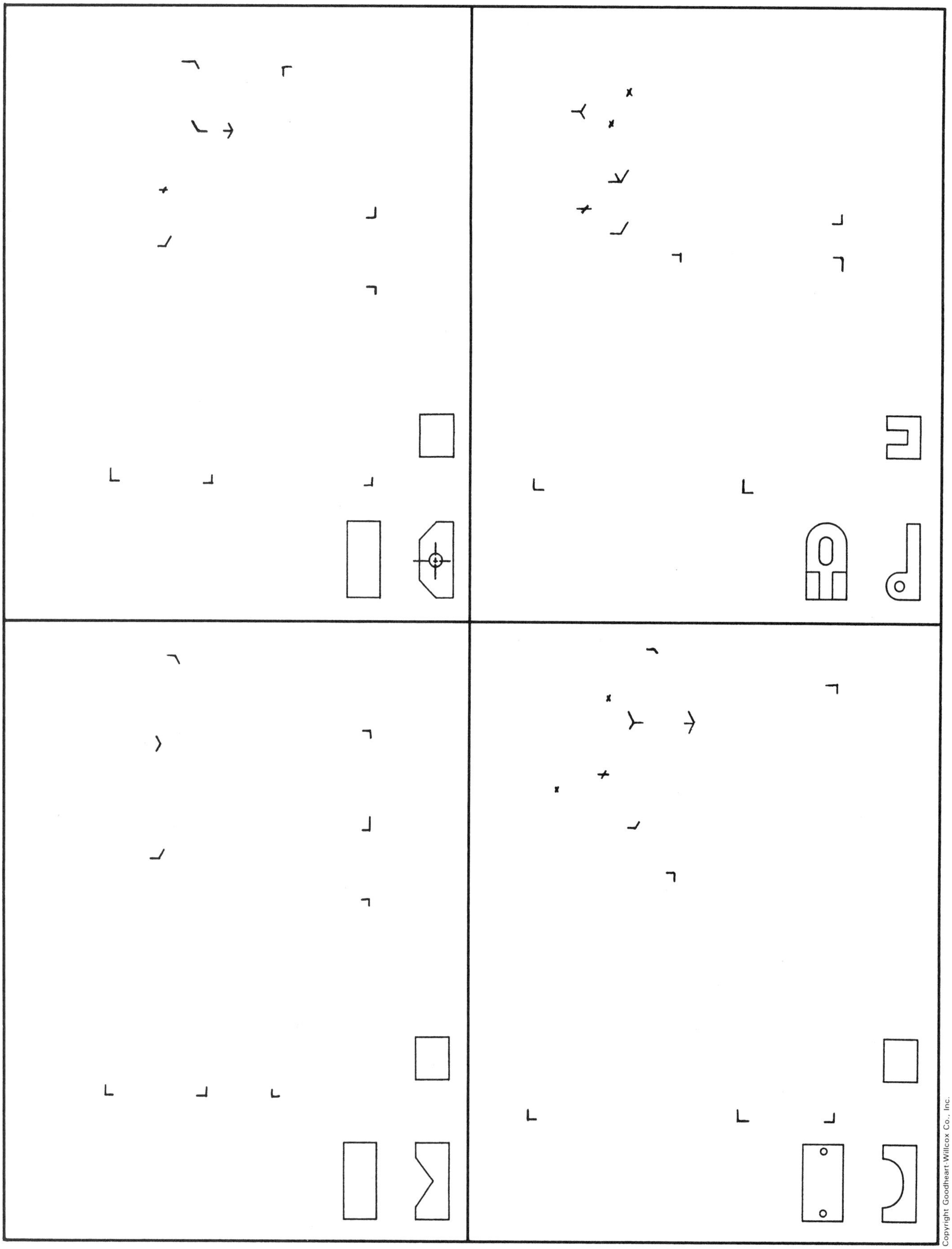

2-13 SKETCHING MULTIVIEWS AND PICTORIALS OF PRODUCTION ITEMS. Sketch the multiviews of the objects shown in the exercise. Add any necessary lines to the multiview projections such as hidden lines or object lines. Be sure to include centerlines. Label the surfaces. Sketch the pictorial view of the object and label the surfaces.

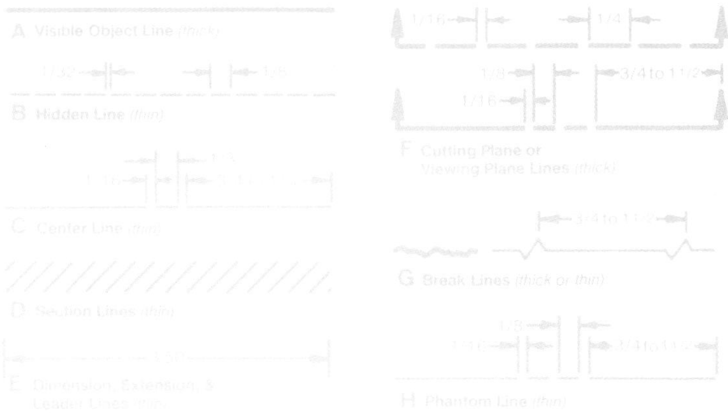

Chapter 3

INSTRUMENT DRAWING

OBJECTIVES

After completing this INSTRUMENT DRAWING chapter, you will be able to:

- ☐ *Select the proper equipment to prepare mechanical drawings.*
- ☐ *Draw horizontal, vertical, and angular lines.*
- ☐ *Draw circles, arcs, and elliptical shapes.*
- ☐ *Use scales in fraction/inch, decimal/inch, and metric measurements.*
- ☐ *Complete geometric constructions and shapes.*
- ☐ *Demonstrate accuracy, neatness, and detail in preparing drawings.*

Drafting is the language of industry used to communicate industrial ideas throughout a manufacturing enterprise. First, ideas are sketched, then they are drawn on tracing paper with instruments, and later transferred to multiple copies or prints. People who work from sketches to develop drawings, tracings, and prints use many skills and techniques that communicate information accurately and efficiently, Fig. 3-1. Drawings may also be created using a screen, a keyboard, and a mouse.

Sketching and instrument drawing can be compared to handwriting and keyboarding. Often, sketching is used to create parts and products just as handwriting is used to form a "rough draft" of a paper, Fig. 3-2. As sketches of parts and products enter the research and development stage, they are revised just as you would revise a rough draft of a paper. When it becomes necessary to communicate ideas with people in other manufacturing areas, the sketches are transformed into neat, precise tracings and prints. Similarly, the final draft of a paper is typed before distributing it for others to read.

Good drawings provide a clear representation of a part of product that leads to a single interpretation. As drawings are distributed within a manufacturing unit, everyone involved must interpret the same meaning. Errors of interpretation may be costly and embarrassing.

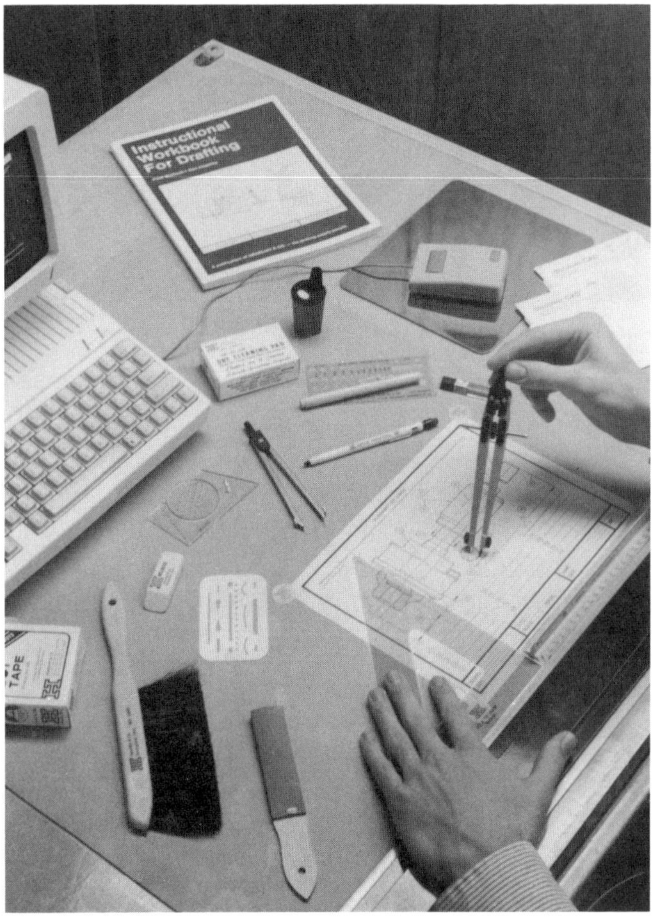

Fig. 3-1. The modern drafter uses a variety of materials, instruments, and equipment. (Hearlihy)

This chapter emphasizes good technique in using instruments to prepare outstanding line work. Each succeeding chapter of this text adds new concepts. Use of these concepts allows you to produce concise drawings that are easily interpreted.

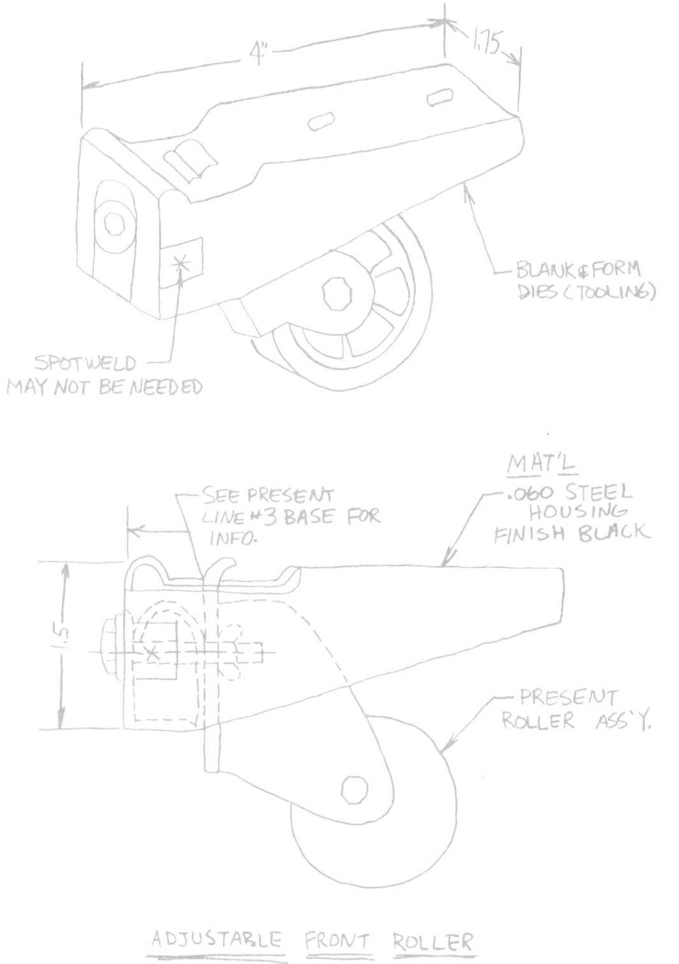

Fig. 3-2. A typical sketch of a design concept for an industrial part. Sketches may be transformed into finished drawings using the instruments and skills learned in this chapter.

FUNDAMENTALS

The major purpose of a design and engineering department is to produce acceptable tracings and prints for new parts and products. After a rough or sketched design is completed by an engineer, graphics personnel decide whether to develop drawings mechanically or with a computer-aided design system, Fig. 3-3.

For drawings developed mechanically, graphic specialists lay out and illustrate the part or product information in a series of views. These views help answer questions and solve problems. Graphics personnel must:

1. Determine the appropriate views.
2. Establish a logical relationship between views.
3. Select an appropriate scale.

After these basic concerns have been satisfied in the initial layout phase, tracings are made for reproducing prints.

Techniques for producing drawings and tracings using basic equipment are discussed and illustrated in this unit of instruction. As your skill and interest grow, additional drafting equipment may be desired to improve your productivity.

COMMON PRACTICES

A primary responsibility of an engineering unit is to produce drawings which are easily interpreted. Good lettering and proper line quality are essential components in producing professional drawings. Lettering must be neat, accurate, and distinctive. Lines must be sharp, dark, and of consistent width, Fig. 3-4.

As you learn to draw with instruments, imagine yourself as a newly-hired drafting detailer working in the drawing room of an engineering department. Be very particular about the quality of your work. Your tracings will be used to make a series of prints that can be easily interpreted by others.

Good drawings involve proper use of drawing equipment. This chapter helps you build confidence in using the basic drawing furniture, materials, and instruments, Fig. 3-5. **Furniture** includes drawing tables or boards and parallel rules, T-squares, or drafting machines. **Materials** consist of various types of pencils, lead, pens, ink, erasers, tape, and

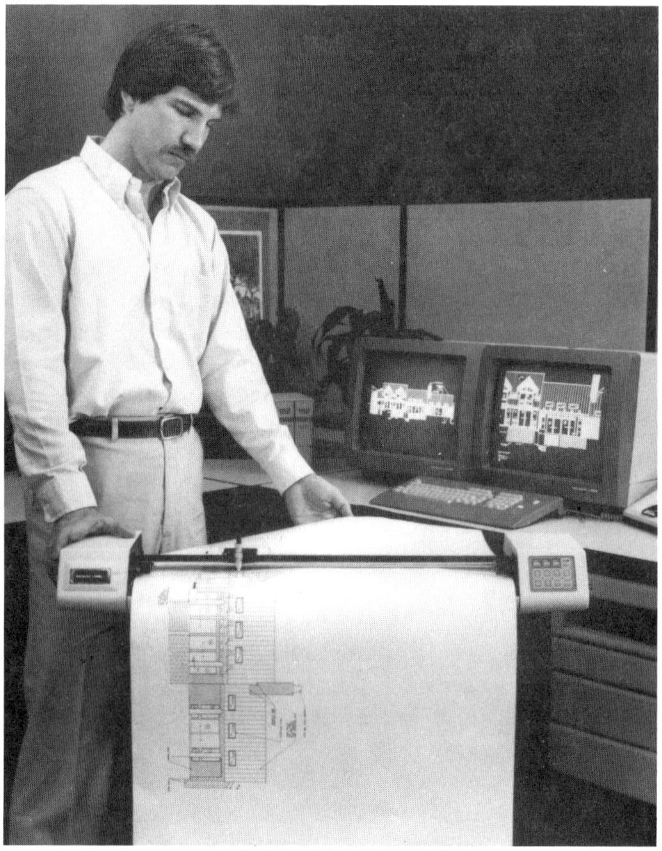

Fig. 3-3. Drawings may be produced mechanically using a computer and a plotter. (Houston Instrument)

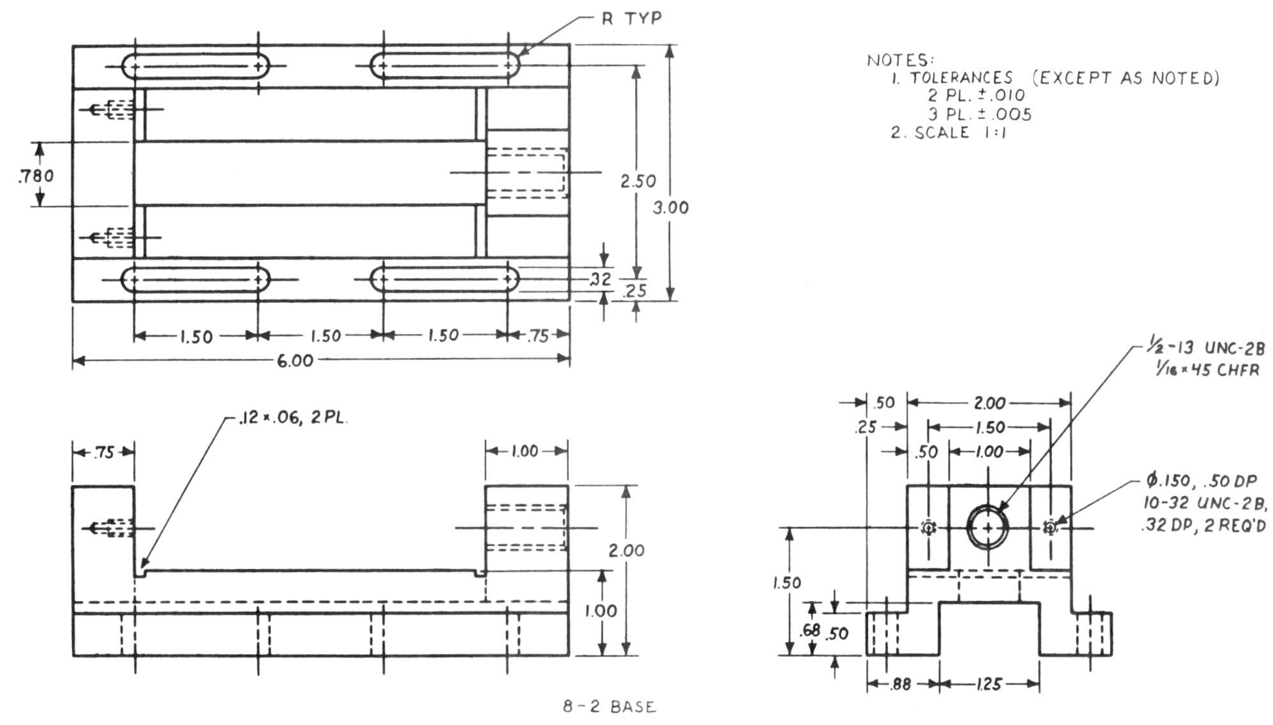

DETAIL DRAWING

Fig. 3-4. This neat and accurate drawing is easy to understand and allows you to visualize the part. (Hearlihy)

Fig. 3-5. Typical mechanical drawing area uses a variety of materials, equipment, and instruments. (Hearlihy)

drawing paper. **Instruments** include triangles, compasses, dividers, scales, and templates.

You should have access to a portable drawing board for completing your homework or for developing ideas when not at your drawing table. A briefcase or tackle box is beneficial for organizing drawing materials and instruments. A three-ring notebook is also necessary for keeping drawings clean and available for reference.

PREPARING THE DRAWING AREA

The drawing board must be flat and smooth. A vinyl cover will improve the drawing surface. Another desirable features is to have the board tilted in a comfortable drawing position.

There are several methods for drawing horizontal lines on your drawing board. A common method is using a **parallel rule** that moves vertically over the board, Fig. 3-6. The rule always remains in a consistent horizontal position.

Another method is to use a **T-square,** Fig. 3-7. The T-square slides vertically along the right or left edge of the drawing board. It is controlled by the non-dominant hand. For example, if right-handed, use your left hand to control the action of the

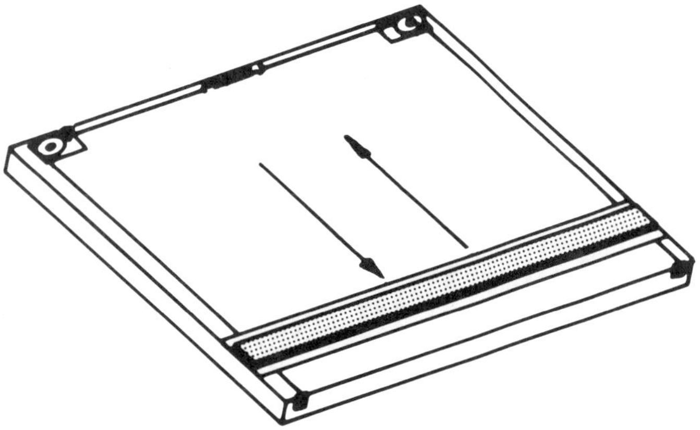

Fig. 3-6. Using a parallel rule.

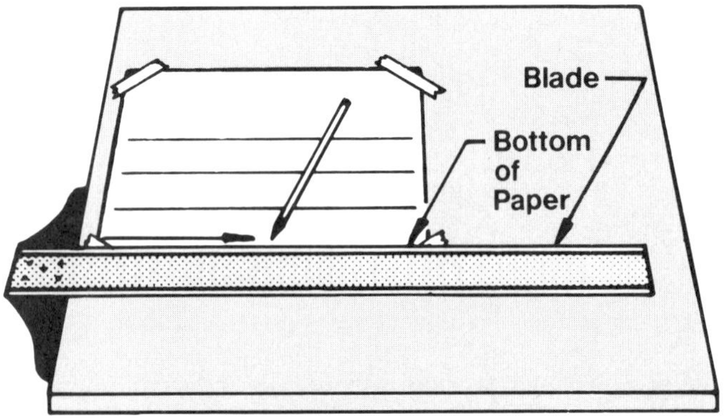

Fig. 3-7. Using a T-square and a drawing board. Hold the head of the T-square firmly against the edge of the board.

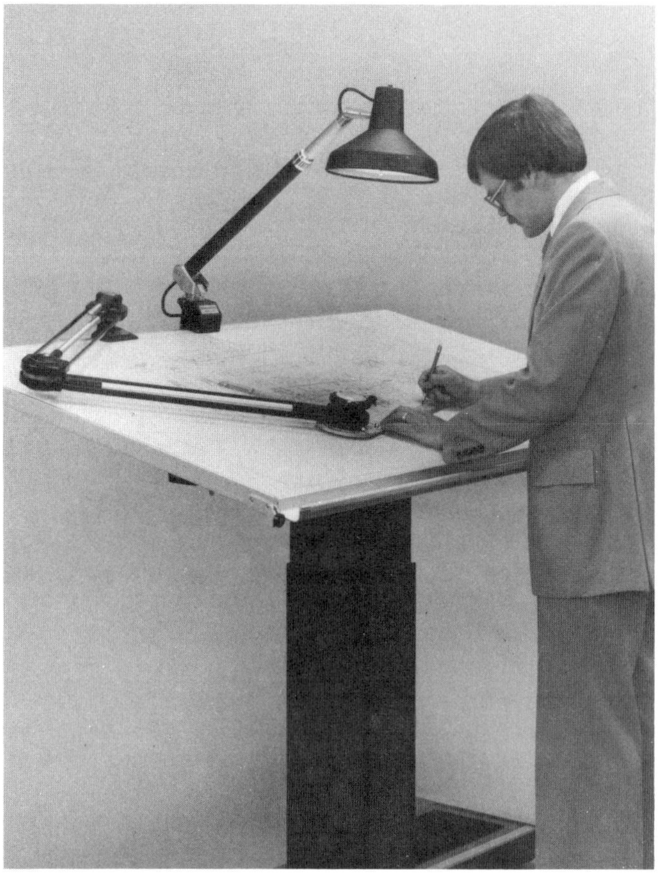

Fig. 3-8. The drafting machine attached to the upper left corner of the board provides accurate horizontal and vertical blades. (Vemco Corp.)

T-square. A smooth, straight drawing board edge is required for the T-square.

Lines can also be drawn with a **drafting machine,** Fig. 3-8. This device is attached to the upper left-hand corner of the drawing board. It has two movable arms connected to a set of horizontal and vertical blades. The machine can be moved around the board while the blades remain in a consistent horizontal and vertical orientation.

Some drafting detailers prefer to use large triangles to maintain horizontal, vertical, and oblique line relationships, Fig. 3-9. This is accomplished by holding the large triangle secure with the non-dominant hand and positioning a second, smaller triangle to draw the necessary lines.

Provide adequate time to become comfortable at your drawing board. Professional line quality evolves from practice with instruments and experience at the drawing board.

SELECTING THE BASIC MATERIALS

Pencils, paper, erasers, and tape are consumable items needed to develop your drawing skills. Various catalogs, your instructor, or your drafting supervisor can provide information about the kinds of materials locally available. Learn which types of materials are acceptable in your school or industry.

Drawing Leads

Pencil lead used in instrument drawing ranges from very soft, HB, to very hard, 9H, Fig. 3-10. The soft leads HB and H are used by those who have a light touch for achieving professional quality finished line work. The medium lead 2H is preferred by many people for most of their drawing. The hard leads, 3H through 9H, may be used for construction and initial layout work. A 2H or 3H pencil, however, is usually recommended for layout and construction work. A 2H or H pencil is used for object lines and finished line work.

The key to selecting the best pencil lead for drawing is to experiment with several different types. Use the ones that work best for you in producing accurate, sharp, and intense lines.

Mechanical Pencils

Two types of mechanical pencils are used for drawing, Fig. 3-11. A **lead holder** uses the same size lead found in wooden pencils. A more convenient

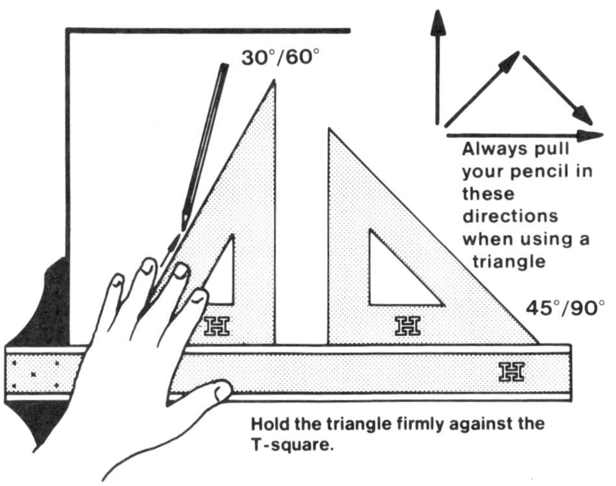

TRIANGLES

Triangles, usually made of clear or tinted plastic, are used for drawing vertical and angular lines. Drafters use two - the 30°/60° triangle which contains 30 degree, 60 degree and 90 degree angles, and the 45°/90° triangle which is made up of two 45 degree angles and one 90 degree angle.

To use a triangle hold it firmly against the top edge of the T-square or parallel rule. Draw a vertical or angular line by placing the pencil point against the triangle and pulling it upward to draw a line from bottom to top. Do not apply too much pressure as it will form grooves in the paper that cannot be removed. Holding the triangle and T-square firmly without movement will insure parallel lines every time.

To prevent smearing when drawing vertical or angular lines, always work from left to right across the sheet.

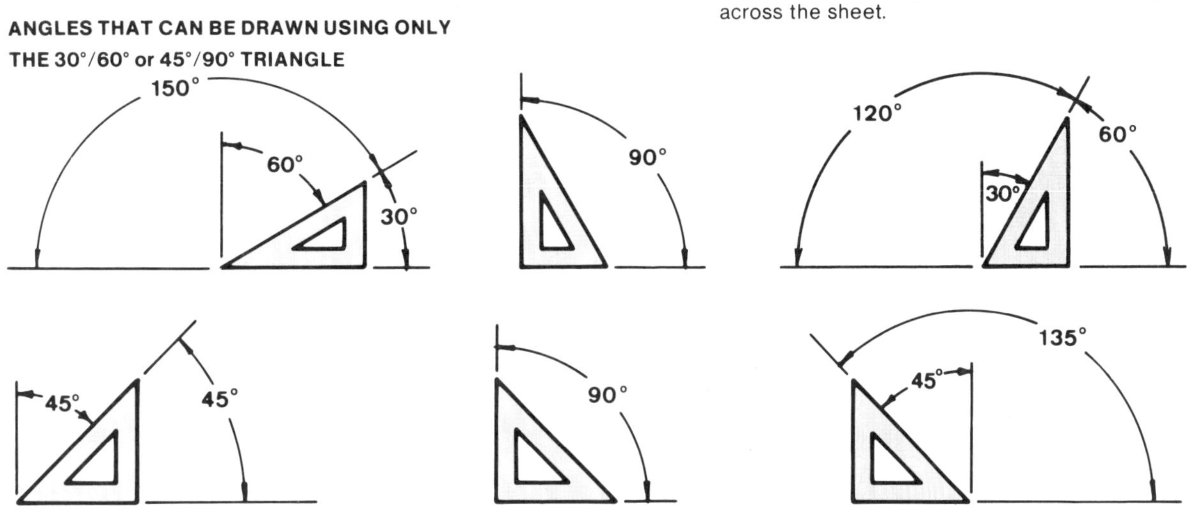

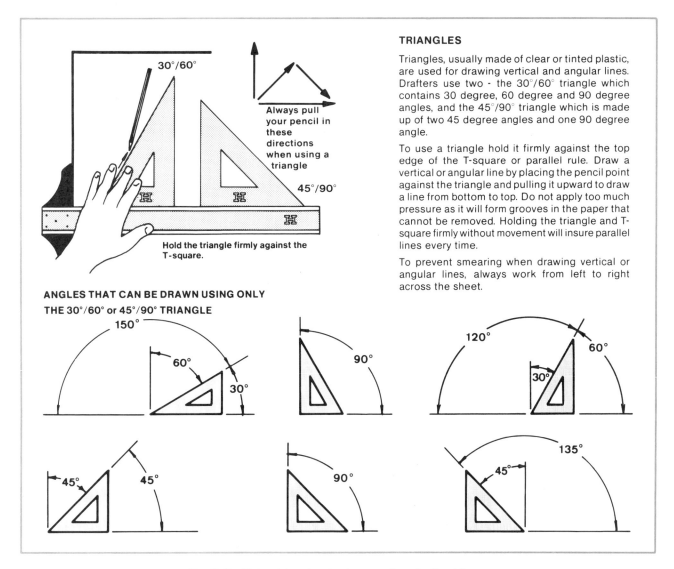

Fig. 3-9. Using triangles to draw various inclined lines.

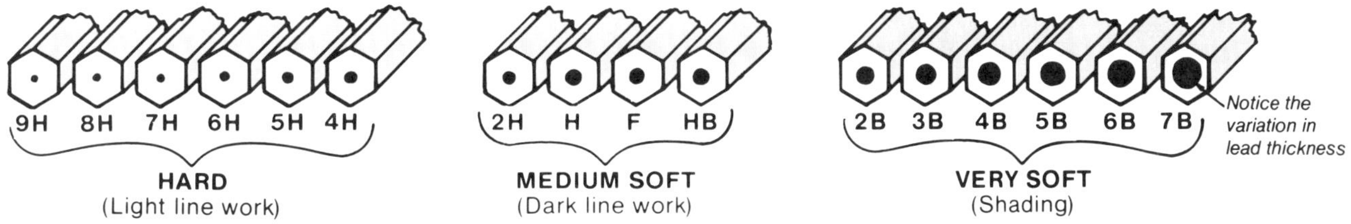

Fig. 3-10. Selection of drawing pencils available for layout work, for dark line work, and for shading. The H, 2H, and HB are most commonly used.

pencil uses fine-line leads that compare to the actual width of the lines being drawn. The lead is "always sharp," whereas the wooden and mechanical pencils with larger lead must be sharpened.

The **.5 mm mechanical pencil** is the most popular size. After making several passes over an object line with a .5 mm lead pencil, you will have a sharp, black, and distinctive line approximately .7 mm wide. The .3 mm size lead is excellent for making centerlines, hidden lines, and section lines.

The lead usually furnished in mechanical pencils is 2H, but harder and soften leads may be purchased, Fig. 3-12. If a lead produces gray lines instead of black, use a softer lead. If the lines smudge, use a harder lead. The 2H, H, and HB leads are commonly used to produce professional line quality.

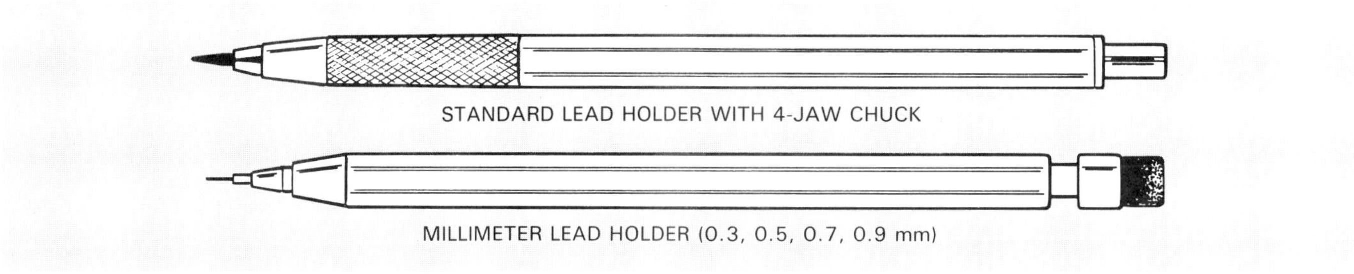

Fig. 3-11. Two different types of mechanical pencils. The 4-jaw chuck lead holder will adapt to any size lead. The millimeter lead holder produces lines of a defined width.

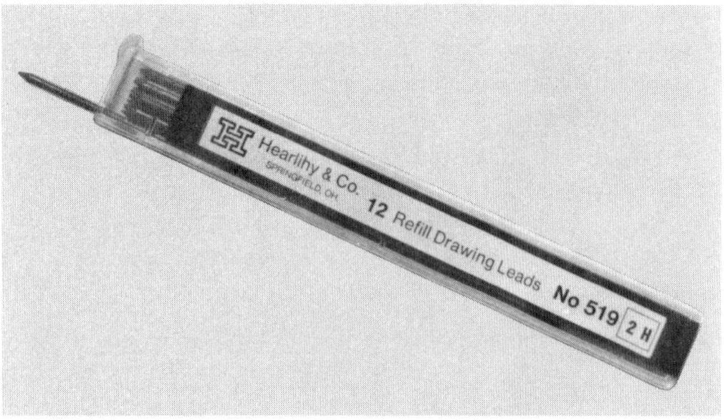

Fig. 3-12. Typical package of drawing leads. Note the hardness of the leads printed on the package.

When lines need to be removed, various erasers may be used, Fig. 3-13. The **ruby red eraser** is commonly used for all-purpose work, because it is inexpensive and effective for erasing. Ask your instructor or local supplier for other suggestions.

Sharpening the Pencil Point

Drafting pencils are sharpened differently than regular pencils. A special pencil sharpener is used to remove the wood, but not the lead, of wood-case drawing pencils. A special pencil pointer or sandpaper is then used to sharpen the lead, Fig. 3-14.

Fig. 3-13. Erasers used in instrument drawing. (Hearlihy)

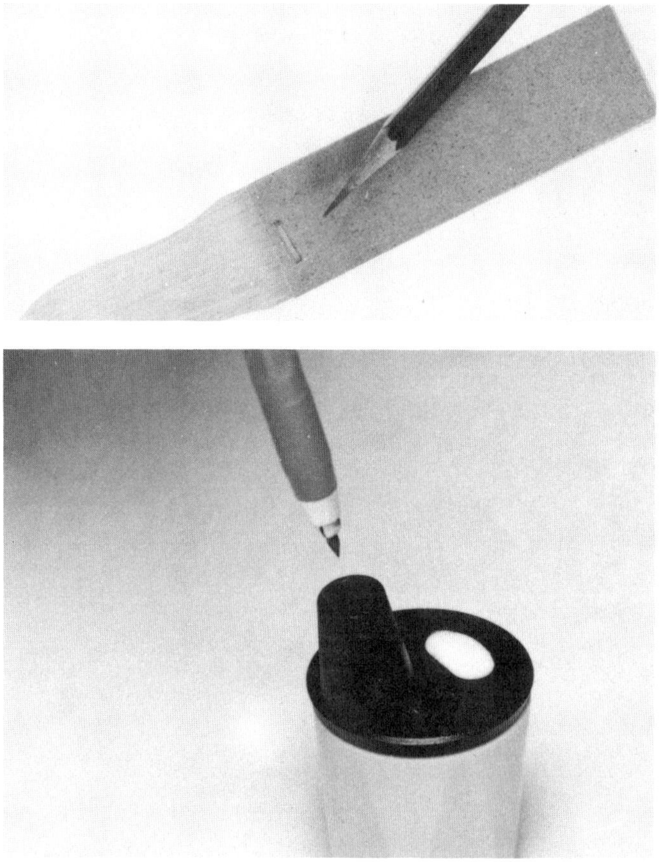

Fig. 3-14. Two methods used to sharpen a pencil. Top. Wood pencil is sharpened using sandpaper. Be sure to remove excess lead to keep your drawing neat and clean. Bottom. Mechanical pointer for the leads used in a mechanical lead holder. (Hearlihy)

Resharpening must be done frequently to maintain uniform line quality.

The lead in lead holders is sharpened with the same procedure as wooden pencils. Fine line mechanical pencils require no sharpening.

TECHNICAL PENS

Many professionals use three technical pens for producing drawings, Fig. 3-15. A 3x0/.25 mm pen

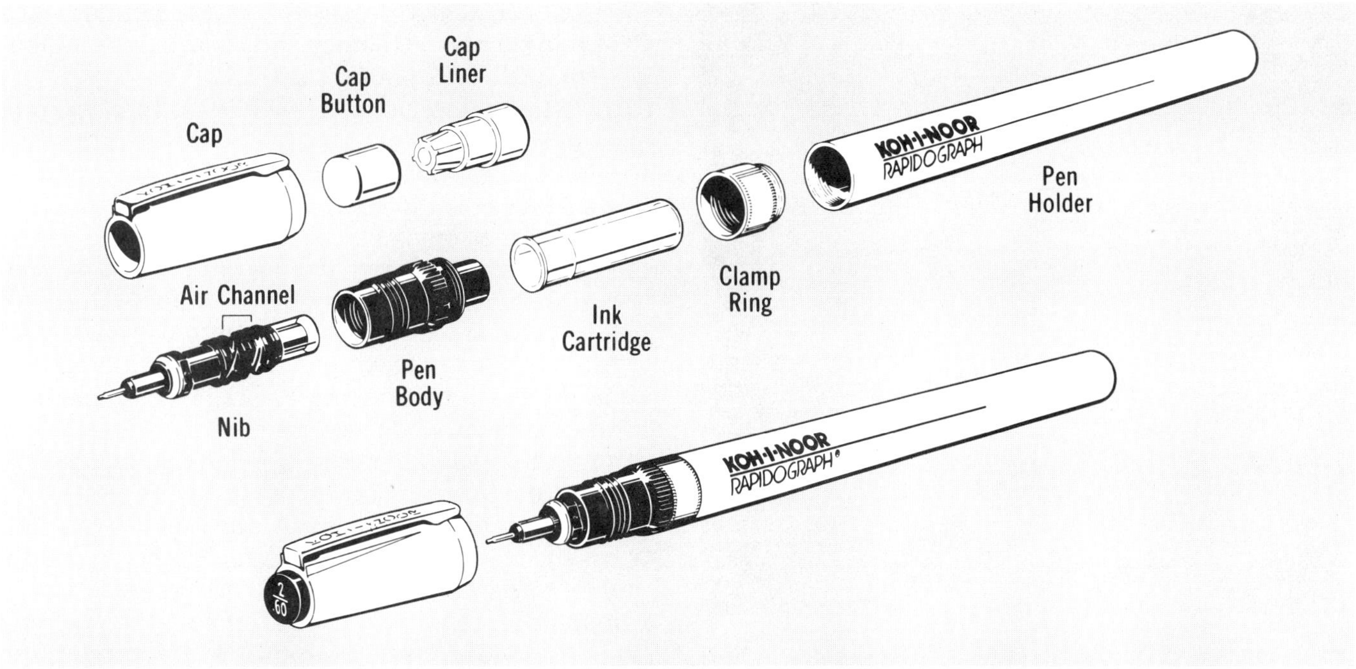

Fig. 3-15. Technical pen used in instrument drawing. The number on the cap is the line width. Keep all parts clean. (Koh-I-Noor)

is used for thin line dimensioning and sectioning. A 1/.50 mm pen is used for thick object lines. A 3/.80 mm pen is used for cutting plane lines or other extra thick lines. Refer to Fig. 3-16 to view the variety of line widths available. The ink used in technical pens is very black, Fig. 3-17. With a little practice, you will find technical pens easy to use. They provide the most professional looking and permanent drawings on tracing paper, vellum, and mylar.

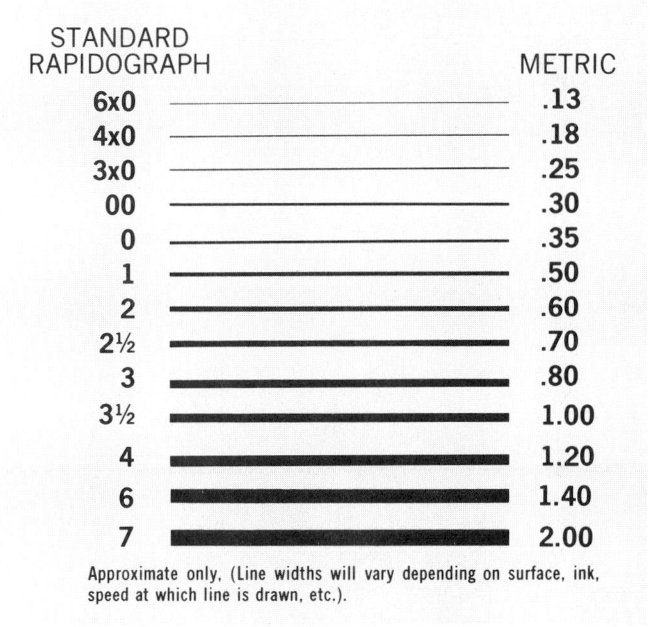

STANDARD RAPIDOGRAPH
METRIC
6x0 .13
4x0 .18
3x0 .25
00 .30
0 .35
1 .50
2 .60
2½ .70
3 .80
3½ 1.00
4 1.20
6 1.40
7 2.00
Approximate only, (Line widths will vary depending on surface, ink, speed at which line is drawn, etc.).

Fig. 3-16. Line widths available in technical drawing pens. Note the standard numbers on the left and the metric sizes on the right. The three most commonly used widths are .25, .50, and .80 mm. (Koh-I-Noor)

DRAWING PAPER, TRACING PAPER, VELLUM AND POLYESTER FILM

Drawing paper varies in size, thickness, color, and surface qualities, Fig. 3-18. The standard sizes of drawing paper are in multiples of 8 1/2 x 11 inches in English, and 210 x 297 millimeters in metric. In the English system, ''A'' size is 8 1/2 x 11 inches,

Fig. 3-17. Ink used in technical pens for drawing on paper and film. (Koh-I-Noor)

Fig. 3-18. Drawing paper is usually sold in reams (500 sheets). The paper should take a pencil line well and also erase well. Ink from a technical pen should not ''feather'' out on good drawing paper.

''B'' size is 11 x 17 inches, ''C'' size is 17 x 22 inches, and ''D'' size is 22 x 34 inches, Fig. 3-19.

Drawing paper is about twice as thick and heavy as regular typing paper. The weight of 1000 sheets of stock drawing paper, measuring 25 x 38 inches, may vary in weight from 60 to 80 pounds. The 60-pound paper is thinner and usually less expensive than the 80-pound paper.

Drawing paper is available in several colors. Cream, light green, or blue tint papers are preferable to white paper because they reduce eye strain. A fine surface finish is recommended to allow for clean erasing. Pencil or ink can be used on drawing paper, but mistakes made with ink are difficult to remove.

A translucent material such as **tracing paper** or **vellum** is used when ''prints'' are to be made from a drawing. Both allow light to pass through them, except where the drawing exists. Tracing paper is less expensive while vellum is more transparent, stronger, and durable. Pencil or ink can be used on either tracing paper or vellum.

Polyester film has the best qualities for drafting and is the most expensive medium. It is dimensionally stable, resistant to tearing, easily erased, highly transparent, and waterproof. Film has a shiny backside and a matte (smooth, even surface free from shine or highlights) side used for drawing. Drawings may be made with lead, plastic lead or ink. Plastic lead has been developed to be used on film. Although regular pencil lead can be used on film, plastic lead is more smudge resistant and easier to erase. The 4S and 3S plastic leads make lines similar to the 2H and H regular pencil leads. Drawing paper is the less expensive material, therefore, it is usually used for layout work and for people learning to draw.

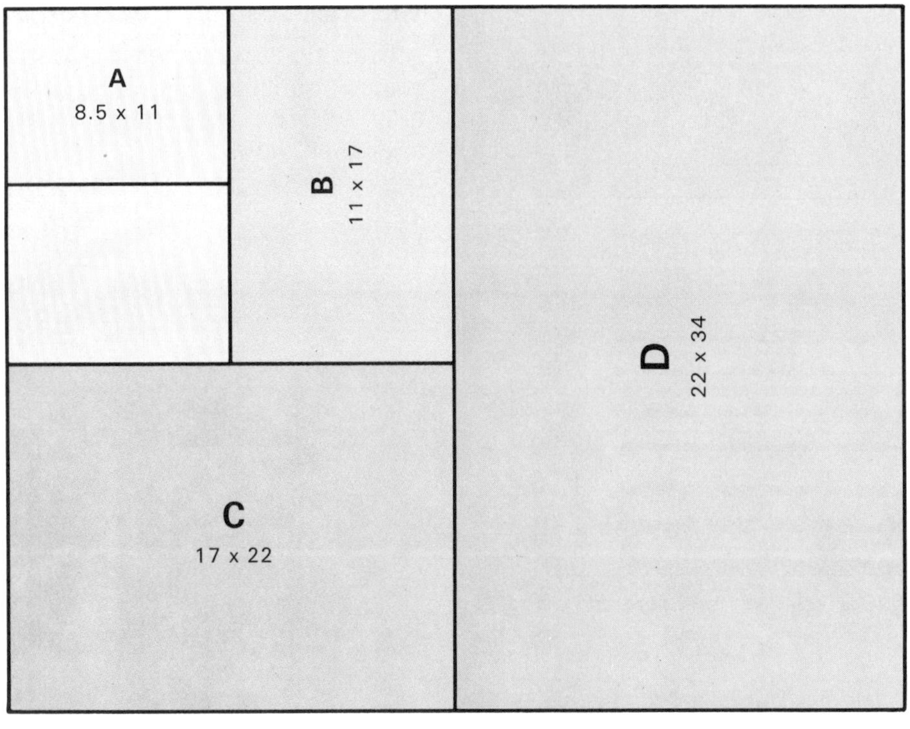

Fig. 3-19. The different sizes of drawing paper are referred to by a letter size. As the letter size increases, the drawing surface doubles.

Fastening the Paper to the Drawing Board

Prior to drawing any lines, fasten the paper to the drawing board with tape or drafting dots, Fig. 3-20. Position the paper by aligning it with the horizontal straight edge of your parallel rule, drafting machine, or T-square, Fig. 3-21. Place a small piece of tape across one of the upper corners. Reposition the paper if necessary, and place a second piece of tape over the other upper corner.

If you must remove the drawing from the board before it is completed, realign it to maintain a parallel relationship.

DRAWING STRAIGHT LINES

All finished lines must be sharp, black, and shiny. You may have to draw over a line several times to make it intense. Lines must be dense so they reproduce well. When drawing is finished, all lines of the same type will be consistently wide. Consistently wide means that each line is the same width throughout its length.

Line Width and Spacing

Lines vary in width and spacing to indicate a variety of situations, Fig. 3-22. **Border lines** provide a boundary for a drawing and are drawn extra thick (0.7-1.0 mm side).

Object lines that create the edges of objects on a drawing are drawn thick (0.5-0.7 mm wide). These object lines are approximately the same width

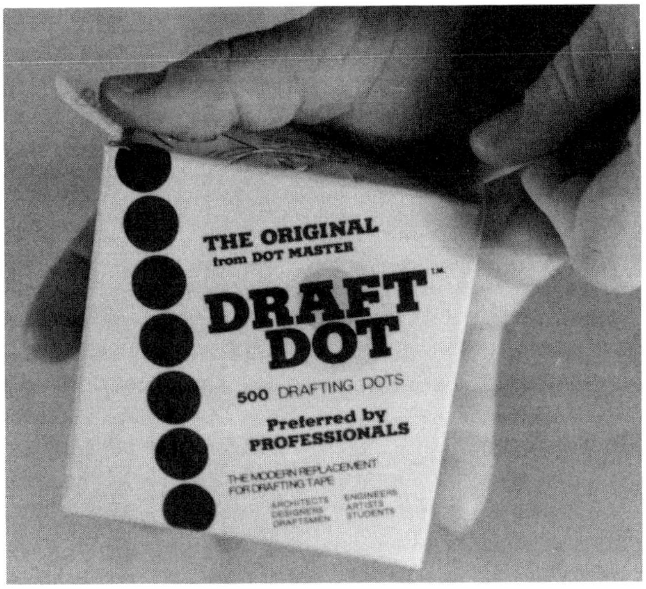

Fig. 3-20. Drafting dots hold the paper to the drawing surface.

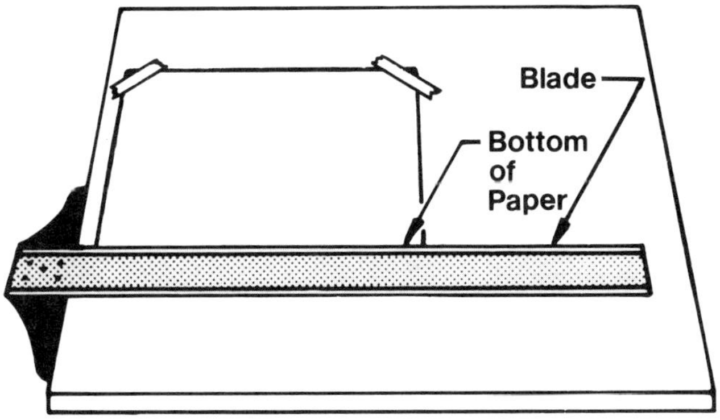

Fig. 3-21. Use a horizontal surface to align the drawing paper before fastening sheet to the board.

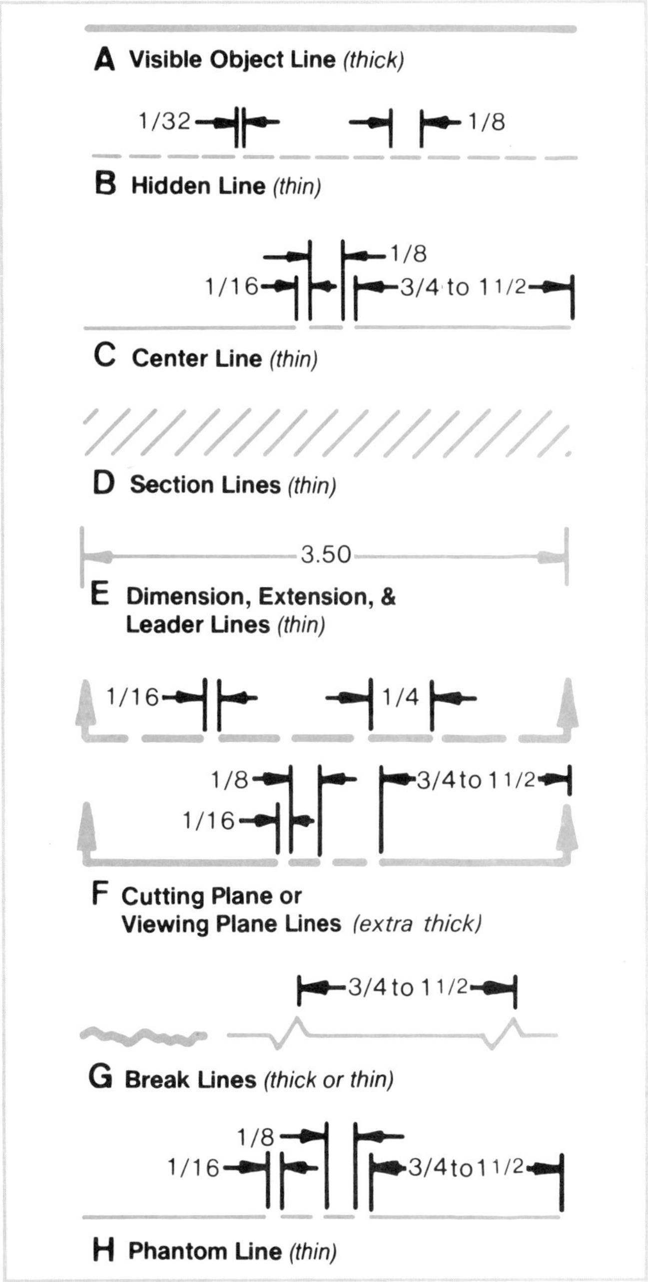

Fig. 3-22. Drafting, the Language of Industry, uses three different line widths to convey different messages. Learn to draw and read all of the lines illustrated above.

as a line made with a ball-point pen. **Cutting plane lines** are thick and broken in a long-short-short-long sequence.

Section lines and lines used for dimensioning are drawn thin (0.35-0.5 mm wide). A thin dashed line represents a hidden surface of an object. A **centerline** is thin and is drawn in a long-short-long sequence.

Guidelines for lettering are drawn as thin as possible. Also, they are drawn just dark enough to be seen.

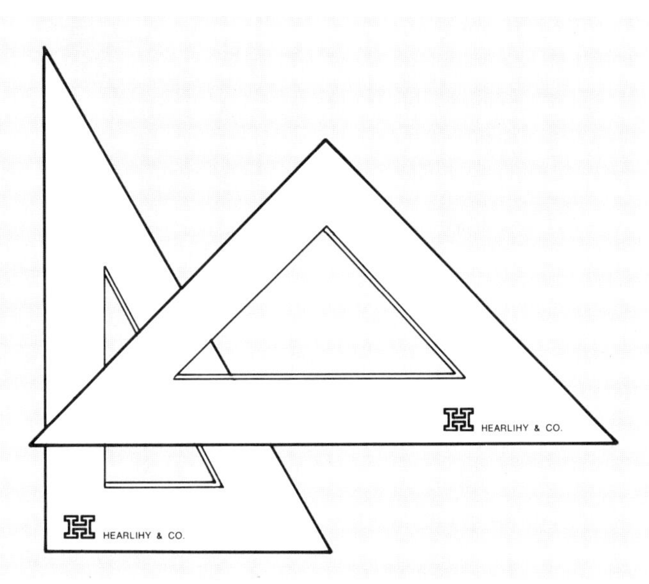

Fig. 3-23. Typical triangles used in instrument drawing.

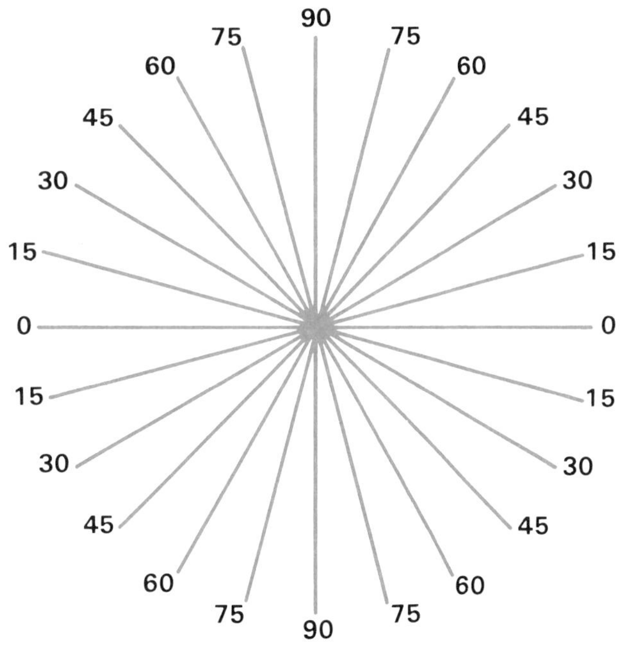

Fig. 3-24. Drawing lines at 15 degree intervals.

Using the 30 x 60 x 90 and 45 x 45 x 90 Triangles to Draw Lines at 15 Degree Intervals

Triangles are often used to draw lines at various angles from the horizontal or X-axis. By using the 45 x 45 x 90 and 30 x 60 x 90 triangles as shown in Fig. 3-23, lines can be drawn at 15 degree intervals as illustrated in Fig. 3-24.

Either triangle may be used to draw a line perpendicular to the horizontal axis to form a vertical line. This is also considered the Y-axis. Begin by drawing horizontal and vertical lines of equal length that intersect to form an **apex** (+), Fig. 3-25.

Lines can be drawn at 45 degree angles with the 45 x 45 x 90 triangle, Fig. 3-26. With the **hypotenuse** or the longest side of the triangle along the parallel rule, draw two lines through the apex of the vertical and horizontal lines. One line slopes upward-right and downward-left at 45 degrees. The other line slopes upward-left and downward-right at 45 degrees.

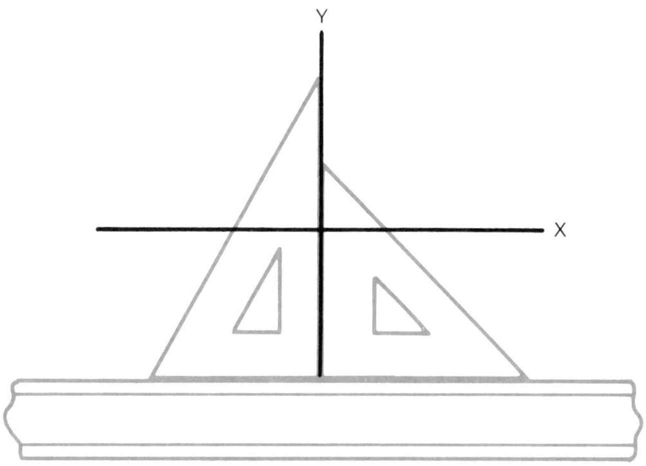

Fig. 3-25. Using triangles to draw horizontal and vertical lines.

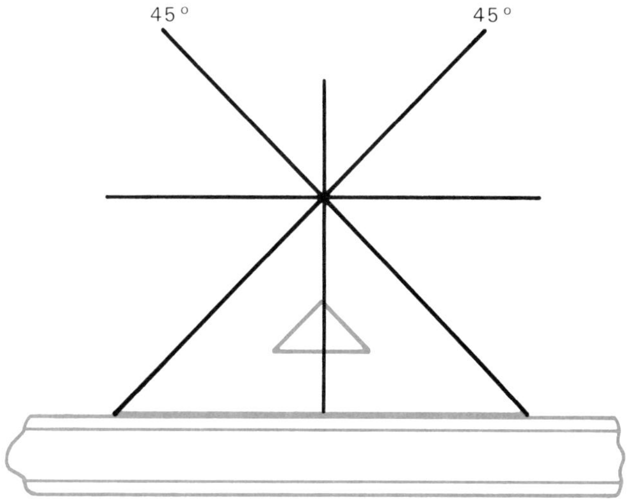

Fig. 3-26. Using a triangle to draw 45 degree lines.

Lines can be drawn at 30 and 60 degree angles with the 30 x 60 x 90 triangle. Place the hypotenuse of the triangle along the parallel rule with the 30 degree angle to the left, Fig. 3-27. Draw a line through the apex that slopes upward-right and downward-left at 30 degrees. Turn the triangle over with the long side along the parallel rule and the 30 degree angle to the right. Draw a line through the apex that slopes upward-left and downward-right at 30 degrees.

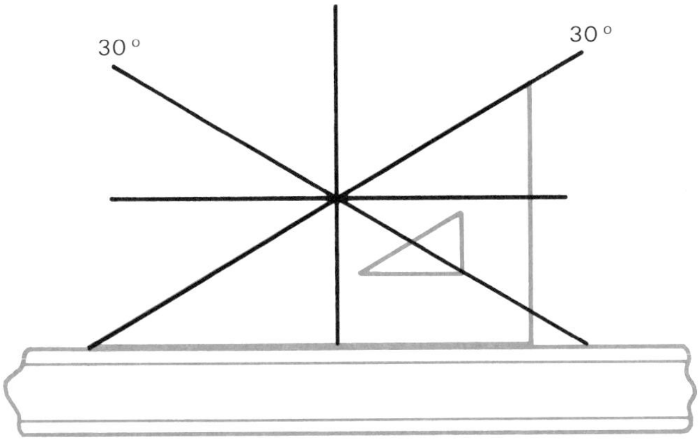

Fig. 3-27. Using a triangle to draw 30 degree lines.

Place the short side of the 30 x 60 x 90 triangle along the parallel rule with the 60 degree angle to the left, Fig. 3-28. Draw a line through the apex that slopes upward-right and downward-left at 60 degrees. Flip the triangle over so the short side is along the parallel rule and the 60 degree angle is to the right. Draw a line through the apex that slopes upward-left and downward-right at 60 degrees.

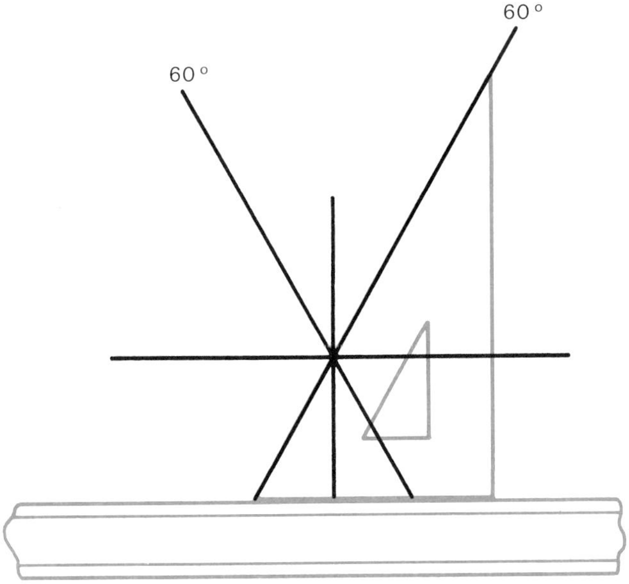

Fig. 3-28. Using a triangle to draw 60 degree lines.

Lines at 15 and 75 degrees to the horizontal axis can be drawn by using the 30 x 60 x 90 and 45 x 45 x 90 triangles.

A line sloping upward-right and downward-left at 75 degrees can be drawn by using both triangles, Fig. 3-29. First, lay the hypotenuse of the 30 x 60 x 90 triangle along the parallel rule with the 30 degree angle pointing to the left. Next, lay the hypotenuse of the 45 x 45 x 90 triangle along the upper side of the 30 x 60 x 90 triangle. A line sloping upward-right and downward-left at 75 degrees can be drawn along the left side of the 45 x 45 x 90 triangle.

The angle is obviously 75 degrees since the 30 and 45 degree angles are added to the horizontal axis.

Leaving the triangles in the previously described arrangement also provides a 15 degrees angle, Fig. 3-30. A line sloping upward-left and downward-

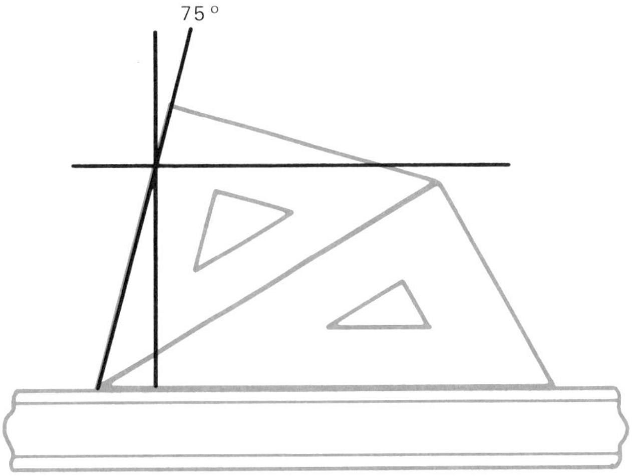

Fig. 3-29. Using two triangles to construct a 75 degree line.

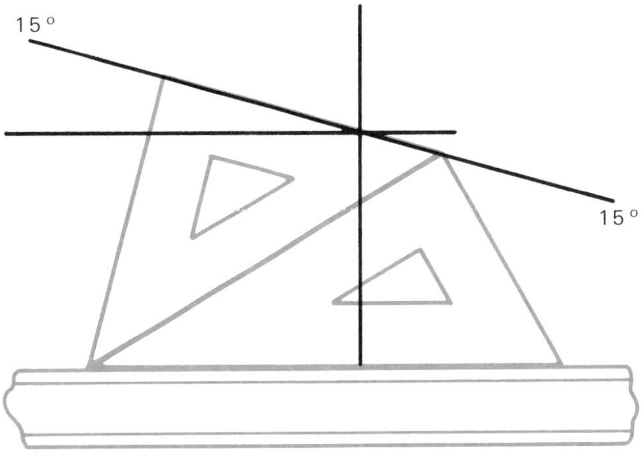

Fig. 3-30. Using two triangles to construct a 15 degree line.

right at 15 degrees can be drawn along the right side of the 45 x 45 x 90 triangle.

A line sloping upward-right and downward-left at 15 degrees can be drawn by using both triangles, Fig. 3-31. First, lay the hypotenuse of the 30 x 60 x 90 triangle along the parallel rule with the 60 degree angle to the left. Next, lay the hypotenuse of the 45 x 45 x 90 triangle along the upper side of the 30 x 60 x 90 triangle. A line sloping upward-right and downward-left at 15 degrees can be drawn along the left side of the 45 x 45 x 90 triangle.

By leaving the triangles in the previously described arrangement, a line sloping upward-left and downward-right at 75 degrees can be drawn along the right side of the 45 x 45 x 90 triangle, Fig. 3-32.

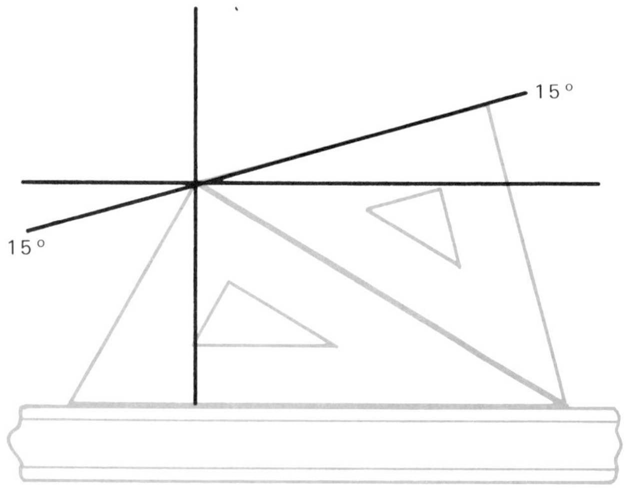

Fig. 3-31. Reverse the lower triangles shown in Fig. 3-30 to draw this 15 degree line.

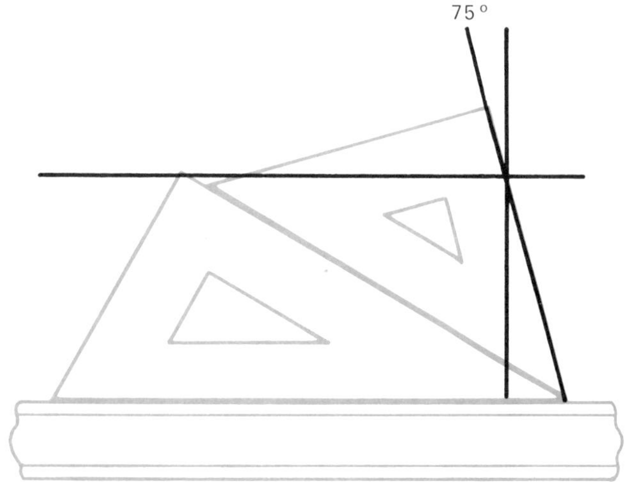

Fig. 3-32. Reverse the lower triangles shown in Fig. 3-29 to draw this 75 degree line.

USING SCALES WITH A DIVIDER OR COMPASS

There are three different drafting scales: the **architect, engineer,** and **metric,** Fig. 3-33. The purpose of each scale is to reduce or enlarge a part or product so it can be drawn and conceptualized. For example, a full-size drawing of a house would not be feasible. Instead, a house plan may be drawn with an architect scale so that "1/4 inch represents 1 foot," (1/4" = 1'). Thus, a room with an 8 foot ceiling would be drawn with a wall being 2 inches high on the plan. Reducing the actual size of a house according to a specific scale allows people to recognize and understand the details of the house or building from a relatively small drawing.

After analyzing a detailed drawing, you will begin to realize the value of measuring instruments. A detailed drawing provides a clear and proportioned image of a product that may be 50 or 100 times larger than the drawing itself. Each item on a detailed drawing has been transferred from a scale using a divider or compass, Fig. 3-34. This process of transferring distances from a scale to the drawing paper is done frequently when drawings are being created. Exercise great care not to damage the surface of the scale when using dividers or a compass. The scale is a precision instrument and should never be used as a straightedge for drawing lines.

Using the Architect's Scale

The **architect's scale** is used in residential and commercial architectural work. It is read in feet, inches, and fractions of an inch. The triangular shaped scale has 11 different scales available, Fig. 3-35. The scale marked with a 16 on the left end is actually full scale. If has inches divided into halves, fourths, eights, and sixteenths.

The other 10 scales provide a broad range of size alternatives for an architect or designer to use. Each of these scales is read in feet, inches, and fractions of an inch. The scales range from large to small in the following order: 3, 1 1/2, 1, 3/4, 1/2, 3/8, 1/4, 3/16, 1/8, and 3/32.

Two scales are combined or folded on top of each other on the ruler.

For example, the zero for the 1/4 scale is at the right-hand side and the 2, 4, 6, etc., are to the left of it. However, the 1/8 scale has the zero at the left-hand side and the 4, 8, 12, etc., are to the right of it. The numerals represent the measurement in feet. Notice that the set of numbers for one scale are placed slightly higher. This makes reading the scale easier. The zero is the starting point for each scale. This means that one scale is read from the left to the right, while the other scale is read from the right to the left.

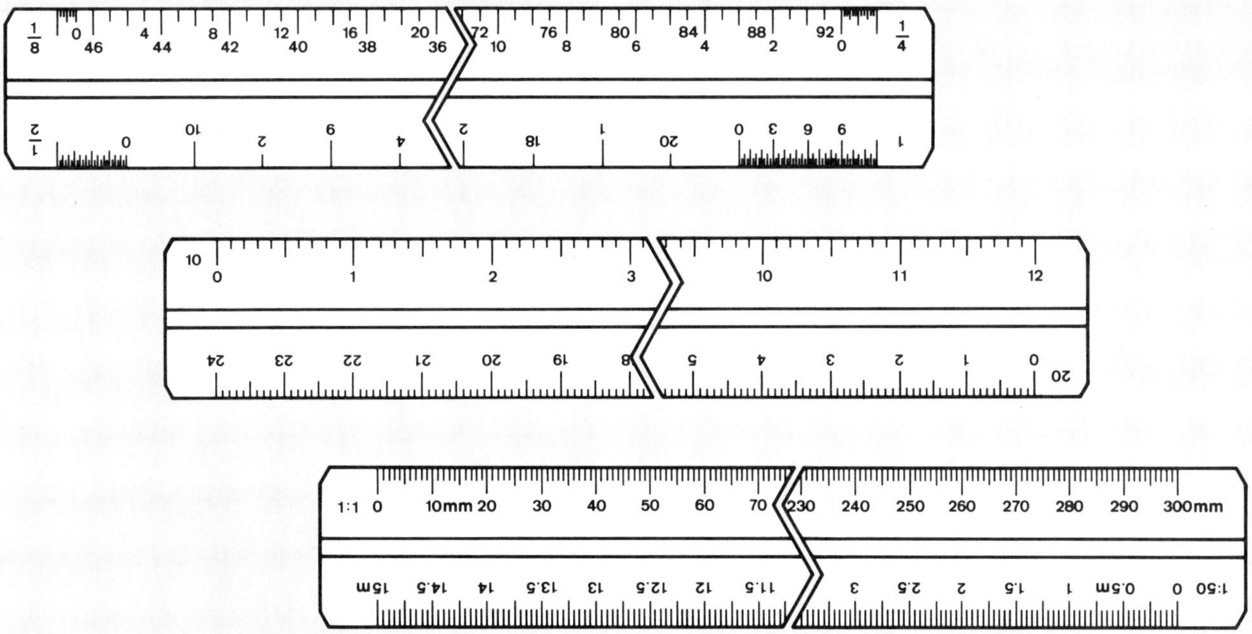

Fig. 3-33. Scales used in instrument drawing. Top—Architect's Scale. Middle—Engineer's Scale. Bottom—Metric Scale.

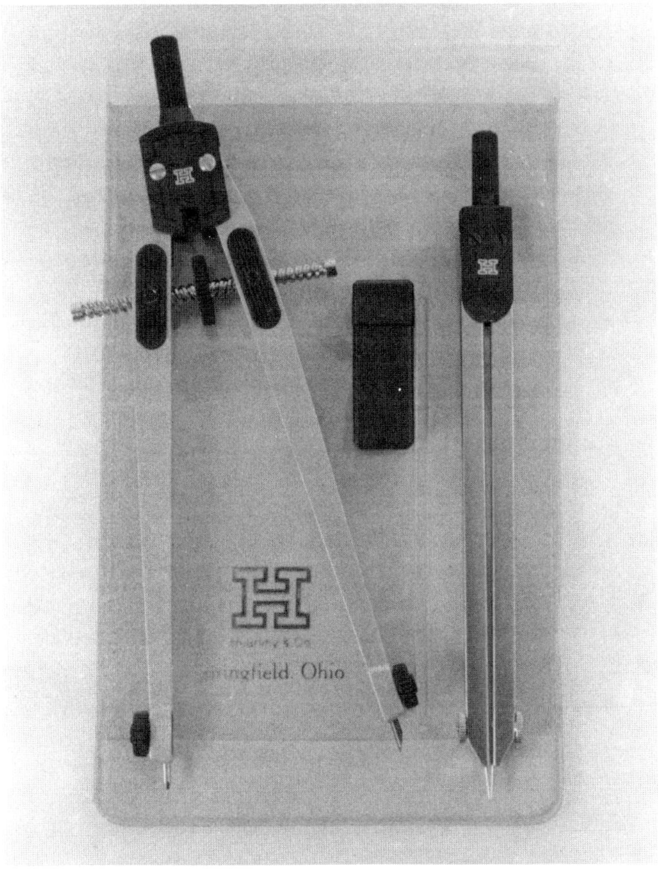

Fig. 3-34. Drafting tools used to transfer dimensions. On the left is shown a compass that is adjusted with the thumb wheel at the top. On the right are dividers which may be easily used. (Hearlihy)

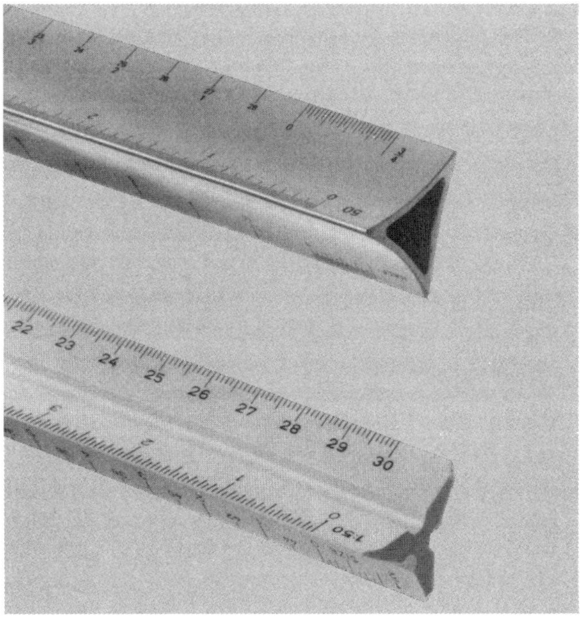

Fig. 3-35. Triangular architect's scales.

Using the small space between the *zero* and the other end is another unique characteristic of the architect's scale. This space is "a foot divided into inches." For example, look at the small hash marks between the zero and the 1/4. Each hash mark represents one inch to the 1/4 scale. The longest hash mark in the middle, represents 6 in. The two shorter hash marks represent 3 in. and 9 in. The shortest hash marks represent 1, 2, 4, 5, 7, 8, 10, and 11 inches from the *zero.* Measuring with the architect's scale is therefore a process of combining the number of feet on one side of the *zero* with the number of inches on the other size of the *zero.*

For example, the architect's scale can be used in designing a small building project such as a small yard barn. Choose the 1 scale since it allows the plans for the 8 ft. x 12 ft. x 8 ft. building to fit on a "C" size drawing sheet. Design windows which are 2 ft. high, 2 ft.-6 in. wide. Using the 1 scale and the divider or compass, position the metal point on the 2. Adjust the other point to the 0 on the left for the 2 ft. dimension. Extend the point left from 0 to the 6 for the 2 ft.-6 in. dimension, Fig. 3-36.

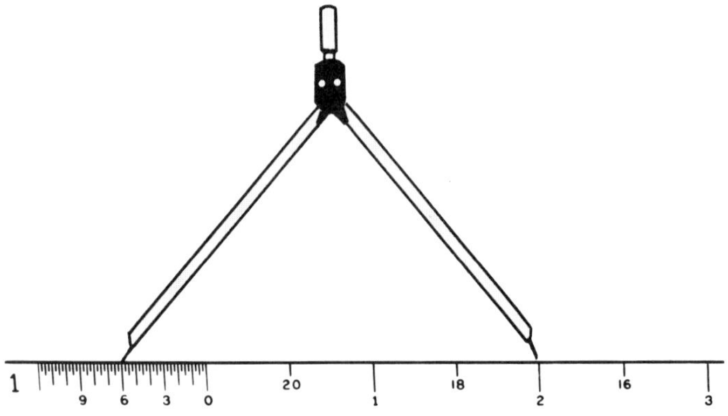

Fig. 3-36. Using dividers to transfer the dimension 2 feet 6 inches from the 1 scale.

The rough opening size for the windows is 2 ft.-1 1/2 in. x 2 ft.-7 1/2 in. Using the 1 scale and divider or compass, place the metal point on the 2. Adjust the other point past the 0 for the 1 1/2 in. and 7 1/2 in. distances. Each long hash mark in the 0, 3, 6, and 9 locations represents a full inch and the smaller hashes represent 1/4 of an inch. The 1 1/2 in. dimension is the sixth hash beyond the 0 and the 7 1/2 in. dimension is the sixth hash beyond the 6.

While becoming acquainted with the architect scale, it becomes obvious the 1/2 scale makes the drawing one half the size of a full scale drawing. The 1/4 scale makes the drawing one fourth the size of a full-scale drawing, and so on.

If the scale for the drawing is designated as 1" = 1', then it is read "one inch represents one foot." It is also important to remember dimensions placed on the drawing are the actual sizes of the product.

Examine each face of the triangularly-shaped scale, to find the following scales:

Find the 16 scale by itself. Invert the scale to locate the 3/32 scale which is read from left to right. The 3/16 scale is read from right to left, Fig. 3-37.

Find the 1 1/2 scale which is read from left to right. The 3 scale is read from right to left. Invert the scale to locate the 3/4 scale which is read from left to right. The 3/8 scale is read from right to left.

Find the 1 scale which is read from left to right. The 1/2 scale is read from right to left. Invert the scale to locate the 1/8 scale which is read from left to right. The 1/4 scale is read from right to left.

Using the Engineer's Scale

The **engineer's scale** is read in decimal inches and is used in engineering work. The triangular shaped scale has six different scales to select. The scale marked with a 10 is actually full scale. In contrast to the common ruler, an engineer's scale has each inch divided into tenths instead of sixteenths.

The five other scales provide wide range of sizes for an engineer's or drafter's use. Each of these scales is read in inches and tenths of an inch. The scales range from the largest to the smallest in the following order: 10, 20, 30, 40, 50, and 60.

For example, An engineer's scale can be used when designing a trailer hitch for a car. Select the 20 scale to draw the hitch because it fits the size of available drawing paper. The trailer ball is located 5.25 in. away from the car bumper. Find the 5.25 in. measurement on the 20 scale, Fig. 3-38. Use a divider or compass and position one metal point on the 0. Adjust the other point to the 5, plus two short marks beyond the 5 to add the .20. Add one-half of the next space to obtain the additional .05 needed for the sum of 5.25 in.

A drawing made with the 20 scale is designated

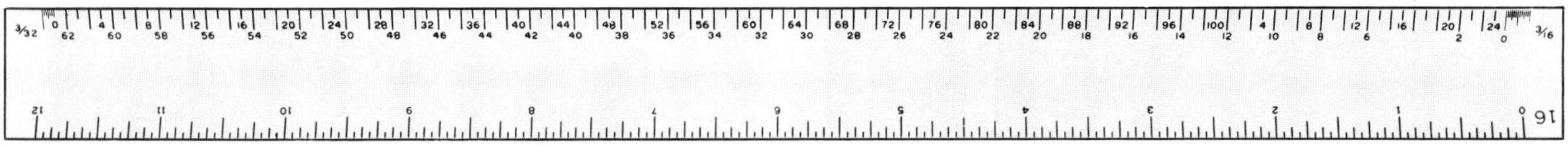

Fig. 3-37. The 3/16 architect's scale is read from the right. Shown here is an example of how to read 4 feet from the right. You should practice the techniques to reading all of the scale.

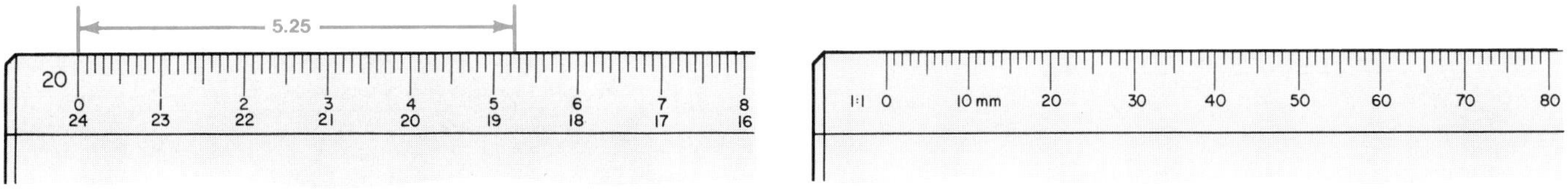

ENGINEER'S SCALE

METRIC SCALE

Fig. 3-38. The 20 scale is read from the left on the engineer's scale. Shown is an example of how to read 5.25 inches from the left.

as 1/2'' = 1'' and is read ''one-half inch represents one inch.'' As you become acquainted with the engineer's scale, you will notice the 20 scale makes a drawing one-half the size of full scale. The 30 scale makes a drawing one-third the size of full scale.

When civil engineers and surveyors begin to prepare drawings for a highway interchange, they may choose to ''draw it to scale'' by using an engineer's scale. The size limitations of the job may cause them to choose the 10 scale and let 1'' = 10' which is read ''one inch represents ten feet.'' The same surveying group may use the 50 scale of the engineer's scale to prepare a map of flat farmland. the scale of their drawing would be 1'' = 500' or read ''one inch represents five hundred feet.''

The engineer's scale is used for many other purposes. Remember, indicate the actual size of the object when dimensioning a drawing.

Examine each face of the triangular shaped scale to find each of the following:

The 10 scale. Invert it to locate the 50 scale.
The 20 scale. Invert it to locate the 40 scale.
The 30 scale. Invert it to locate the 60 scale.

Using the Metric Scale

The **metric scale** is used worldwide in engineering and architecture. The metric system has been called the international language of measurement. Its basic unit of measurement is the meter (m). The meter was established in the late 1700s as one ten-millionth (1/10,000,000) of the distance from the earth's equator to the poles

When comparing the English and metric units of measurement, the length of the meter is slightly longer than a yard (36 in.); 1 meter = 39.37 inches. The millimeter (mm) is the shortest metric unit of measure. There are approximately 25 millimeters in an inch; 25.4 mm = 1 inch. The kilometer (km) is the longest unit of measure in the metric system and is approximately six-tenths of a mile.

Linear measurement in the metric system is based on the unit of ten, which is similar to the system used in counting money. For example, compare a meter (m) to ten dollars ($10.00), a millimeter (mm) to one cent ($0.01), and a kilometer to ten-thousand dollars ($10,000.00). To change meters to millimeters, move the decimal three places to the right and to change meters to kilometers, move the decimal three places to the left. A millimeter is one/thousandth (1/1000) of a meter and a kilometer is a thousand (1000) meters.

The triangular metric scale has six different scales available. The scale labeled 1:1 is the full scale. The same scale could also be used for 1:10, 1:100, 1:1000, etc. to reduce the scale of a project to 1/10th, 1/100th, or 1/1000th of its actual size respectively. Other scales commonly used include: 1:1.25, 1:2, 1:2.5, 1:5, and 1:7.5.

For mechanical engineering purposes, measurements are made in millimeters (mm), also called ''mills.'' As auto body designers create the shape of an automobile, its side may be over 4000 mills long. A part such as a radio knob may have a diameter of 20 mills.

A full-size drawing of the side of the automobile is useful for the designers, but not very practical to duplicate and distribute to others. Imagine shrinking the actual size of the sideview of an automobile to fit on an 8 1/2 in. x 11 in. drawing sheet. Using the 1:1.25 scale reduces the dimension slightly and the 1:2 scale reduces it to half size. The 1:2.5 scale makes it smaller yet, and the 1:5 scale reduces it to 1/5 its actual size. The 1:2 scale converted to the 1:20 scale is 1/20 of the actual size and is the most appropriate for fitting the automobile on the 8 1/2 in. x 11 in. drawing sheet.

An architect or civil engineer commonly use the meter (m) as a standard unit of linear measurement. Their choice of scale varies, based upon the size of structure and the size of drawings needed. For example, a road map may have the scale of 1:500.000. The map is one five-hundred-thousandth of the actual size of the land. Note that a period is used between thousands in the metric system as compared to a comma in the English system.

DRAWING ARCS AND CIRCLES

There are two methods for making arcs and circles. One is with the compass and the other is with a template. Either method produces a sharp, black, and uniform curve. The curve may be redrawn several times to make it look professional.

Using the Compass for Drawing Arcs and Circles

When using a **compass,** the lead must be sharpened with a piece of sandpaper. Adjust the lead so it is slightly shorter than the metal pointer. Adjust the compass with the thumb of the dominant hand to the correct radius while the appropriate scale is held in the other hand. Be careful not to damage or mark the scale.

To draw the arc or circle, locate the point where two centerlines intersect, and then press the compass point lightly into the paper. Tilt the top of the compass slightly forward and draw the arc in the same direction, Fig. 3-39. Continue drawing around the circle until the lines of the arc are sharp, black, and uniform.

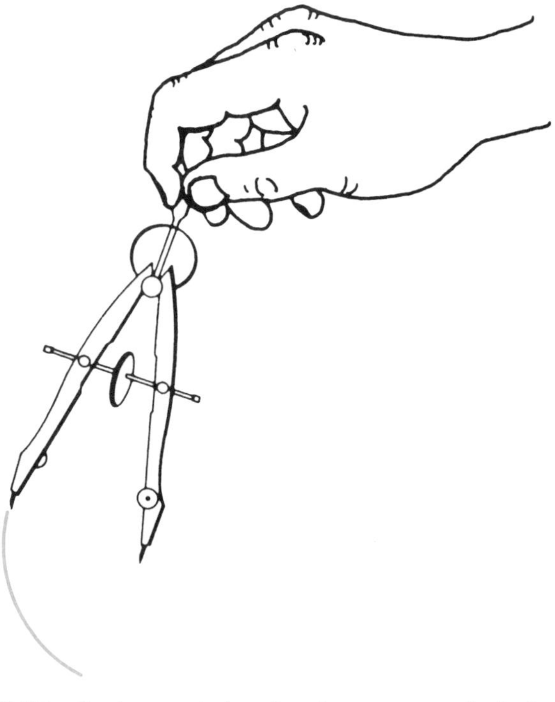

Fig. 3-39. To draw a circle using the compass, tilt the instrument in the direction of travel.

Using a Circle Template for Drawing Arcs and Circles

The same results described using a compass may be achieved by using a **circle template,** Fig. 3-40. Locate the correct size circle and match the centerlines on the template with the centerlines on the drawing. Hold the template in position and traverse or trace around the circle template with a pencil until the circle is sharp, black, and of uniform width.

COMPLETING GEOMETRIC CONSTRUCTIONS

In the ancient Greek language, the term geometry means "to measure the earth." Geometry and geometric constructions were used thousands of years ago by the Greek, Egyptian, and Babylonian cultures. Geometry has been used for centuries to design and build roads, structures, and industrial products as well as to study astronomy. Modern designers, engineers, and drafters utilize geometric construction techniques to solve problems quickly and accurately, Fig. 3-41.

The study of geometry and geometric constructions involves many interesting relationships about points, lines, and planes. As you learn to use the basic drawing instruments and follow the procedures in this chapter, you will be creating common geometric shapes. You will also be preparing to solve problems related to lengths, areas, and volumes of geometric shapes in various situations.

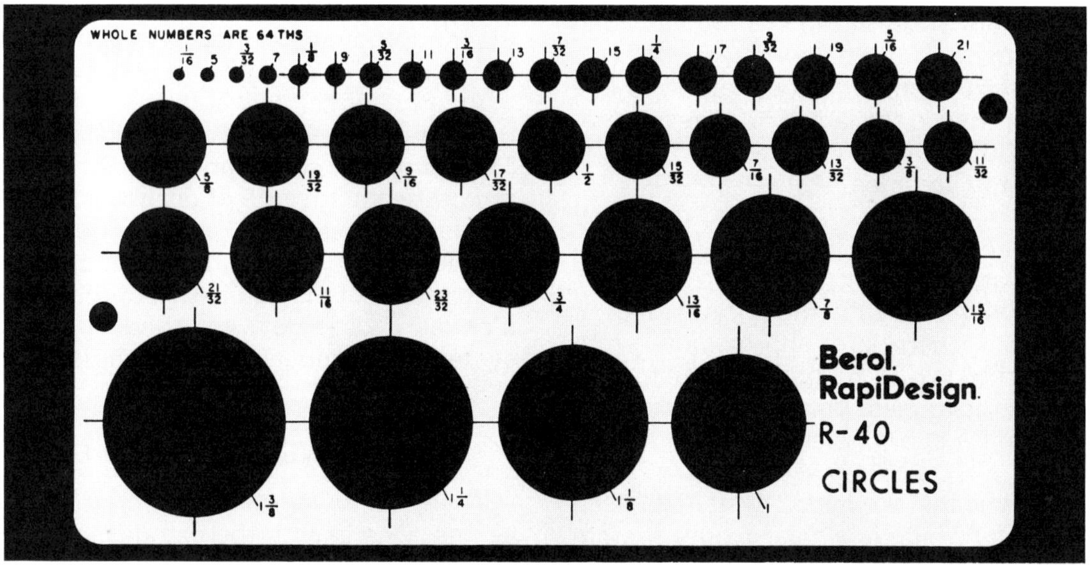

Fig. 3-40. Use of the circle template saves time, especially for small arcs and circles. To align the template properly, carefully line up the centerlines.

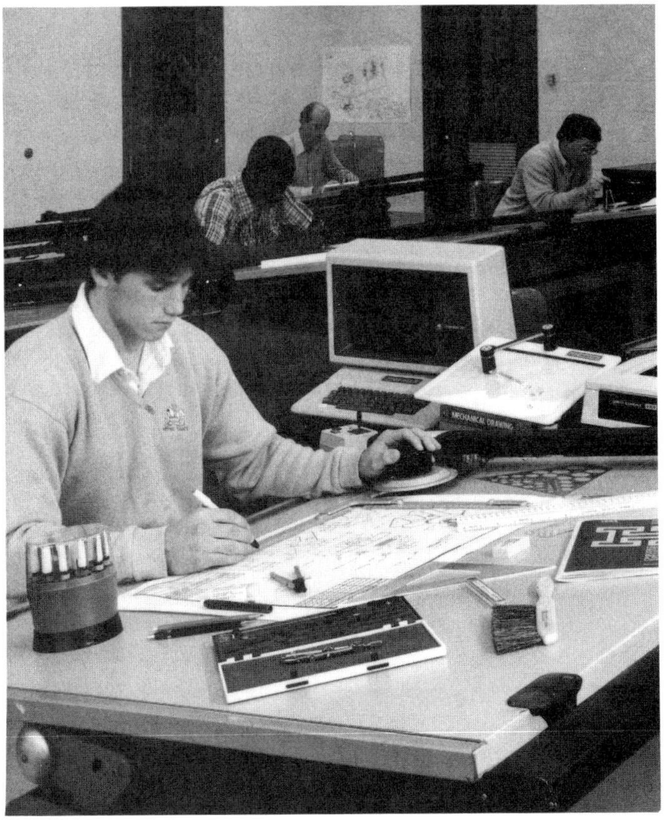

Fig. 3-41. The modern drafter has many tools to select from including templates and the computer.

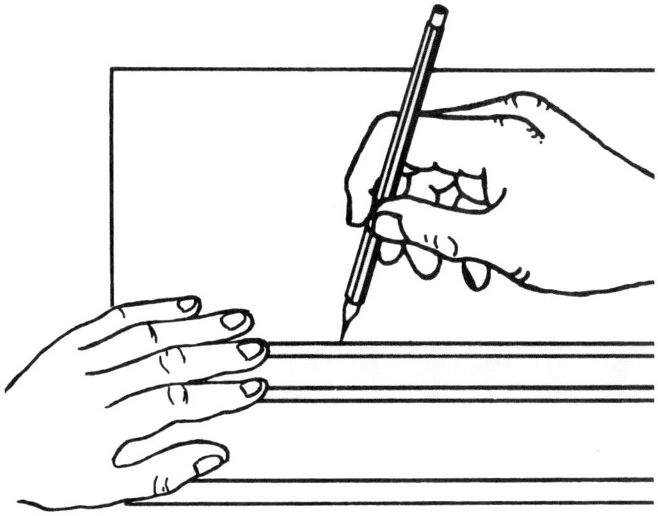

Fig. 3-42. Drawing horizontal lines along a parallel rule.

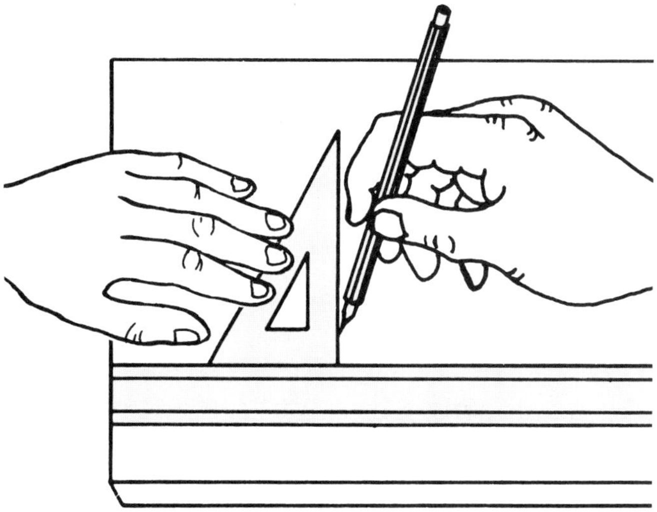

Fig. 3-43. Drawing vertical lines along a triangle placed on the parallel rule.

The following series of geometric construction procedures involves problems related to lines, angles, and polygons (many sided figures). While completing common construction procedures, you will become competent in using the drafting tools, instruments, and materials. Speed, accuracy, and enjoyment will increase with practice.

CONSTRUCTING LINES

Lines on drawings are used to communicate ideas. To communicate the ideas clearly and consistently, lines are always drawn very black and intense. When drawing with a pencil, pass over a line several times until it becomes dark enough to look professional.

Drawing Parallel Lines

Horizontal lines may be drawn from given points by placing the pencil on the first point, position the parallel rule in contact with the pencil, and draw the line, Fig. 3-42. Place the pencil on the second point, reposition the parallel rule, and draw the line. Repeat the process until all horizontal lines are drawn.

Vertical lines are drawn by positioning the parallel rule below the lines to be drawn. Position one side of a triangle along the parallel rule so the vertical lines can be drawn along the other side, Fig. 3-43. Place the pencil on the first point, slide the triangle across the parallel rule until it comes in contact with the pencil. Hold the parallel rule and triangle with one hand. Draw the vertical line along the vertical side of the triangle with the other hand. Move to the next point and repeat the process.

Constructing a Line Perpendicular to a Given Point on a Line

Adjust your compass from point P to the shortest end of line AB, Fig. 3-44. Position the pointer of the compass at point P and swing an arc segment over line AB at (a) and at (b). Adjust the compass larger to increase accuracy, if space permits. Position the pointer at point (a) and swing an arc segment above point P. Without changing the compass

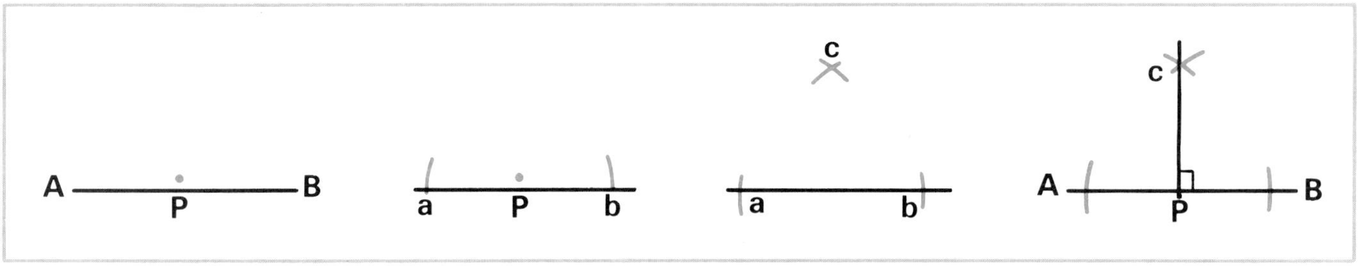

Fig. 3-44. Constructing a perpendicular line at a given point

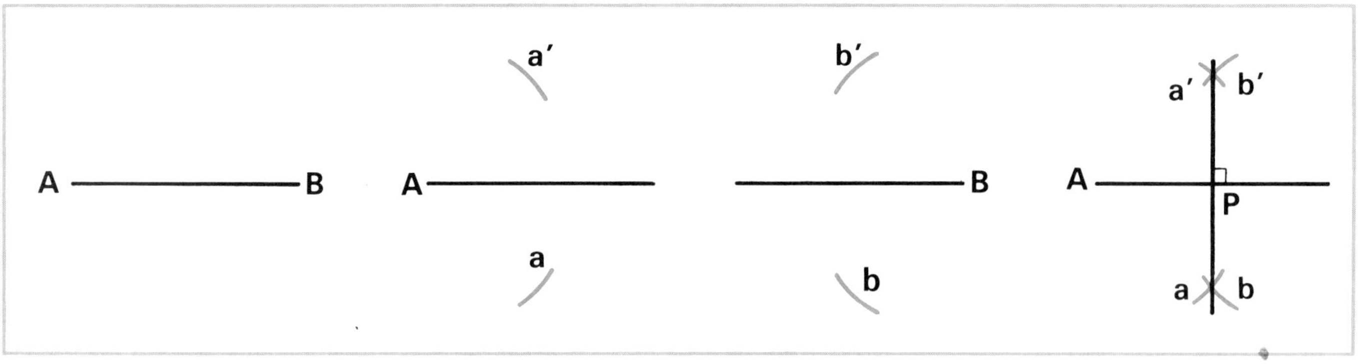

Fig. 3-45. Constructing a perpendicular bisector to a given line.

setting, swing another arc segment from point (b) above point P. The two arcs intersect at point (c). A line connecting points (c) and P is perpendicular to the given line AB.

Constructing a Perpendicular Line Bisecting Another Line

Adjust your compass to a radius of about 3/4ths the length of the given line AB, Fig. 3-45. Sharpen your compass lead for all construction lines. Position the pointer of the compass at A and swing arc segment (a′) and (a) above and below line AB. Without adjusting the compass, position the pointer on point B and swing arc segments (b′) and (b) above and below line AB. Draw a line connecting the intersection of (a′b′) with (ab). Line (a′b′-ab) is perpendicular to and bisects line AB at point P.

Dividing a Line into Equal Segments

First, select a unit of measure that is easy to recognize and close to the same size of one of the segments. For example, if a 4 5/16 in. line is to be divided into three equal segments, select 1 inch at the unit, Fig. 3-46. It is easy to recognize and it is close to the size of each of the segments.

Construct a line away from one end of the given line at an angle as shown. From the given line, mark off and label consecutive units along the construction line with a divider or along a scale.

Construct a line connecting the end of the given line (x) with the last unit on the construction line (y). Construct additional lines parallel to line (xy) from each unit through the given line.

The lines parallel to (xy) divide the given line into equal segments. A given line may be divided into

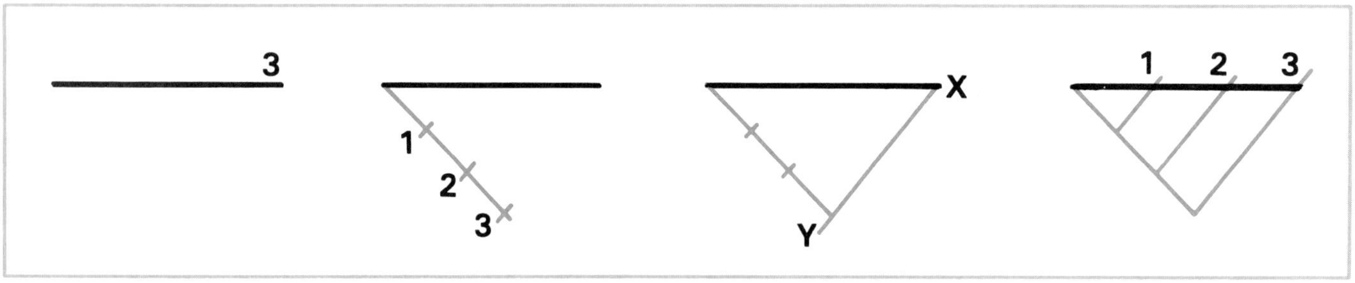

Fig. 3-46. Dividing a line into equal segments.

any number of equal parts quickly and accurately by using this simple procedure.

Drawing Angular Lines (Bearing)

Civil engineers, astronomers, sailors, and pilots are a few of the professionals who use the earth's North and South poles as a reference, Fig. 3-47.

On a 360 degree circular scale, North (N) is designated as the 0 or 360 degree direction and South (S) is at 180 degrees. East (E) is at 90 degrees and West (W) is at 270 degrees. Further subdividing, NE is at 45 degrees, SE is at 135 degrees, SW is at 225 degrees, and NW is at 315 degrees. These lines may be drawn by using a parallel rule and a 45 x 45 x 90 degree triangle.

By adding subdivisions at 22.5 degree intervals, the clockwise notations are as illustrated: N, NNE, NE, ENE, E, ESE, SE, SSE, S, SSW, SW, WSW, W, WNW, NW, NNW. The 22.5 degree intervals are drawn by bisecting the 45 degree angles. The procedure for bisecting an angle is described later in this chapter under the side head of Bisecting an Angle.

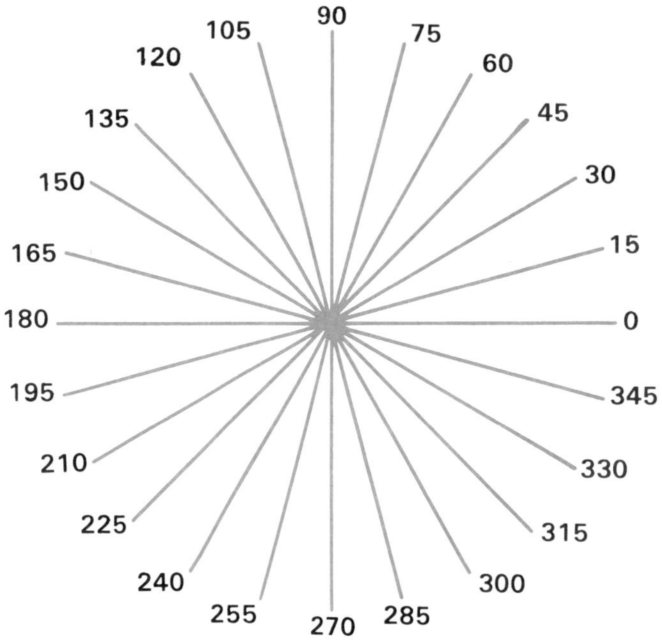

Fig. 3-48. Circular scale showing degrees starting at mathematical X-axis being 0 degrees.

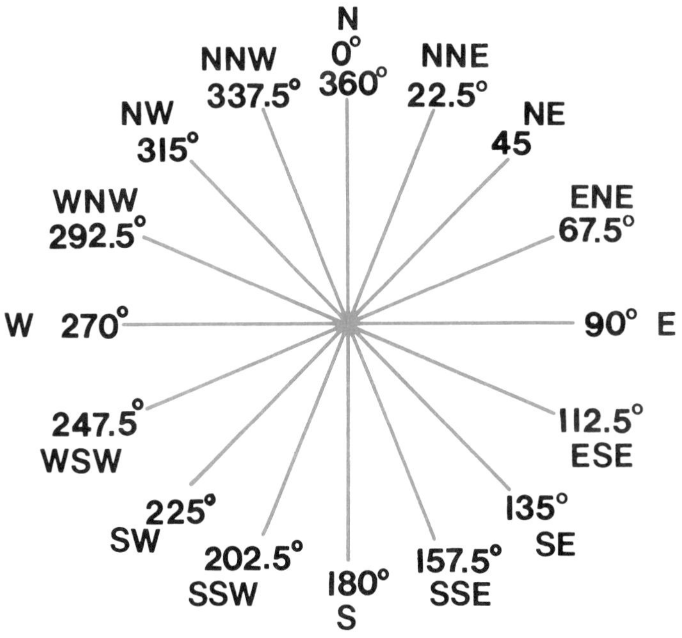

Fig. 3-47. Circular shape showing degrees and directions starting at North being 0 degrees.

Drawing Angular Lines

Mathematicians use a system for designating the direction of angular lines, in degrees, in a counterclockwise direction. The horizontal, X-axis, is to the right, 0 degrees, and left, 180 degrees. The vertical, Y-axis, is upward, 90 degrees, and downward, 270 degrees, Fig. 3-48. The X and Y-axes intersect at point 0,0. From this center point, right is +X, left is −X, upward is +Y, and downward is −Y.

Using a 360 degree circular scale, the angular lines are identified from 0 degrees on the right, in a counterclockwise direction. Angular lines may be drawn at 30, 45, 60, and 90 degrees with the triangles separately. By combining the two triangles, the additional 15 degree intervals can be drawn. Refer to the use of triangles earlier in this chapter.

Note the following angular relationships of the lines in Fig. 3-48.

A line sloping upward-right at 15 degrees, slopes downward-left at 195 degrees.

A line sloping upward-right at 30 degrees, slopes downward-left at 210 degrees.

A line sloping upward-right at 45 degrees, slopes downward-left at 225 degrees.

A line sloping upward-right at 60 degrees, slopes downward-left at 240 degrees.

A line sloping upward-right at 75 degrees, slopes downward-left at 255 degrees.

A line sloping upward-left at 105 degrees, slopes downward-right at 285 degrees.

A line sloping upward-left at 120 degrees, slopes downward-right at 300 degrees.

A line sloping upward-left at 135 degrees, slopes downward-right at 315 degrees.

A line sloping upward-left at 150 degrees, slopes downward-right at 330 degrees.

A line sloping upward-left at 165 degrees, slopes downward-right at 345 degrees.

Constructing an Angle Equivalent to a Given Angle

Adjust the compass for the length of the legs of the angle to be transferred, Fig. 3-49. With the compass pointer at the apex of angle A, draw an arc on each leg at (a) and (a′). With the same compass setting, position the pointer at B and draw arcs (b) and (b′) in the general area where the new angle will be located. Draw a line from B through (b).

Readjust the compass to the distance from (a) to (a′) which creates point (c). Transfer this distance to create the new angle. Position the pointer at (b) and draw an arc to intersect with the (b′) to locate (c′). Now, construct the new angle by drawing a line from B through point (c′).

If the angle to be transferred is an intervals of 15 degrees (15, 30, 45, etc.), it may be quicker and easier to use the triangles to transfer angles. The triangles can be used individually to draw 30, 45, 60, and 90 degree angles.

Bisecting an Angle

Adjust the compass slightly smaller than the length of the lines representing the angle, Fig. 3-50. With the pointer at apex X, swing an arc that crosses both lines at (x) and (x′). Swing equal arcs from (x) and from (x′) that intersect at point Y. A line connecting X and Y bisects the angle.

Constructing Triangles (Given three sides)

Adjust the compass to the length of side EG, Fig. 3-51. Swing an arc from point E in the general area of G. Draw line EG. Adjust the compass to the length of a second side, FG. Swing an arc from point G to (g) the general area where you expect point F to be located. Adjust the compass to the length of side EF. Swing an arc from point E to (e) so that it intersects with arc Gg to form point F. Now, construct the triangle by drawing lines between points G/F and E/F.

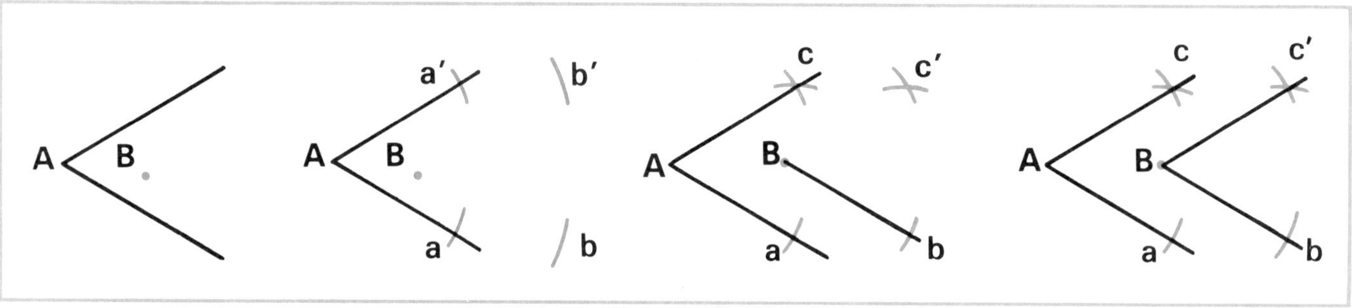

Fig. 3-49. Constructing an angle equal to a given angle.

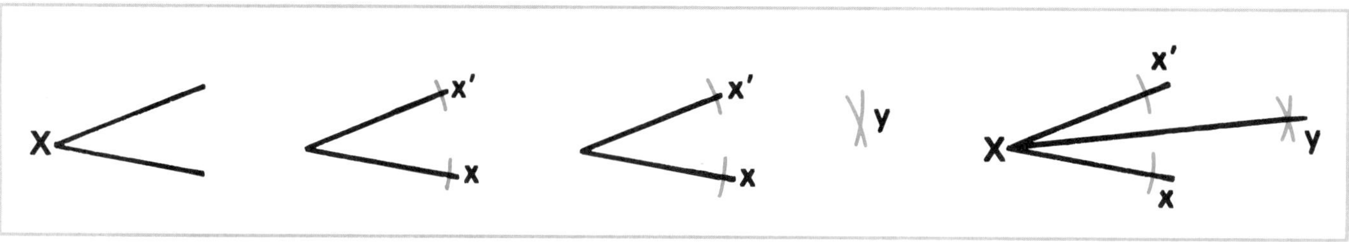

Fig. 3-50. Bisecting an angle.

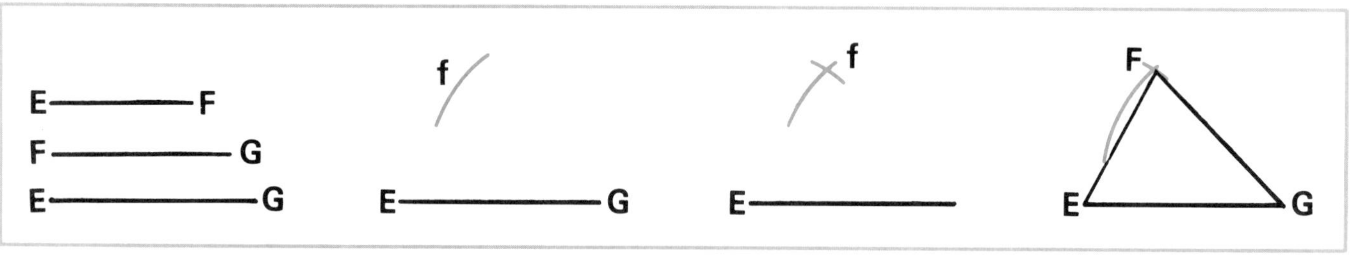

Fig. 3-51. Constructing a triangle using the three given sides.

Constructing Triangles (Given two sides and an included angle)

Adjust the compass to the length of a given side JK, Fig. 3-52. Swing an arc from point J to the general area of K, and draw side JK. Construct angle J by transferring the given angle as described earlier in this chapter.

Adjust the compass to the length of the second side JM. Swing an arc from point J to locate point M. Draw a line between K and M to complete the triangle.

Constructing Triangles (Given two angles and the included side)

Adjust the compass to the length of the given side NO, Fig. 3-53. Swing an arc from point N to the general area of O, and draw side NO.

Construct angle N at point N and angle O at point O by transferring these given angles as described earlier in this chapter.

If necessary, lengthen one or both of the sides to locate point P and complete the triangle.

Constructing Right Triangles (Given one side and one angle)

Adjust the compass to the length of given side RS, Fig. 3-54. Swing an arc from point R to the general area of S, and draw side RS.

Transfer the given angle S to given line RS as you have learned.

Draw a line at a right angle to line RS from R to T by constructing a line perpendicular to line RS as described earlier in this chapter.

Constructing a Square (Given the length of the sides)

The **square** has four equal sides at right angles to each other. A square is one of the many four-sided figures called **quadrilaterals.**

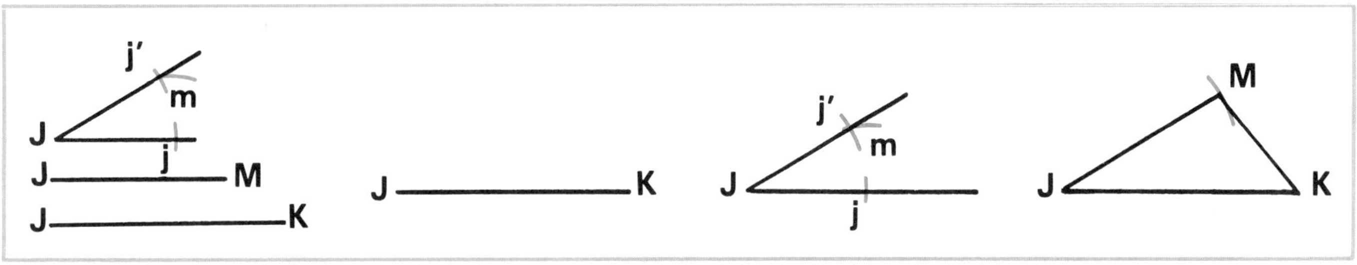

Fig. 3-52. Constructing a triangle using the two given sides and the included angle.

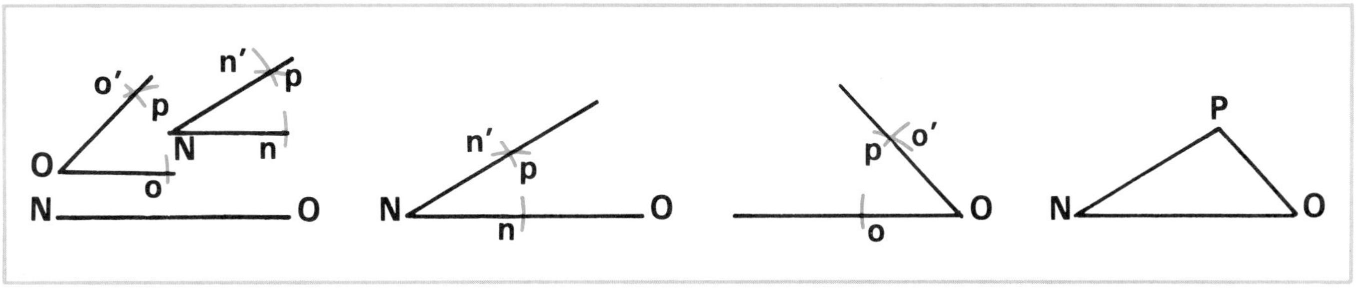

Fig. 3-53. Constructing a triangle using one side and two angles.

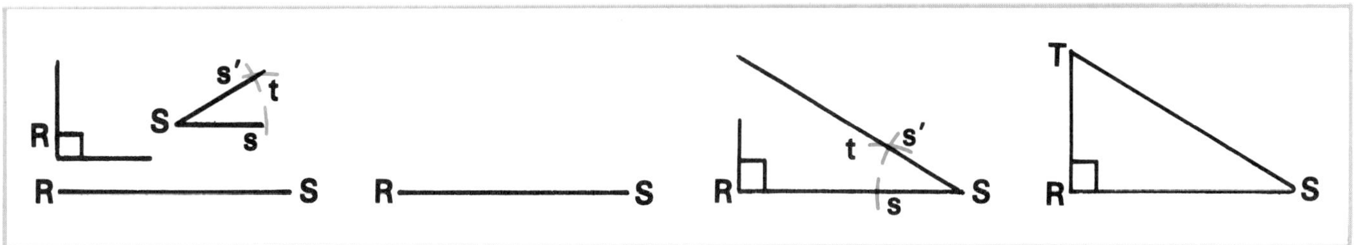

Fig. 3-54. Constructing a right triangle using one given side and one given angle.

When drawing a square, adjust the compass to the length of a side and draw side ST, Fig. 3-55. Draw lines perpendicular to S and T. Use the compass to mark the lengths of SV and TU. Draw a line between V and U to complete the square.

Constructing a Rectangle (Given the length of the sides)

A **rectangle** has two opposite sides that are of equal length parallel to each other and constructed with right angles. Since the opposite sides of a rectangle are parallel, it is sometimes referred to as a right angle **parallelogram.**

To draw a rectangle, adjust the compass to the length of a side and draw side WX, Fig. 3-56. Draw lines perpendicular to line WX at W and X and use the compass to mark the lengths of WZ and XY. Draw a line between Z and Y to complete the rectangle.

Constructing a Rhomboid (Given the length of the sides and an angle)

A **rhomboid** is a parallelogram without right angles. A rhomboid is constructed similar to a rectangle or square when the length of the sides and an included angle are given.

Adjust your compass to the length of side PQ and draw the line, Fig. 3-57. Transfer the given angles at P and at Q as described above. Adjust your compass to the length of lines PS and QR and draw them from P and Q. Draw a line between S and R to complete the rhomboid.

Constructing a Trapezoid (Given the length of the base, the altitude, and the included angle)

A **trapezoid** is a four-sided figure with a base parallel to an opposite side. The distance between these parallel sides is referred to as altitude. The other two sides are inclined from the base at the same angle, but toward each other.

To construct a trapezoid, adjust the compass to the length of the base TU and draw it, Fig. 3-58. Next, construct an altitude perpendicular to the base and indicate the given length (h). Draw a line parallel to the base through point (h).

Construct the given angle at T and at U so both angles slant inward or outward toward the top at V and W to complete the trapezoid.

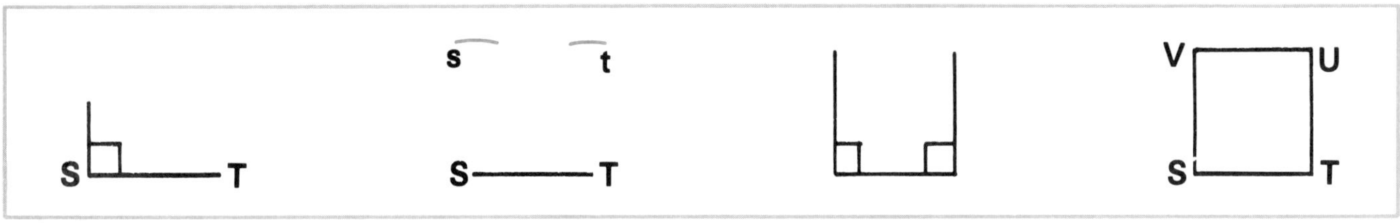

Fig. 3-55. Constructing a square given the length of one side.

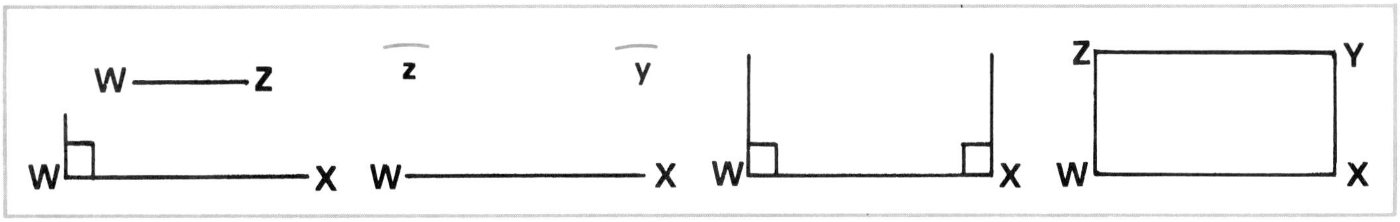

Fig. 3-56. Constructing a rectangle given the length of two sides.

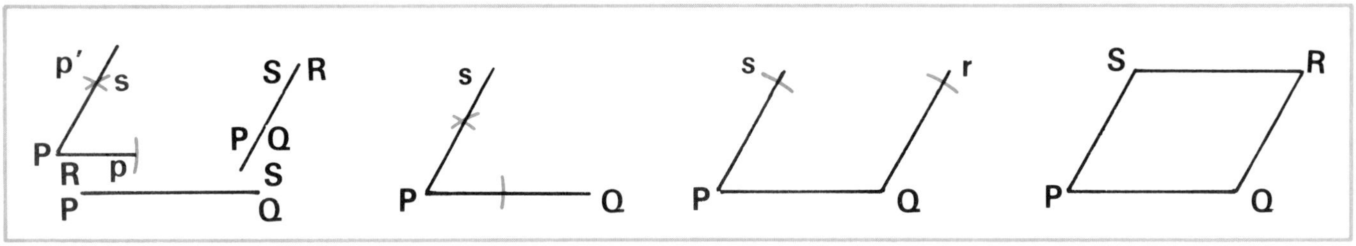

Fig. 3-57. Constructing a rhomboid given the length of two sides and one angle.

CONSTRUCTING ARCS, CIRCLES, AND LINES

Circular shapes are more difficult to draw than straight lines. With practice, circular lines will look consistent with straight lines. When curved lines and straight lines flow together, first make the curves, then construct the straight lines. It is easier to fit a straight line to an existing curve than a curve to an existing straight line. Keep your lead sharp to ensure accuracy. After inspecting the correctness of the layout, darken the curves and lines so they flow together smoothly.

Constructing Circles (Given the radius and the center)

The first step in drawing circles with a given radius involves adjusting the compass to the given radius on a scale, or selecting the diameter (radius x 2) on a circle template.

Position the compass point at the center or position the template over the centerlines. Make the same circle several times in each direction to create a professional looking circle, Fig. 3-59.

Constructing Circles (Given two points on the circumference and the radius)

First connect two given points to form chord CD, Fig. 3-60. Then, construct a perpendicular bisector to the chord as described in this chapter.

Adjust the compass to the given radius R with the scale. Swing an arc from C or D to cross the line that bisected the chord. This locates the center of the circle P.

Position the compass point at the center of the circle P. Check to see that the lead passes through the points, and draw the circle.

Constructing Circles (Given three points on the circumference)

First, connect the three points to form two chords EF and FG, Fig. 3-61. Then, construct a perpendicular bisector to each of the chords.

Extend these two perpendicular bisectors until they intersect to locate the center of the circle P.

Position the compass point at the center of the circle. P. Adjust the compass to the given points, and draw the circle.

Constructing a Line Tangent to a Circle

When drawing a line tangent to an existng circle, the line enters the circle and becomes one with the circle. The line leaves the circle in a smooth, consistent manner. The point where line HI is one with the circle is called the **point of tangency,** T, Fig. 3-62. A radius drawn to a point of tangency forms a right angle with line HI.

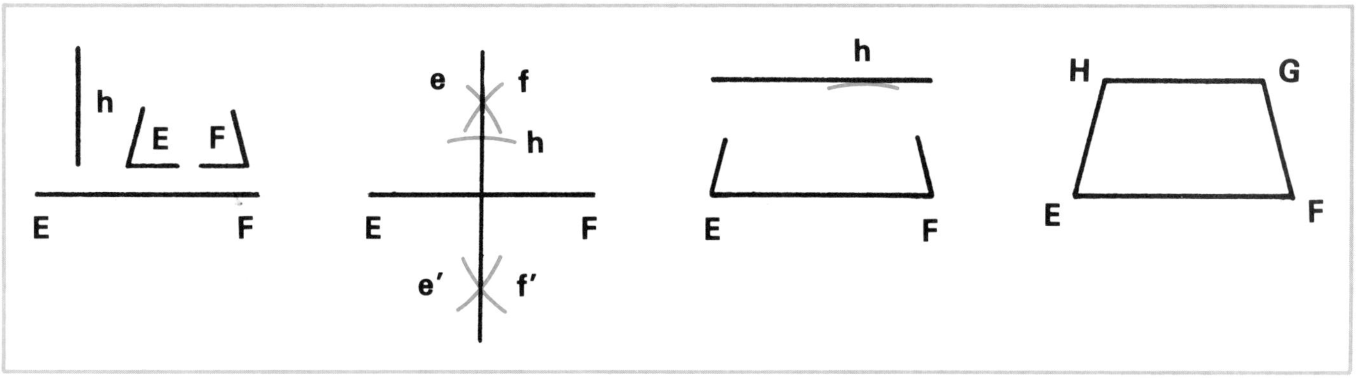

Fig. 3-58. Constructing a trapezoid given the length of the base, the altitude, and the included angle.

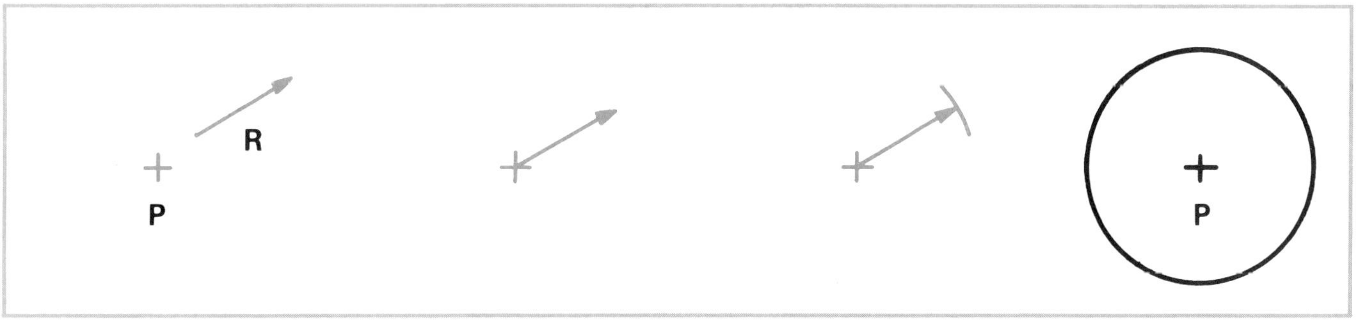

Fig. 3-59. Constructing a circle given the radius and center the point.

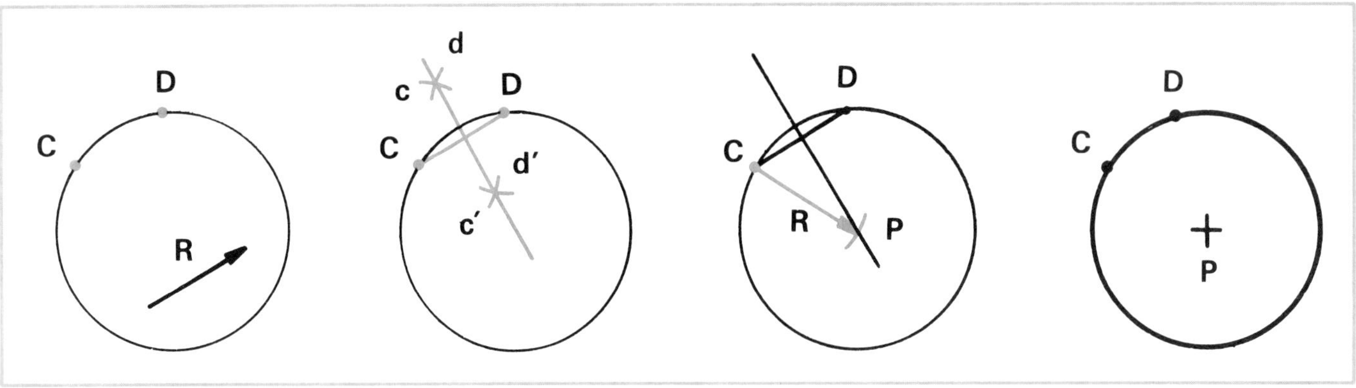

Fig. 3-60. How to construct a circle given two points on the circumference and the radius.

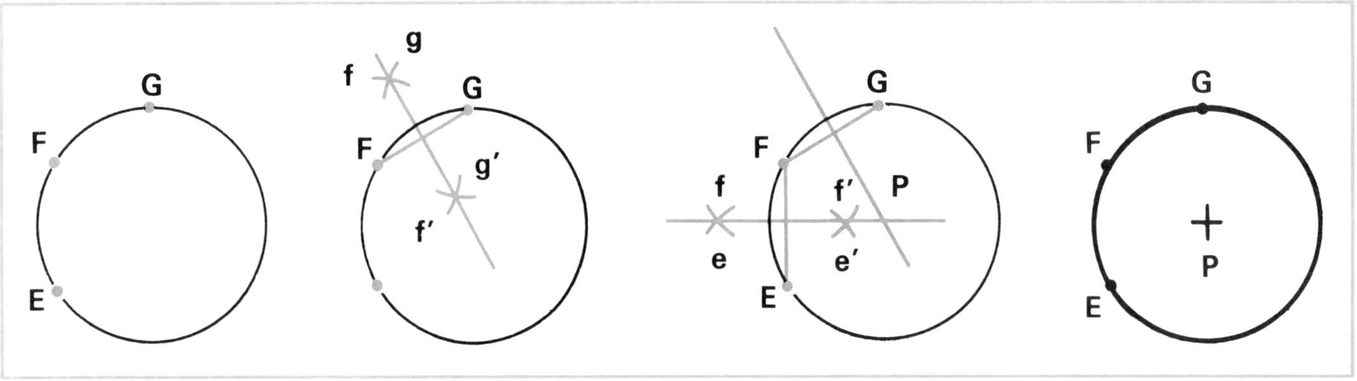

Fig. 3-61. Constructing a circle given three points on the circumference.

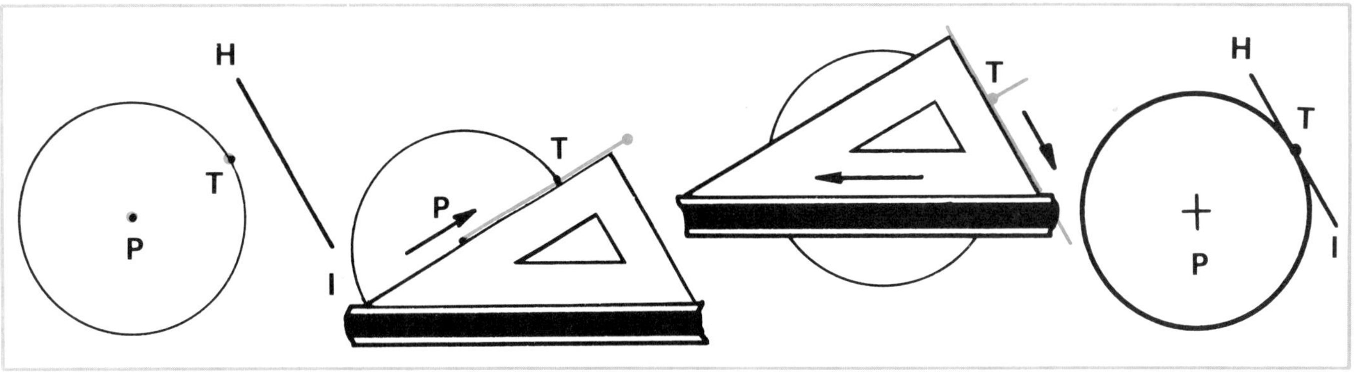

Fig. 3-62. Constructing a line tangent to a circle.

Locating the center of the circle and the point of tangency are the first steps in drawing a line tangent to a circle. When the hypotenuse of the 45 x 45 x 90 triangle laying against the parallel rule, position one side of the triangle to pass through both the center of the circle and the point of tangency.

Move the triangle along the parallel rule to the position where the line is tangent to the circle. Draw the line.

A circle being drawn tangent to a line enters the line, intersects the line, and leaves in a smooth, consistent manner. The point where the circle becomes one with line JK is called the **point of tangency** T, Fig. 3-63. The center of the circle lines on a line perpendicular to the given line JK from the point of tangency T.

Locating the center of the circle is accomplished in two steps. First, with the hypotenuse of the 45 x 45 x 90 triangle laying along the parallel rule, position one side of the triangle to pass through line JK with the 90 degree angle of the triangle at point T.

Second, draw a line along the other side of the triangle from T. Transfer the radius from T to the center at point P. Draw the circle from its center point P around tangent to line JK.

Constructing an Arc Tangent to Two Lines

When drawing a given arc, it should flow very smoothly in both directions into the two given straight lines like a curve on a highway. With an arc radius given, the center of the arc that connects the two straight lines is a "radius distance," R, away from each line, Fig. 3-64.

The first step in locating the center of the curve is to construct a line parallel to each of the given lines. These lines are a radius distance away and in an area between the two given lines. To accomplish this, adjust the compass to the size of arc radius R. Swing two arcs, R, from each end of the given line.

Draw a light line tangent to each pair of arcs. These two construction lines will be parallel to the given lines and a "radius distance" away from them. The point where these two construction lines intersect, X, is the center of the arc to be drawn.

With the center at X, draw the arc tangent to the two given lines.

Constructing an Arc Tangent to a Circle and a Line

When drawing the given arc, make it flow smoothly into the circle and into the line. The center of the arc is the given "radius distance," R, away from the circle and away from the straight line, Fig. 3-65.

To locate the center of the arc, construct a line parallel to the given line, at a radius distance away, and in an area between the line and the circle. To do this, adjust the compass to the given radius of arc R. From each end of the given line, swing a light arc, R, in a perpendicular direction with the given line and in an area between the given line and circle.

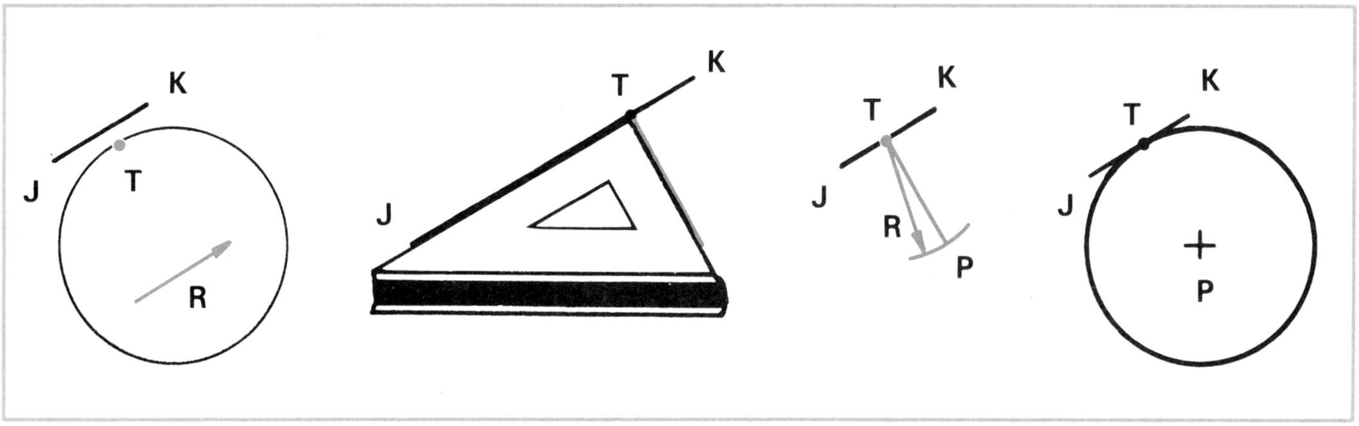

Fig. 3-63. Constructing a circle tangent to a given line.

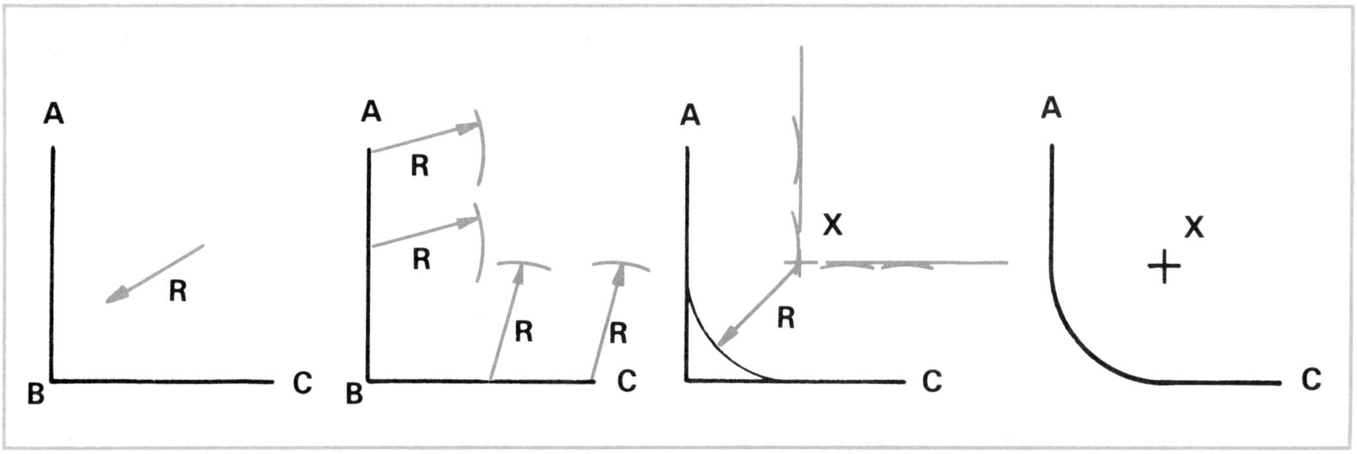

Fig. 3-64. Constructing an arc which is tangent to two lines.

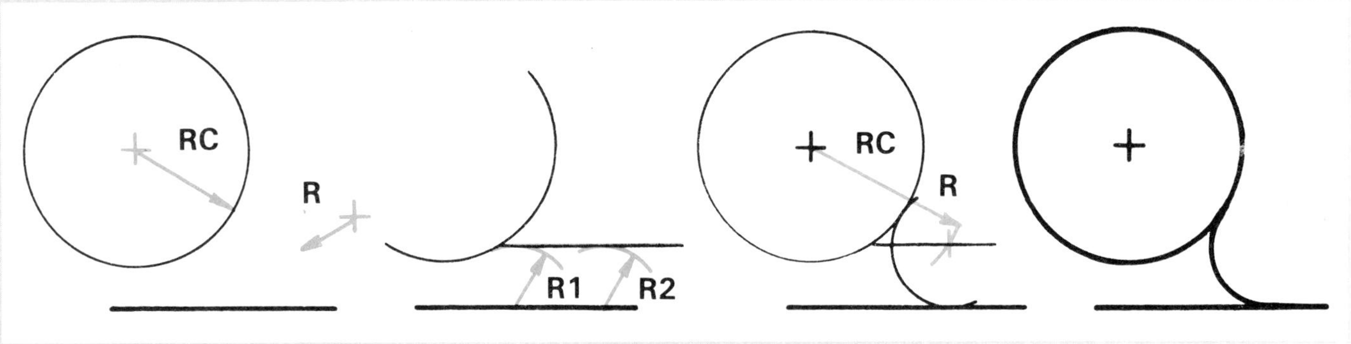

Fig. 3-65. Constructing an arc which is tangent to a circle and a line.

Draw a light construction line tangent to the two arcs.

Next, add the radius of the given arc, R, to the radius of the circle, RC. With the compass at the center of the circle, strike arc R + RC through the light construction line. The center of the arc is at X. With the compass adjusted to R, draw the arc connecting the given line with the given circle.

Inscribing an Equilateral Triangle and a Square

The sum of the angles in any triangle is equal to 180 degrees. An equilateral triangle has equal length sides and equal angles of 60 degrees.

To draw an equilateral triangle within a given circle, use 60 degree angle of the 30 x 60 x 90 degree triangle, Fig. 3-66. Use the 60 degree angle with the parallel rule to draw the two inclined sides. Use the parallel rule to draw the horizontal base. Draw the triangle from the 12 o'clock position down to the 4 o'clock and 8 o'clock positions. With the 30 degree angle pointing upward, draw lines downward-left and downward-right until they touch the circle. Complete the triangle with a horizontal line connecting the ends of the slanted lines and circle.

To inscribe a square, use the 45 x 45 x 90 degree triangle over the parallel rule to draw diagonals through the center of the circle, Fig. 3-66. Lay the hypotenuse of the triangle against the parallel rule. Move the triangle until one of the 45 degree sides is over the center of the circle. Draw a diagonal through the center of the circle. move the triangle over so the other 45 degree side is over the center of the circle and draw the other diagonal.

Draw the square by connecting the points where the circle and diagonals intersect with the two vertical and horizontal lines.

Constructing a Pentagon

A **pentagon** is a five-sided polygon. It is constructed by locating five equally spaced points on a circle and connecting the five points with straight lines.

A procedure for dividing a circle into five equal parts involves three steps. First, bisect a radius of circle AB, Fig. 3-67. Second, adjust the compass from the point where the radius is bisected, C, to the top of the circle, D. Swing an arc to intersect with radius CD at point E. Third, adjust your compass to distance DE. Mark the circle in five equal parts.

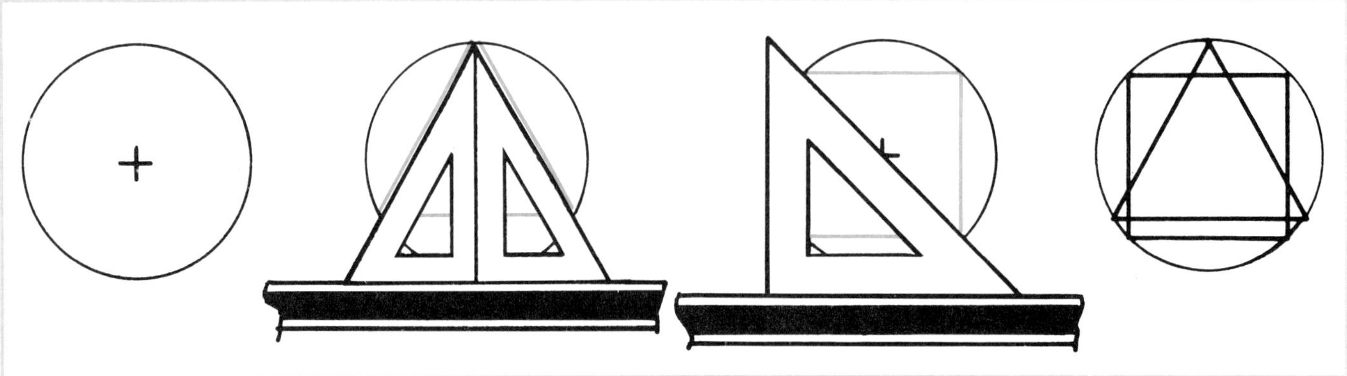

Fig. 3-66. Drawing a equilateral triangle or a square within a given circle.

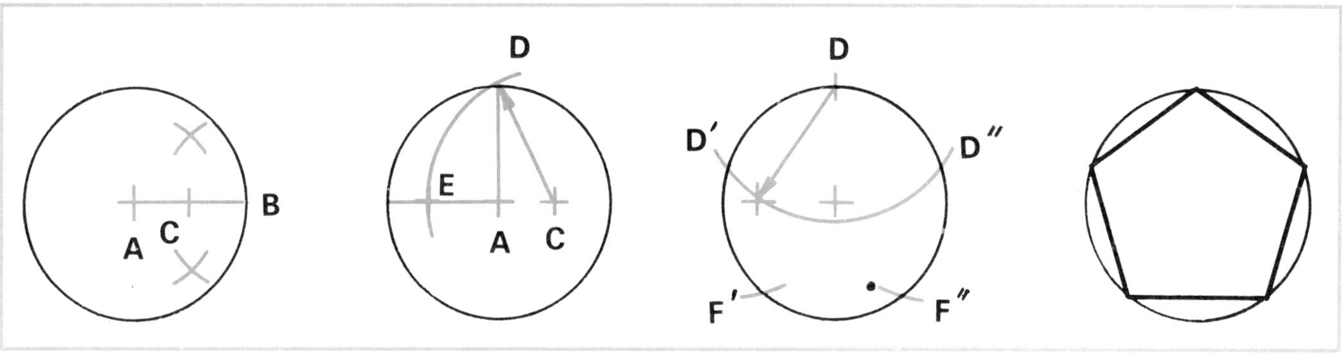

Fig. 3-67. Pentagons can be constructed following these steps.

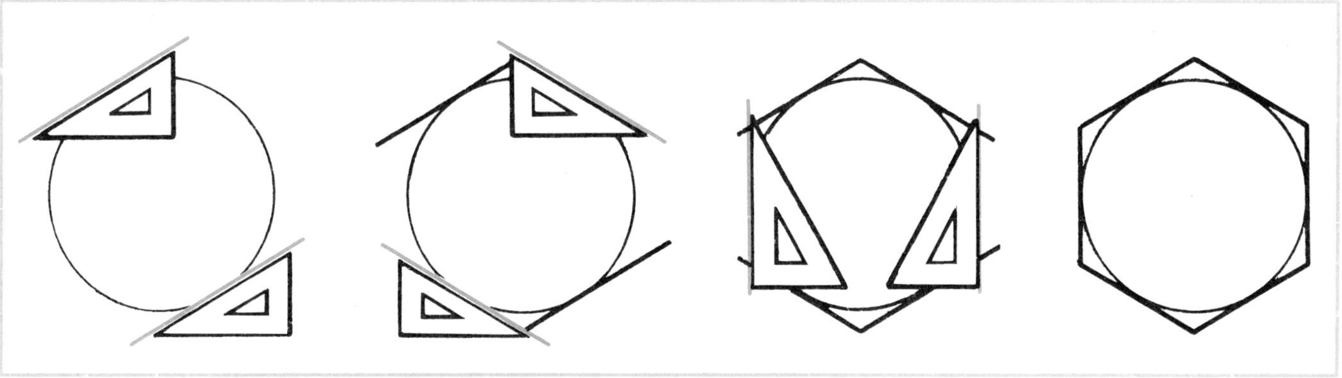

Fig. 3-68. Hexagons are constructed following these steps.

Draw the pentagon by connecting the five marks on the circle with straight lines.

Constructing a Hexagon Outside of a Circle

A **hexagon** is a six-sided polygon. It can be drawn on the outside of a circle by using the 30 x 60 x 90 degree triangle and parallel rule.

First, draw a circle with a diameter equal to the "distance between the sides" of the hexagon, Fig. 3-68. With the 30 degree angle to the left side, draw a light line tangent to the circle at the 5 o'clock position. Move the parallel rule upward. Draw a light line tangent to the circle at the 11 o'clock position.

Turn the triangle over so the 30 degree angle is to the right side. Draw a light line tangent to the circle at the 1 o'clock position. Move the parallel rule down to draw a light line tangent to the circle at the 7 o'clock position. Using the vertical side of the triangle, draw light lines tangent to the circle at the 3 and 9 o'clock positions.

Repeat the process making the light lines dark and professional looking.

Constructing an Octagon Outside of a Circle

An **octagon** is an eight-sided polygon. It is constructed on the outside of a circle with a 45 x 45 x 90 degree triangle and parallel rule.

First, draw a circle with a diameter equal to the "distance between the sides" of the octagon, Fig. 3-69. Place the hypotenuse of the triangle over the parallel rule. Draw a light line tangent to the circle at the 4:30 o'clock position. Move the parallel rule upward. Draw a light line tangent to the circle at the 10:30 o'clock position.

Use the other side of the triangle and draw a light line tangent to the circle at the 1:30 o'clock position. Move the parallel rule downward and draw a light line tangent to the circle at the 7:30 position.

With a vertical side of the triangle, draw vertical lines at the 3 and 9 o'clock positions. Draw horizontal lines at the 12 and 6 o'clock positions with the parallel rule.

Repeat the procedure to make all the lines dark, sharp, and black.

Constructing an Ellipse by the Four-Center Method

One method used to construct an ellipse used for an isometric drawing is called the **four-center method.** Use a 30 x 60 x 90 degree triangle and compass for the procedure.

First, locate the center point. Draw centerlines for the ellipse at a 30 degree angle, see Fig. 3-70.

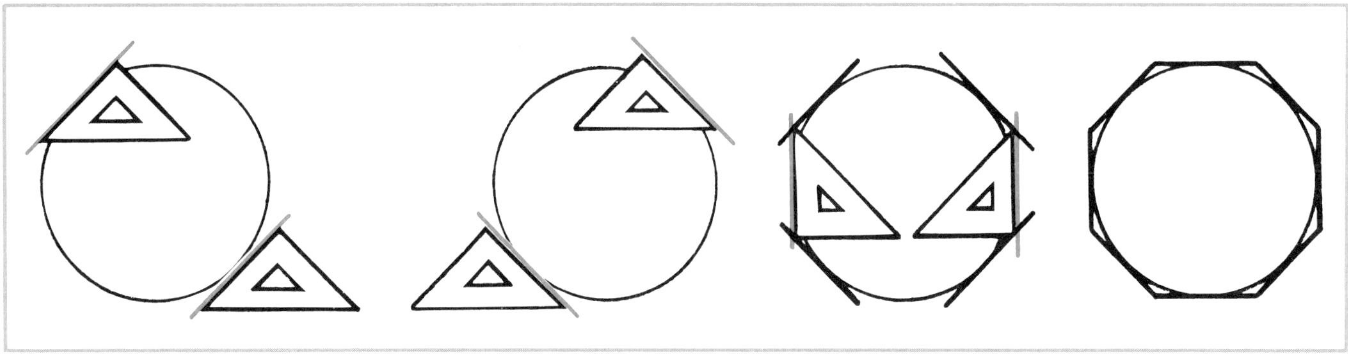

Fig. 3-69. Octagons may be constructed following these steps.

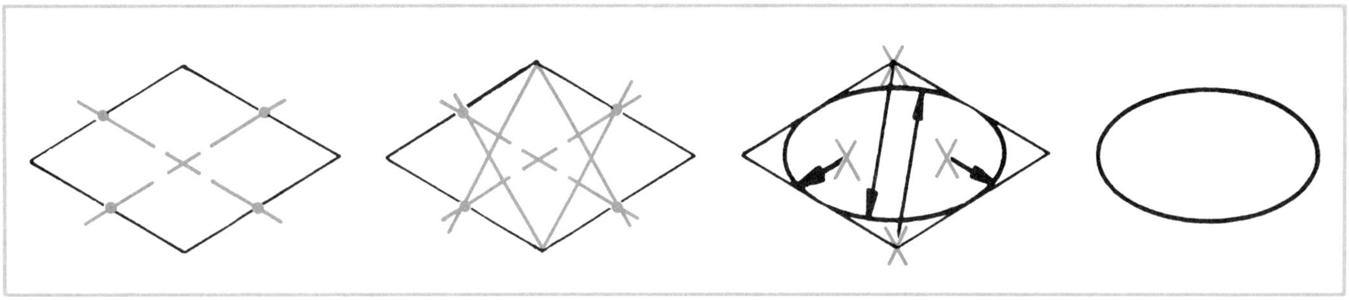

Fig. 3-70. Ellipses can be constructed following this four-center method.

Determine the radius for the ellipse. Mark each centerline with a "dot" at a distance from the center point equal to the radius.

Second, use a sharp pencil to lightly construct lines to locate the four centers of the ellipse. Construct lines at a 60 degree angle from each dot until they intersect to the left, right, above, and below the original center point. These four points of intersection are the four centers used to draw the ellipse.

Finally, set the compass to the small radius and swing an arc on the left and right sides. Set the compass to the larger radius and swing an arc at the top and bottom until the four arcs join smoothly.

SUMMARY

This chapter should be used by you as a reference for selecting drawing materials and supplies, and using them correctly and efficiently.

Each of the following problems has been designed to help you practice the use of the instruments efficiently and apply various geometric constructions in drawing situations. You should be aware of the criteria listed here to be used to evaluate your work. This self-evaluation will help to train you to produce professionally looking results.

1. Draw lines that are of consistent width and intensity.
2. Draw arcs and circles of consistent width and intensity.
3. Complete geometric constructions correctly and accurately.
4. Use the triangles efficiently.
5. Read and interpret the architect's scale.
6. Read and interpret the engineer's scale.
7. Read and interpret the metric scale.
8. Letter notes professionally.
9. Make lines, arcs, and circles flow together smoothly.

Chapter 3—INSTRUMENT DRAWING
Review What You Have Learned

Write all of your answers on a separate sheet of paper. Do not write in this textbook.

Essay:

1. Write a descriptive paragraph comparing freehand sketching with instrument drawing. Be sure to include an explanation of the tools and materials required for each operation.
2. Write a direct and to the point description of the proper method to follow in drawing a circle using a compass.

Multiple Choice: Carefully read the statements below and write the letter of the best answer for each of the items on your answer sheet.

3. The most common lead hardness in pencils is:
   a. HB.
   b. H.
   c. 2H.
   d. 4H.
   e. 9H.
4. Using both the 30 x 60 x 90 and the 45 x 45 x 90 degree triangles, lines can be drawn at:
   a. 15 degrees.
   b. 30 degrees.
   c. 45 degrees.
   d. 75 degrees.
   e. All of these.
5. Most mechanical pencils have lead that is what size?
   a. 0.1 mm.
   b. 0.3 mm.
   c. 0.5 mm.
   d. 0.7 mm.
   e. 1.0 mm.
6. An architectural scale contains all *but* which of the following?
   a. Feet.
   b. Decimals.
   c. Inches.
   d. Fractions.
   e. 16ths.
7. Which scale would be used for drawing an object half size when using the engineer's scale?
   a. 1/2.
   b. 1:5.
   c. 20.
   d. 16.
   e. 50.
8. Straight lines may be drawn with:
   a. A parallel rule.
   b. A T-square.
   c. A drafting machine.
   d. Triangles.
   e. All of these.
9. When using an architectural scale to draw a house to "quarter scale," use:
   a. 0.25.
   b. 1:25.
   c. 1/4.
   d. 40.
   e. 1:4.

True or False: Carefully read the statements below. Write a "T" on your answer sheet for the statements which are true. For the statements which are false, write an "F." Rewrite each false statement so it becomes true.

10. If your lines and lettering are too light, use a harder pencil lead. True or False?
11. A 4H pencil is recommended for lettering. True or False?
12. An HB pencil is used for making guidelines. True or False?
13. The term "60 pound paper" means that 1000 sheets of standard size (28" x 38") paper weighs 60 lbs. True or False?
14. Lines at 30 degrees, 60 degrees, and 90 degrees from the horizontal can be drawn when using a 30-60-90 degree triangle. True or False?
15. A scale is used to draw an object to actual, expanded, or reduced size. True or False?
16. Actual size numerals are always used to dimension an object drawn to an enlarged size or to a reduced size. True or False?

Completion: After studying this chapter, read the incomplete sentences below. Write the missing word or words on your answer sheet.

17. Arcs and circles are drawn with __________ or __________.
18. When drawing a house plan to quarter scale, 1/4 __________ represents 1 __________.
19. The scale selected for a drawing is determined by matching the size of the __________ and the size of the __________.
20. A divider is used to transfer distances from a __________ to a __________.
21. When using an architectural scale, the large divisions in the center represent __________ and the fine divisions on the ends represent __________.
22. When using the engineer's scale, the __________ scale would make the drawing one-half the size.

Matching: Match the list of drawing equipment in column A with their uses in column B.

Column A	Column B
23. Parallel rule/ T-square.	a. Draw to size.
24. Pencils/pens.	b. Draw arcs and circles.
25. Triangles.	c. Draw horizontal lines.
26. Compass/template.	d. Draw vertical/ angular lines.
27. Scales.	e. Draw lines.

Match the paper sizes in column A with the measurements in column B.

Column A	Column B
28. A.	a. 5 1/2 x 8 1/2.
29. B.	b. 8 1/2 x 11.
30. C.	c. 11 x 17.
31. D.	d. 17 x 22.
	e. 22 x 34.

Match the kinds of lines in column A with line widths in column B.

Column A	Column B
32. Border.	a. Thicker than 1.0 mm.
33. Object.	b. 0.7—1.0 mm.
34. Cutting plane.	c. 0.5—0.7 mm.
35. Section.	d. 0.3—0.5 mm.
36. Hidden.	e. Thinner than 0.3 mm.
37. Center.	
38. Guide.	

Match the bearing direction in column A with the degrees in column B.

Column A	Column B
39. North.	a. 0 - 360 degrees.
40. South.	b. 90 degrees.
41. East.	c. 135 degrees.
42. West.	d. 180 degrees.
	e. 270 degrees.

Match the mathematical direction in column A with the degrees in column B.

Column A	Column B
43. Right.	a. 0 - 360 degrees.
44. Left.	b. 90 degrees.
45. Up.	c. 135 degrees.
46. Down.	d. 180 degrees.

Match the mathematical X and Y values in column A with the direction in column B.

Column A	Column B
47. X+.	a. Upward.
48. X−.	b. Downward.
49. Y+.	c. To the right.
50. Y−.	d. To the left.
	e. In or out.

Practice What You Have Learned: On a blank 8 1/2 in. x 11 in. sheet of drawing paper, make a neat instrument drawing of the following objects to improve your skills and techniques.

Portable carrying case for CD's and tapes.

A clock face with unique markings for hours of the day.

A design logo for a new company which sells pizza. Use your instruments to develop the logo.

DRAWING PARALLEL LINES: Draw parallel, horizontal and vertical lines through each of the given points.

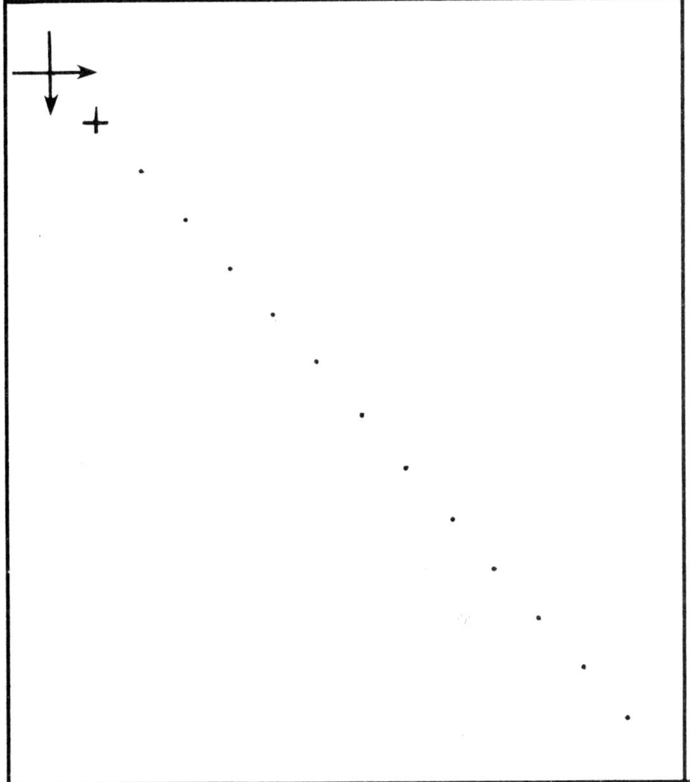

BISECTING LINES: Locate the center of each given line and indicate the center point with a short line.

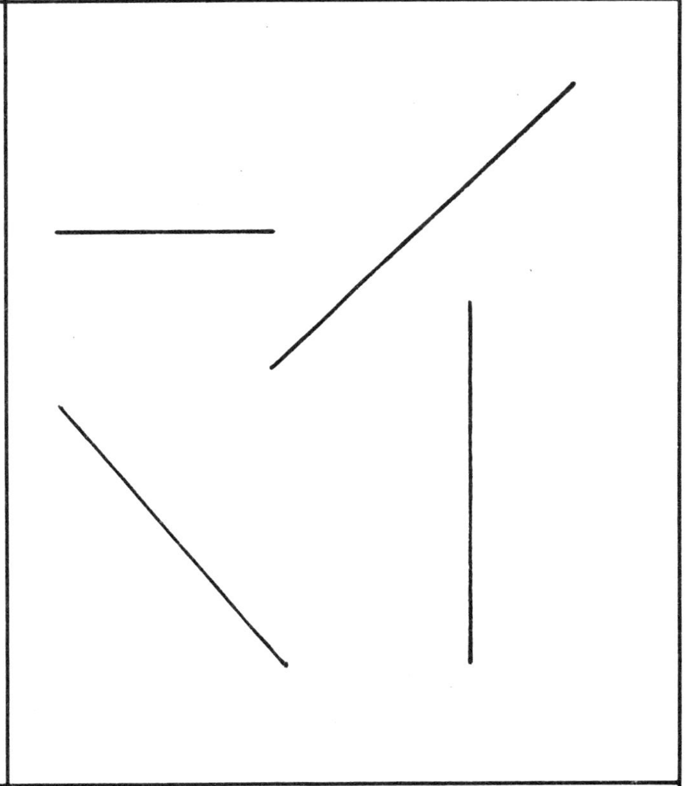

PERPENDICULAR BISECTING LINES: Construct 2'' line that bisects and is perpendicular to each given line.

DIVIDING LINES INTO EQUAL SEGMENTS: Divide each given line into segments of equal length as specified.

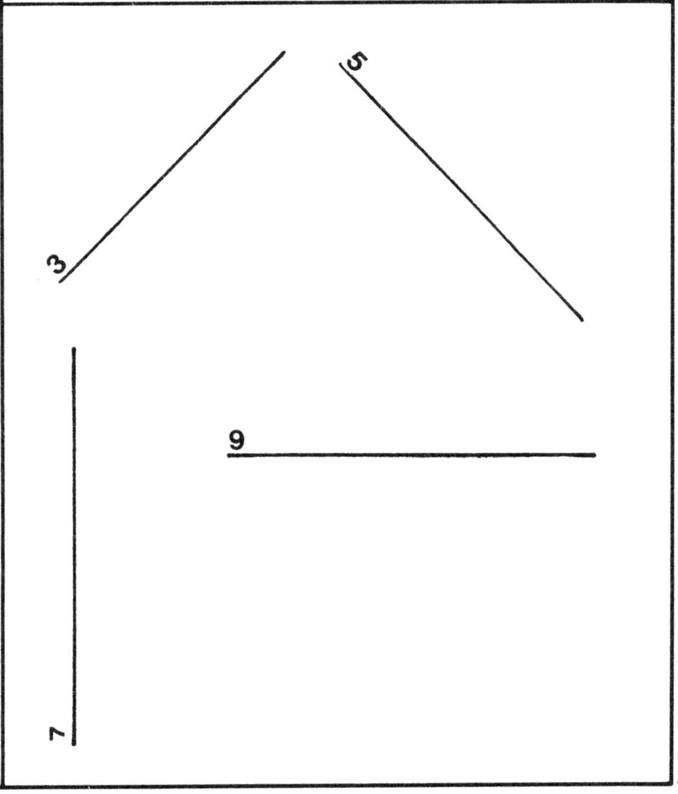

3-1 CONSTRUCTING STRAIGHT LINES. Using instruments, follow the directions given to draw this exercise on a separate sheet of paper. You will practice drawing parallel horizontal and vertical lines, bisecting lines, constructing perpendicular bisecting lines, and dividing lines into equal segments.

DRAWING ANGULAR LINES (BEARING): Draw lines, 1'' long, away from the given points at 22.5° intervals. Label each line with direction and degrees. (North is upward at 0°/360°, east is to the right at 90° etc.)

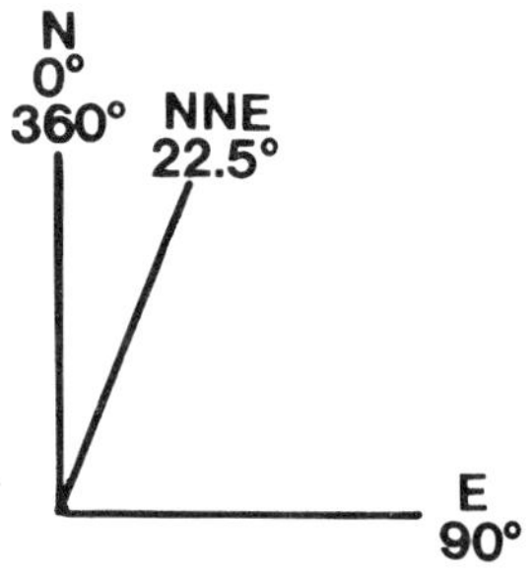

DRAWING ANGULAR LINES (MATHEMATICAL): Draw lines, 1 1/4'' long, away from the given point at 15° intervals. Label each line with degrees. (To the right is 0°/360°, upward is 90°, etc.)

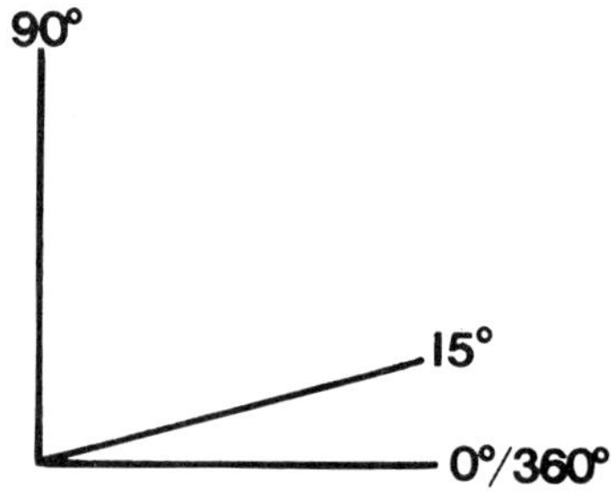

TRANSFERRING ANGLES: Reconstruct each of the four angles at the designated points.

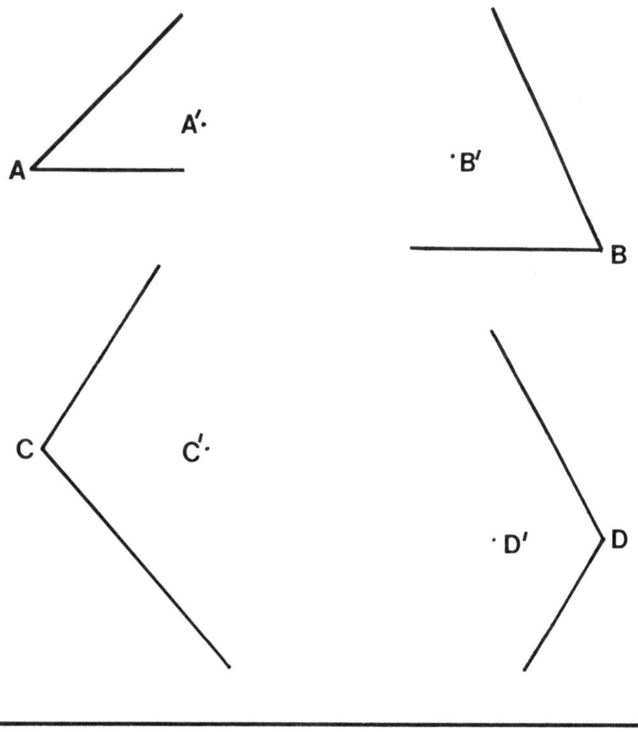

BISECTING ANGLES: Bisect each of the four given angles.

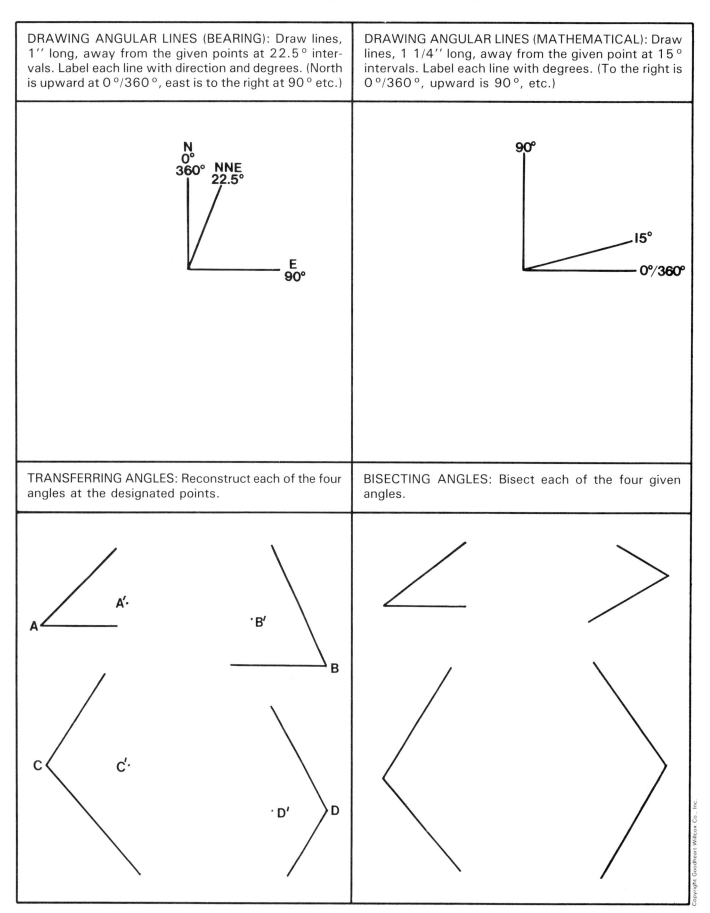

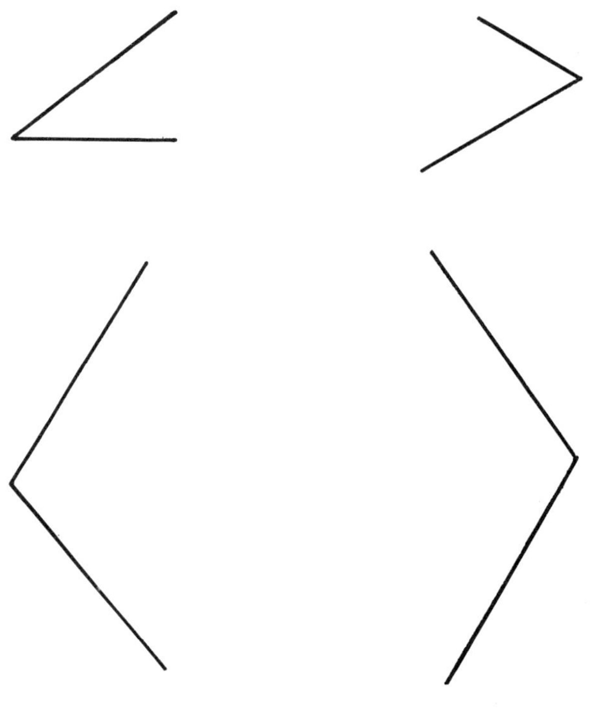

3-2 CONSTRUCTING ANGLES. Using instruments, follow the directions provided to practice three exercises: drawing angular lines, transferring angles, and bisecting angles.

CONSTRUCTING TRIANGLES (SIDES GIVEN): Construct each of the three triangles with sides given. Label the triangle with 1) three equal sides as "equal lateral" 2) two equal sides as "isosceles."

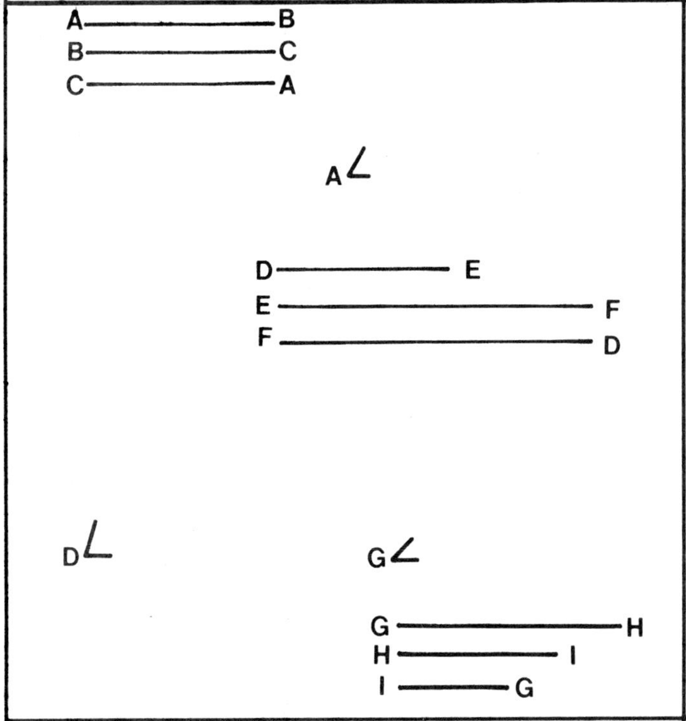

CONSTRUCTING TRIANGLES (2 SIDES / INCLUDED ANGLE GIVEN): Construct each of the three triangles with two sides and the included angle given. Label the triangle with all angles less than 90° as "acute" and those with an angle larger than 90° as "obtuse."

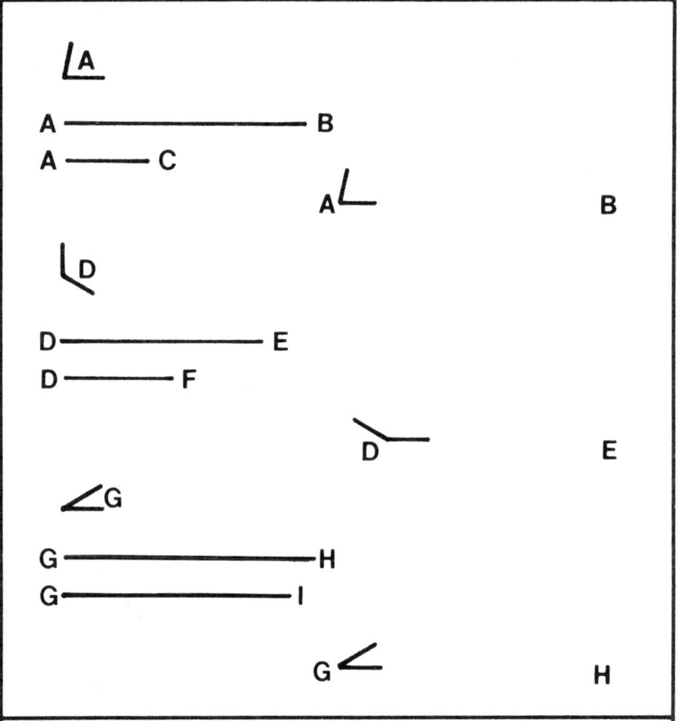

CONSTRUCTING TRIANGLES (2 ANGLES / INCLUDED SIDE GIVEN): Construct the three triangles with two angles and the included side given. Label the acute and obtuse triangles.

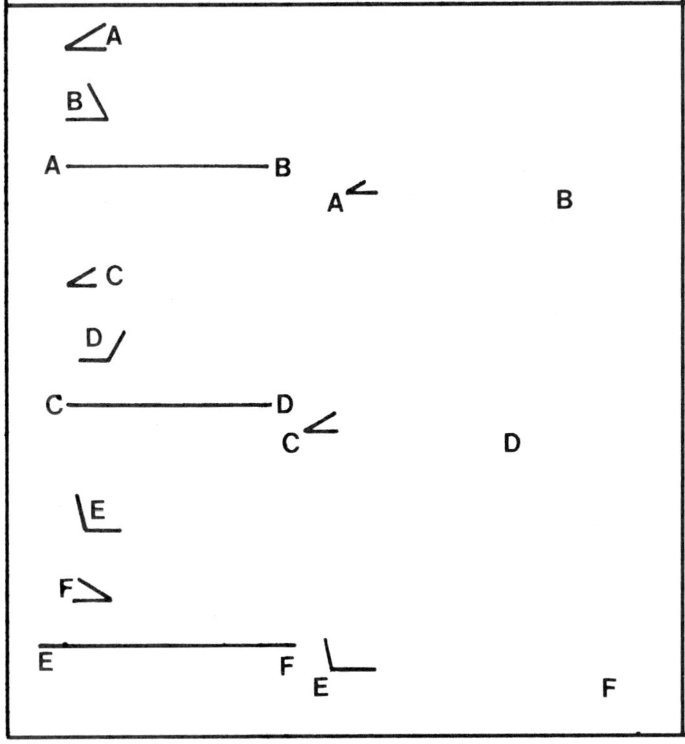

CONSTRUCTING RIGHT TRIANGLES: Construct the three right triangles with one side and one angle given. Label each hypotenuse and right angle.

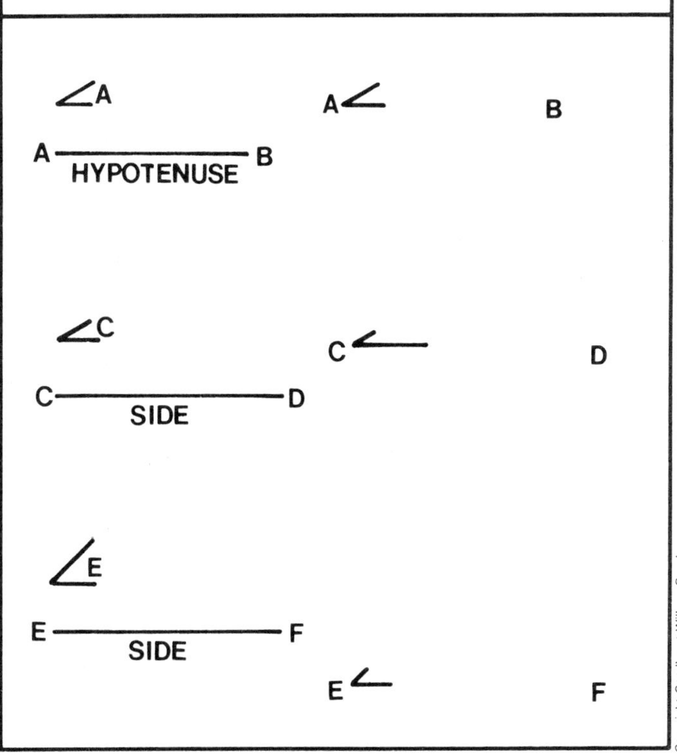

3-3 CONSTRUCTING TRIANGLES. Follow the directions provided to practice what you have learned in this chapter to construct triangles. You will use three sides given, two sides and the included angle given, two angles and the included side given, and one side and one angle given for a right triangle.

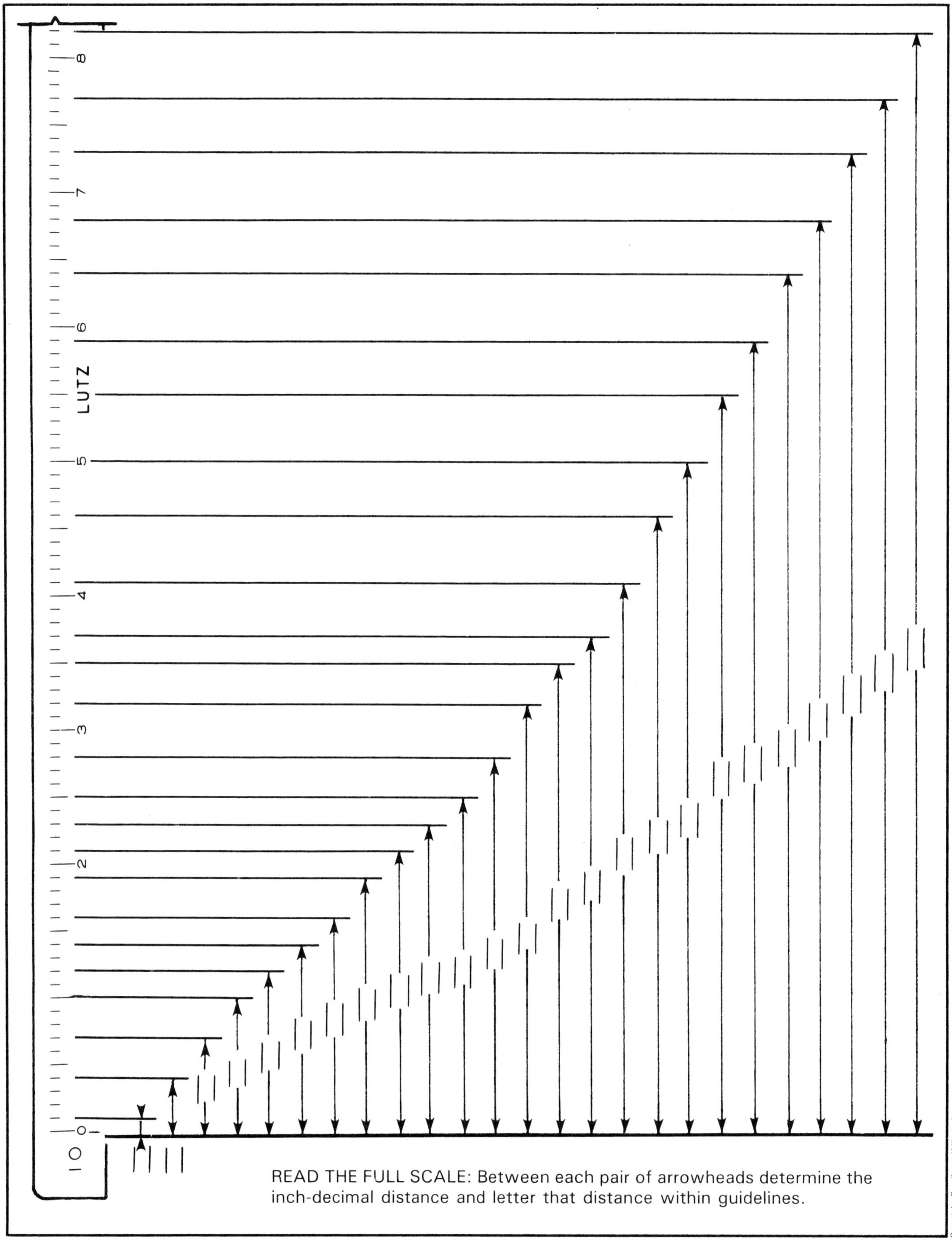

READ THE FULL SCALE: Between each pair of arrowheads determine the inch-decimal distance and letter that distance within guidelines.

3-4 READING THE ENGINEER'S SCALE.

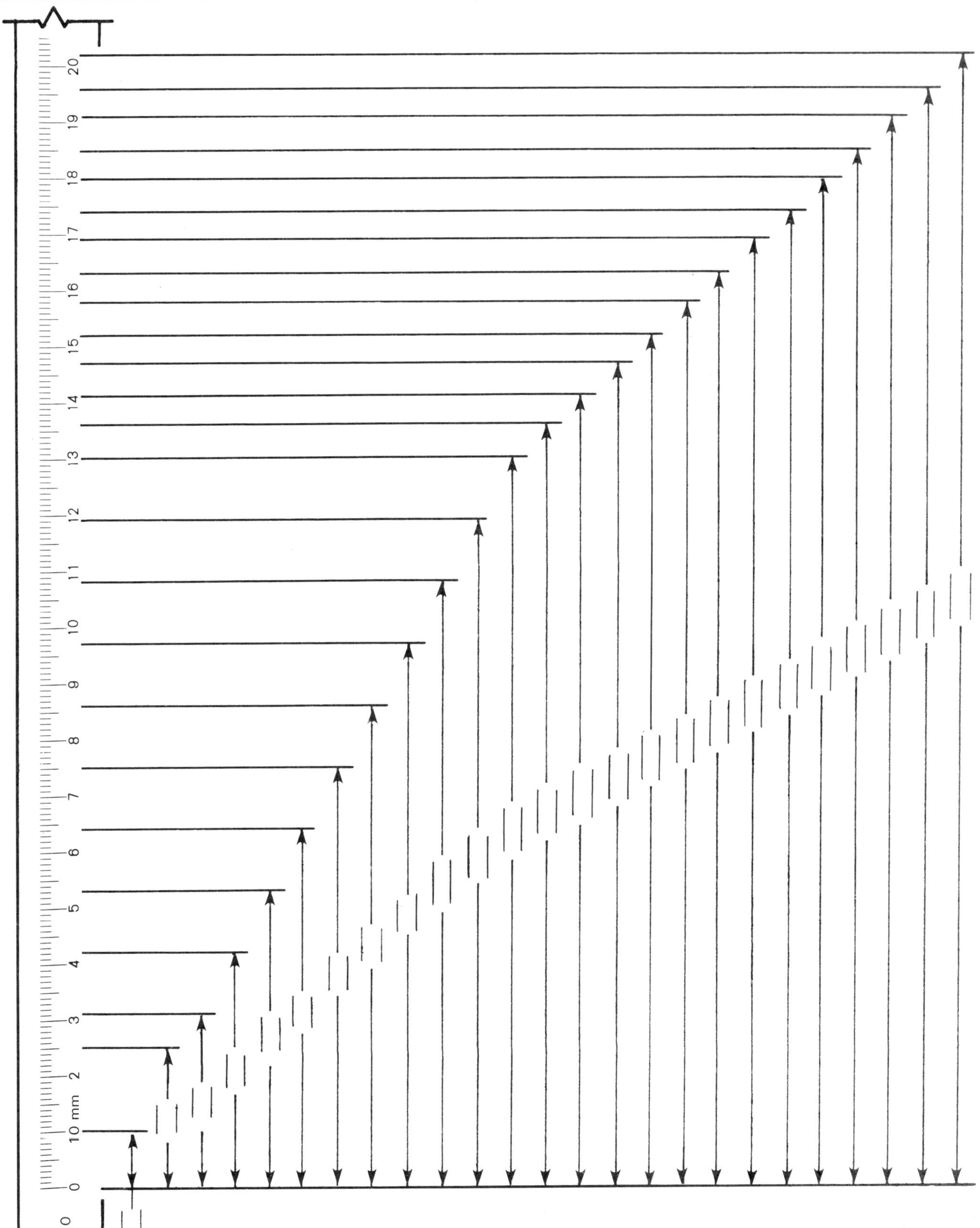

READ THE FULL SCALE: Determine the millimeter disance between each pair of arrowheads and letter than distance within the guidelines.

3-5 READING THE METRIC SCALE.

CONSTRUCTING SQUARES: Construct five squares with the length of their sides as follows: 1'', 1.5'', 2'', 2.5'', and 3''.

CONSTRUCTING RECTANGLES: Construct five rectangles with the lengths of their sides as follows: 20 mm and 25 mm, 35 mm and 40 mm, 45 mm and 50 mm, 55mm and 60 mm, and 75 mm and 80mm.

CONSTRUCTING PARALLELOGRAMS: Construct three parallelograms with the length of their sides and angles as follows: .75'' and 1'' at 45°/135°, 1.75 and 1.75'' at 60°/120°, and 2.5'' and 2'' at 75°/105°.

CONSTRUCTING TRAPEZOIDS: Construct three trapezoids with the base length, height and angles as follows: 75 mm, 80 m, and 75°/105° angles; 50 mm, 30 mm, and 60°/120° angles; and 20 mm, 8 mm, and 45°/135° angles.

3-6 CONSTRUCTING QUADRALATERALS. On a separate sheet of paper, use your instruments to construct the shapes described in the directions. You will gain practice in constructing squares, rectangles, parallelograms, and trapazoids.

CENTER RADIUS: Construct cencentric circles from the given center point with the following diameters: 3'', 2 1/2'', 2'', 1 3/4'', 1 1/2'' x 1 1/4'', 1'', 3/4''.

CENTER AND POINTS ON THE CIRCUMFERENCE: Construct three circles by using the three given points. One point is the center and the other two are on the circumference of each circle.

THREE POINTS ON THE CIRCUMFERENCE: Construct four circles by using the three given points on the circumference of each circle.

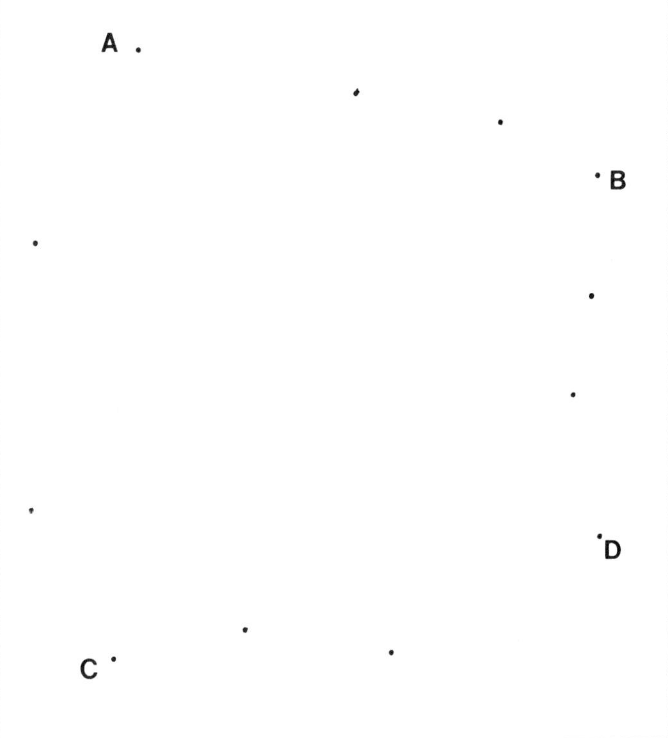

CHORD AND RADIUS: Construct four circles by using the given chords and radii of A), .75'', B) .875'', C) 1'', and D) .5''.

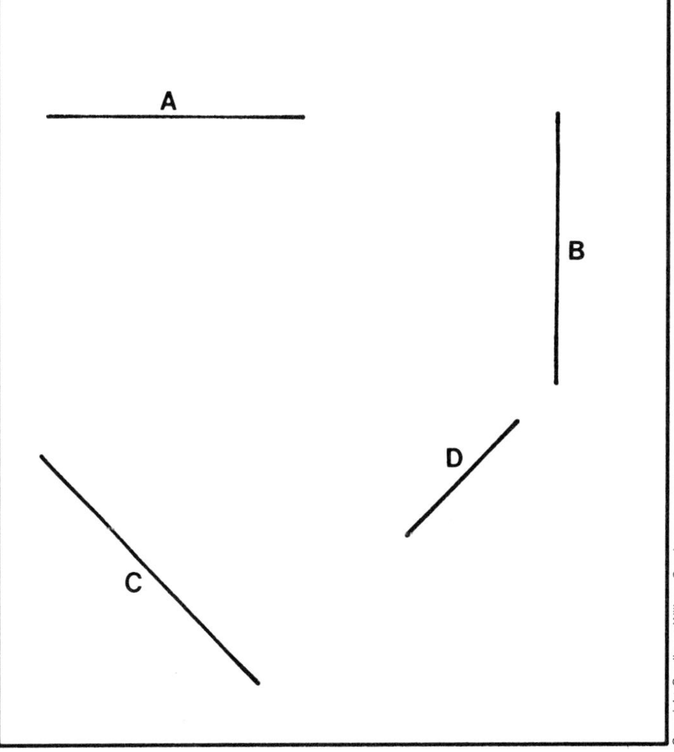

3-7 CONSTRUCTING CIRCLES. Use instruments to practice constructing circles. You will use a center point and a diameter, a center point and points on the circumference, three points on the circumference, and a cord and radius.

LINE AND CIRCLE: Construct A) a line tangent to a given circle and B) a 25 mm radius circle tangent to a given line.

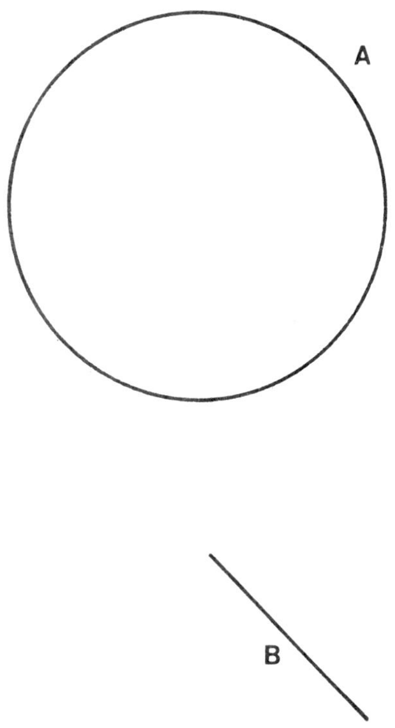

TWO LINES AND AN ARC: Construct aracs of A) 2'', B) 2 1/2'', C) 1'' tangent to the given lines.

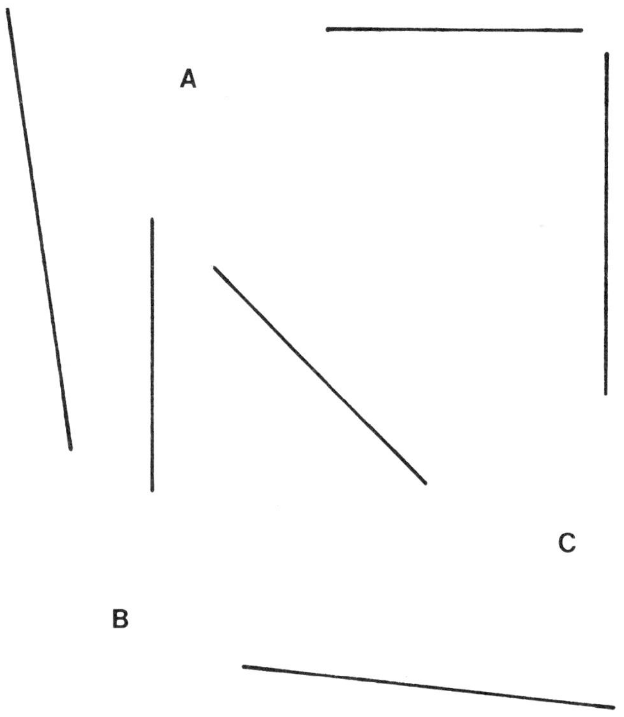

CIRCLE AND ARC: Construct arcs of A) 1'', B) 1 1/4'', and C) 1 1/2'' tangent to the given circles.

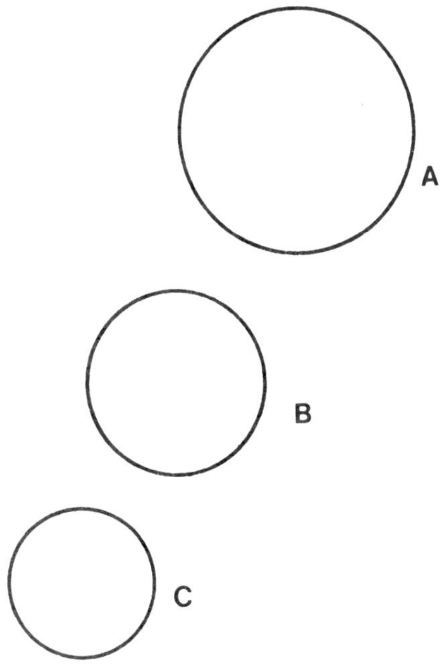

SEMICIRCLES AND CIRCLES: Construct circles and semi-circles as follows, A) two 12 mm radius semi-circles tangent to the upper two given circles and B) a 19 mm circle above and a 25 mm semi-circle below the lower two circles and tangent to them.

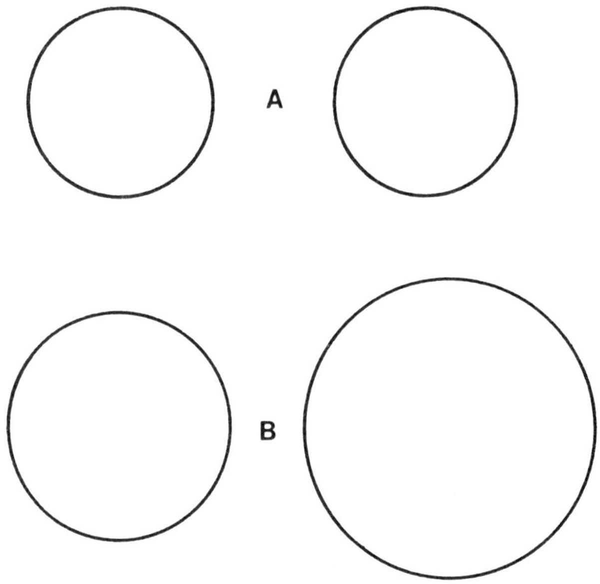

3-8 CONSTRUCTING TANGENTS. Practice will be provided in constructing tangents using a line and circle, two lines and an arc, a circle and an arc, and semicircles and circles.

INSCRIBED TRIANGLES AND SQUARES: Construct a 3″ diameter circle, an inscribed triangle, and an inscribed square.	PENTAGONS: Construct a pentagon within a 75 mm diameter circle.
+	+
HEXAGONS: Construct a hexagon, tangent to the outside of a 2.5″ diameter circle.	OCTAGON: Construct an octagon tangent to the outside of a 75 mm diameter circle.
+	+

3-9 CONSTRUCTING POLYGONS. Using instruments, carefully follow the directions to inscribe a triangle and a square in a circle, and to construct a pentagon, a hexagon, and an octagon.

READ THE SCALES: Determine the inch-fraction distance between each pair of arrowheads and letter that distance within the guidelines.

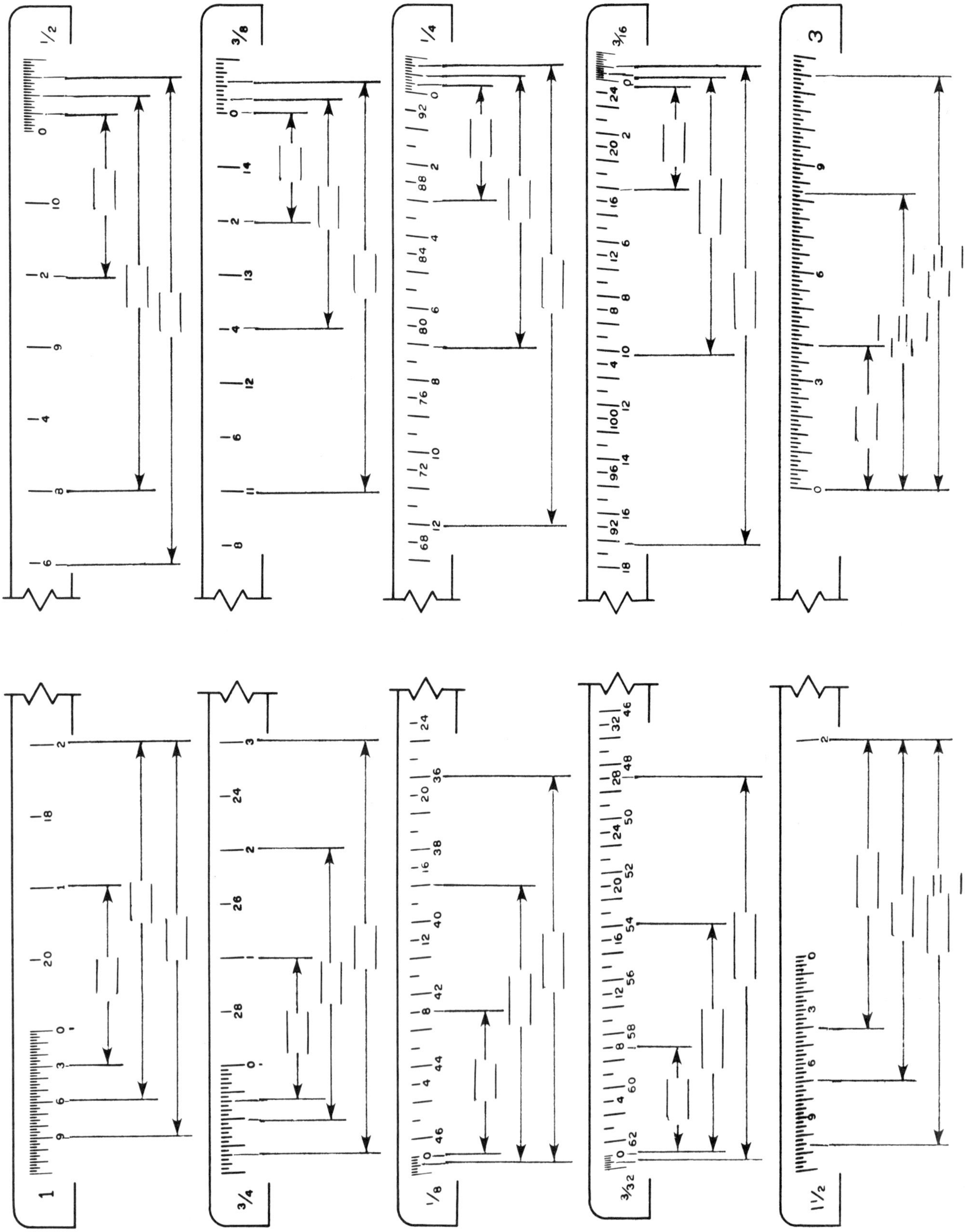

3-10 READING THE ARCHITECT'S SCALE.

READ THE SCALES: Determine the millimeter/meter distance between each pair of arrowheads and letter that distance within the guidelines.

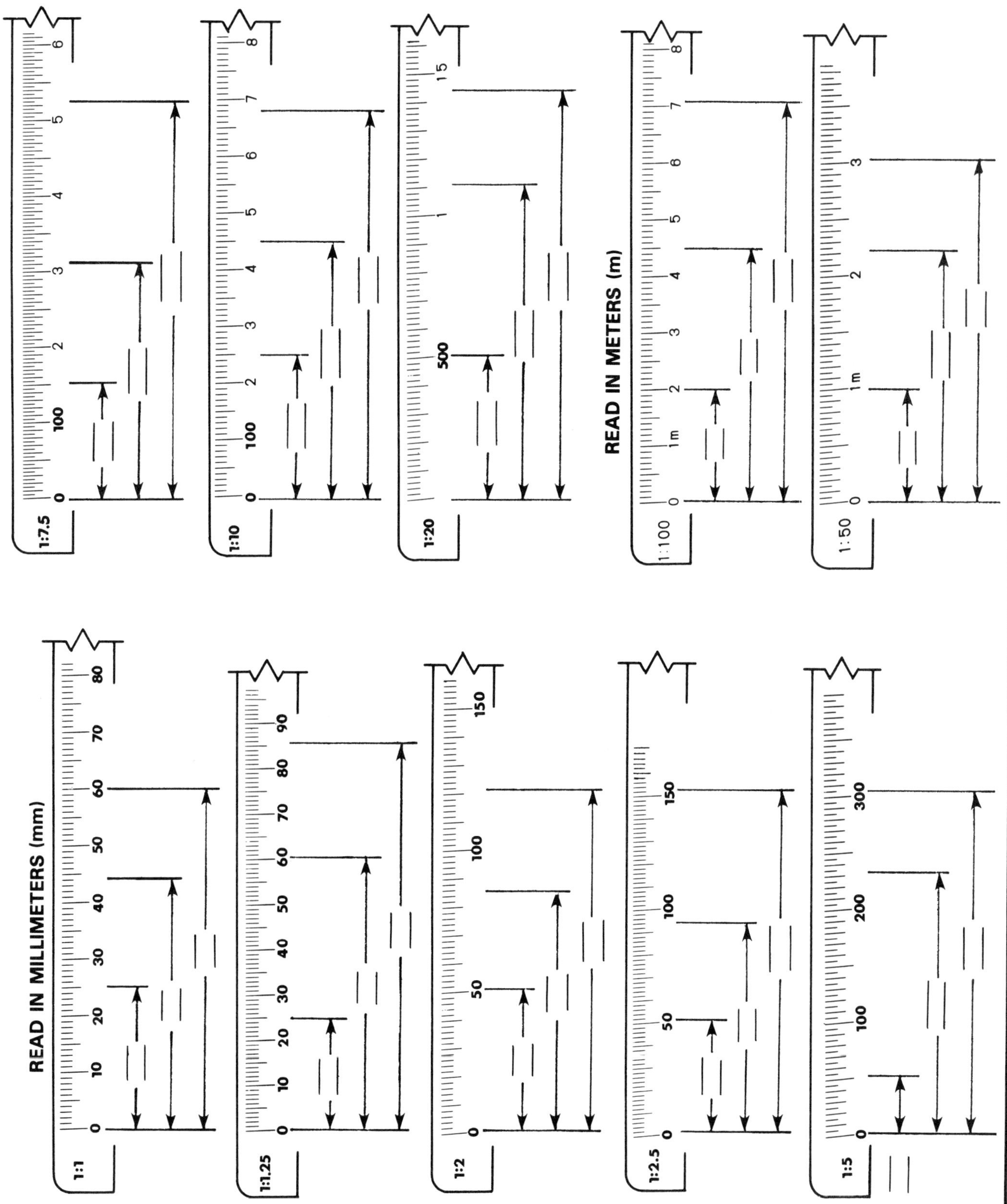

3-11 READING THE METRIC SCALE.

READ THE SCALES: Determine the inch-decimal distance between each pair of arrowheads and letter that distance within the guidelines.

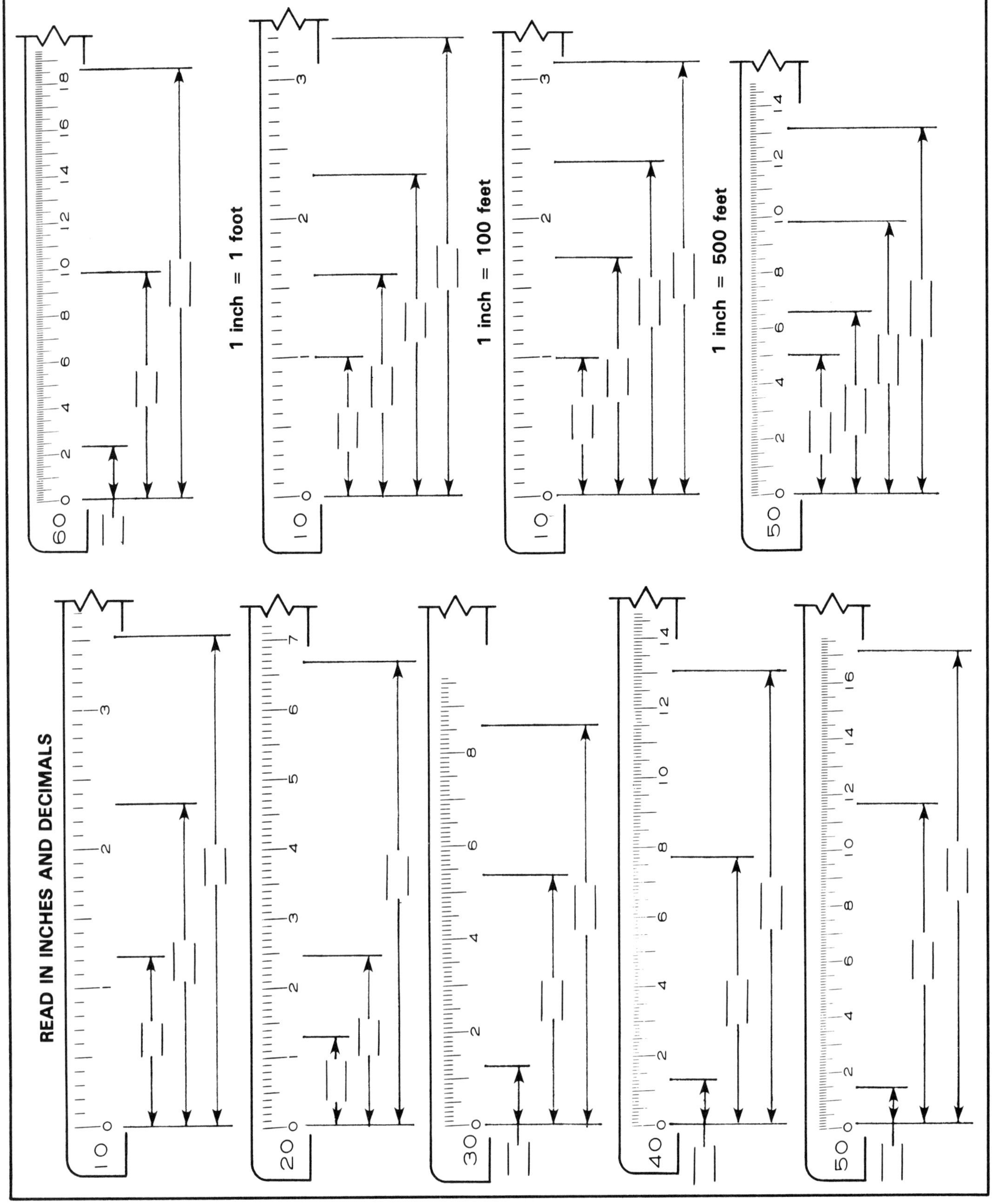

3-12 READING THE ENGINEER'S SCALE.

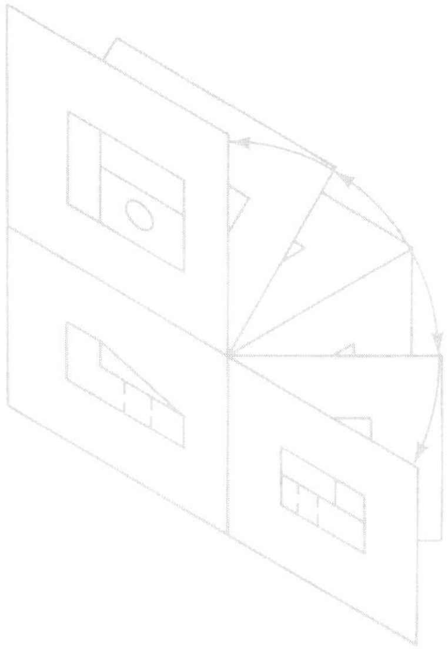

Chapter 4

PROJECTING IMAGES

OBJECTIVES

After completing this chapter on PROJECTING IMAGES, you will be able to:

- ☐ *Visualize multiview images from pictorial drawings, real objects, and ideas.*
- ☐ *Draw multiview projections from pictorial drawings, real objects, and sketches.*
- ☐ *Visualize isometric images from multiview drawings.*
- ☐ *Prepare isometric drawings.*
- ☐ *Draw the first auxiliary views of a surface.*
- ☐ *Develop solutions to surface pattern problems.*

Sketches solidify or capture ideas that flow from the minds of designers. **Drawings** communicate the necessary information to make the ideas a reality. **Pictorial views** provide a vivid image. **Multiview drawings** show specific details about size and shape. Fig. 4-1 shows a building brick as a pictorial and as a multiview drawing.

Our culture is rich with examples of products illustrated on flat two-dimensional surfaces. These flat illustrations create three-dimensional images of products in the mind. For example, the pages of mail-order catalogs and advertisements in magazines contain thousands of photographs. Each printed two-dimensional picture provides the customer with an instant three-dimensional image of available merchandise. Additionally, a two-dimensional surface of a television screen provides three-dimensional images of products.

While cameras and printing presses provide vivid images of products that already exist, the products and ideas created by designers, engineers, and architects are recorded and communicated as two-dimensional sketches. Sketches are revised as ideas or concepts develop, and become drawings. Both sketches and drawings communicate product information before prototypes are constructed.

Drawings and sketches include pictorials. Pictorials, like photographs, provide an instant three-dimensional image of products.

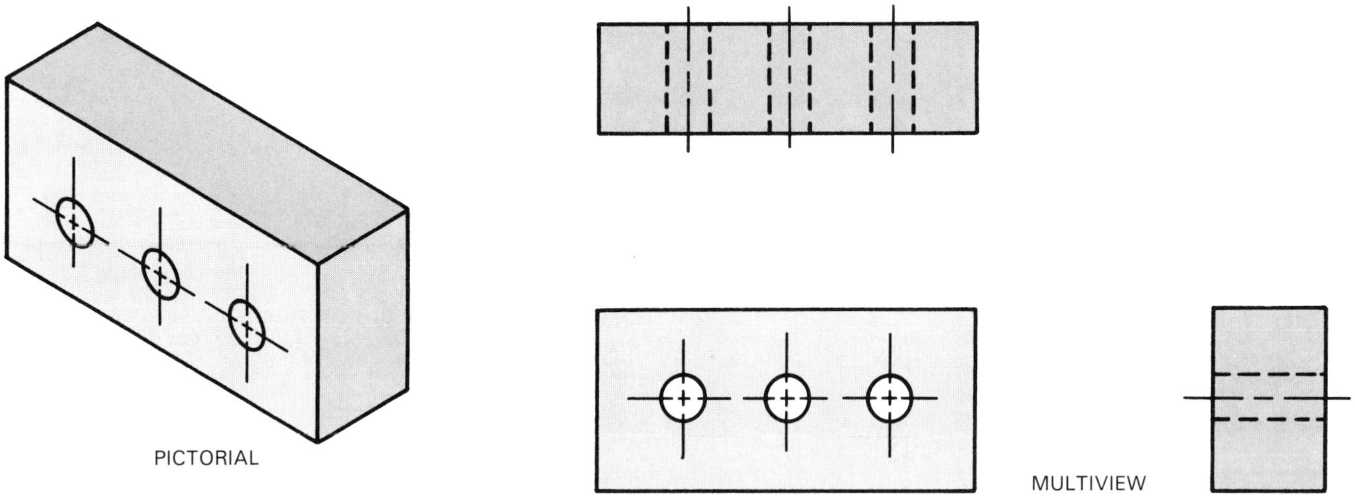

Fig. 4-1. Comparison of a building brick as a pictorial drawing and as a multiview drawing.

Isometric pictorial views, however, can be produced quickly and provide similar information as precise pictorials. Therefore, isometric sketches and drawings are commonly used to communicate three-dimensional images of products. Multiview drawings provide specific size and shape information about a product. Both isometric and multiview sketches are essential in providing product information.

FUNDAMENTALS

Multiview drawings represent an essential part of the language of industry. They typically include top, front, side views of an object. Multiviews provide two-dimensional images of specific surfaces. These surfaces are independent views of the object. Experienced drafters can look at the top, front, and side views of an object, and they can visualize a three-dimensional image of the object. An experienced drafter can record this image of the object as an isometric sketch.

A brick is an example of a product with parallel surfaces. The top and bottom are parallel, the sides are parallel, and the front and back are parallel. Both isometric and multiview drawings have parallel lines. These lines are often called **parallel lines of projection.** An isometric view of the building brick contains sets of parallel lines. Refer to Fig. 4-2 and note that three lines are vertical lines (V), three lines slant upward to the right (R), and three lines slant upward to the left (L). In a pictorial, the parallel lines represent the edges of the object.

The multiview projection of the building brick has a top view, front view, and side view, Fig. 4-3. Each view is drawn with two sets of parallel lines. Each line in a multiview represents a surface of the brick. For example, in Fig. 4-4, the upper horizontal line in the front view represents the top surface of the brick. As a viewer is positioned at eye level with the top of the brick, the top surface appears as a line.

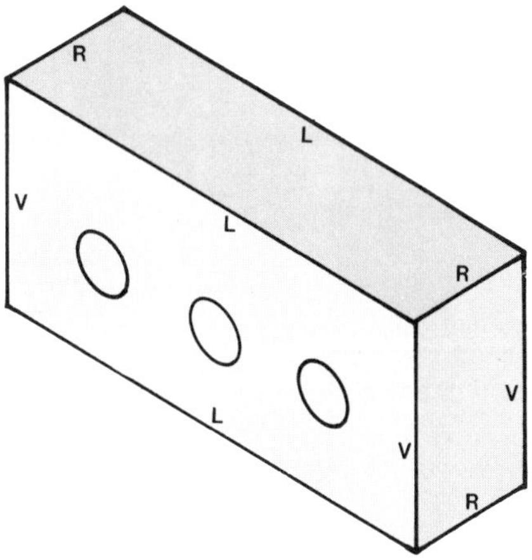

Fig. 4-2. The isometric view of a brick is easily drawn using three sets of parallel lines.

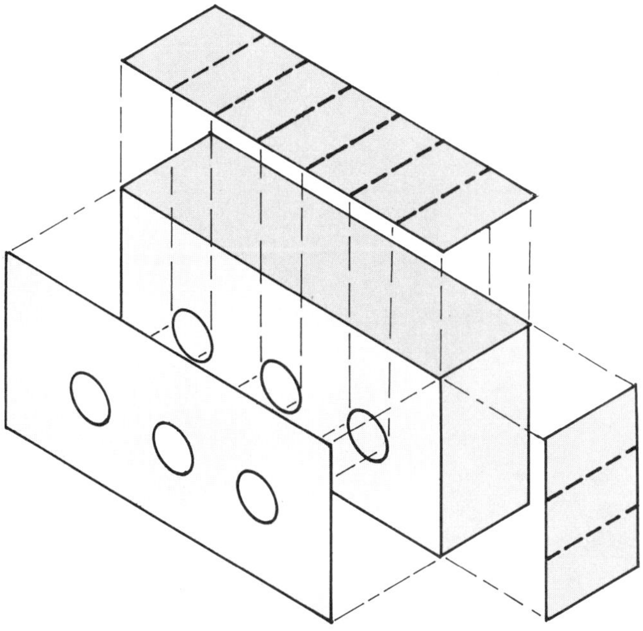

Fig. 4-3. Multiview projections show three views and use more lines than isometric drawings to show the edges.

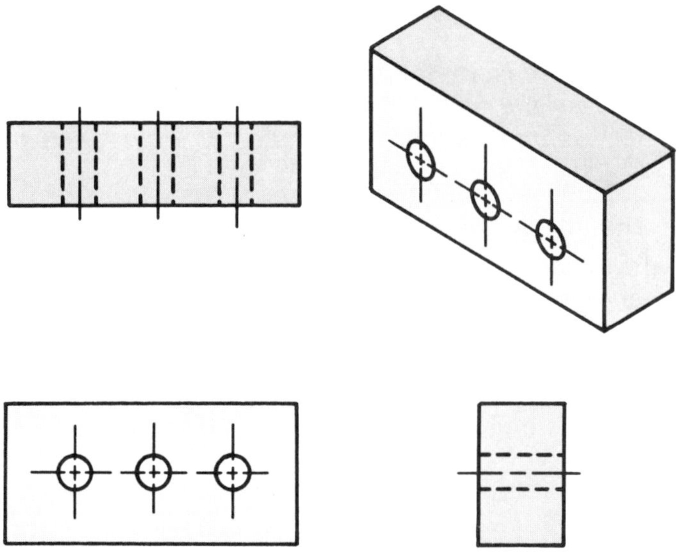

Fig. 4-4. In a multiview drawing, each of the lines represents a surface in another view.

Before going on, you need to know that the placement of multiview projections with respect to each other is of utmost importance. The United States of America arranges views according to **third-angle projection.** Many other countries arrange views according to first-angle projection.

Although most of your work will be in third-angle projection, the European and Oriental style uses the first-angle projection. As a beginner drafter, you should understand the relationship between the views. With interdependence among nations, you may encounter drawings in first-angle projection. In this activity, you will first learn to construct in the third-angle projection. After you have mastered these techniques, you will learn about first-angle projection later in this chapter.

DEVELOPING MULTIVIEW PROJECTIONS IN THIRD-ANGLE

Projecting images involves visualization. Visualizing the top, front, and right side of a three-dimensional part is essential. Visualizing images quickly and accurately requires an understanding of the arrangement of views.

Identifying Lines of Sight for Isometric and Multiview Drawings

Lines of sight are imaginary lines that extend from the observer's eye to points on an object. Lines of sight are always parallel. As you can see in Fig. 4-5, the shaded, flat front surface appears as a straight line or edge view when viewed from above.

Visualizing Top, Front, and Side Views

One way to visualize and draw the top, front, and side views of a product is to begin with its isometric view. The image seen from directly above the isometric is the top view, Fig. 4-6. Likewise, the front view is the image seen from the front. The right side view is the image seen from the right side of the isometric view.

Each view represents the exact size of the object. The front view indicates the exact length and height, Fig. 4-6. The top view indicates the exact length and depth. The right side view indicates the exact height and depth.

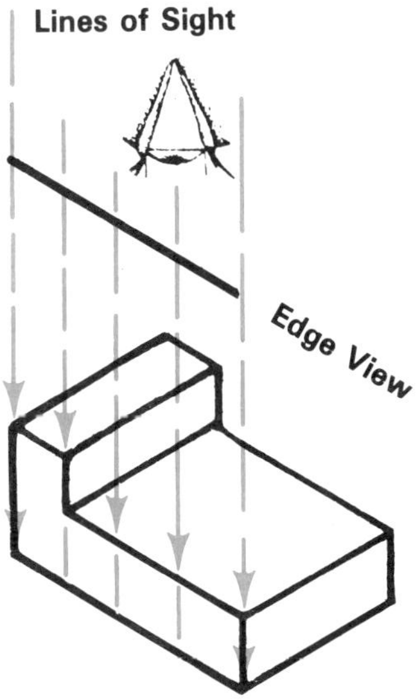

Fig. 4-5. Lines in multiview drawings represent the edge of a surface.

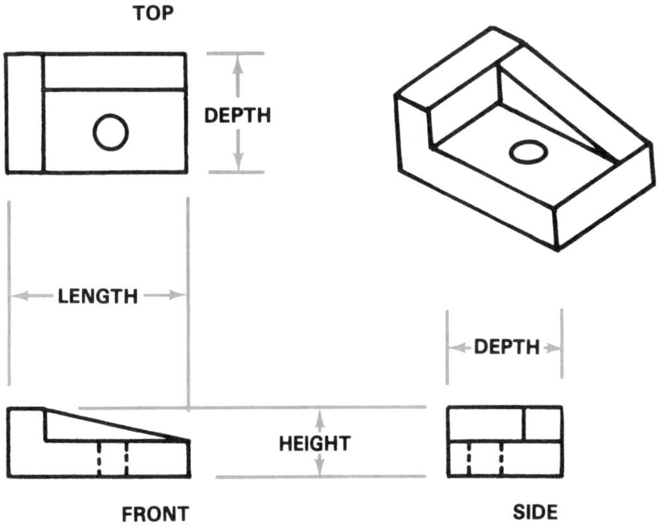

Fig. 4-6. Multiview drawings convey the exact length, height, and depth of the product.

Establishing Planes of Projection for Isometric and Multiview Drawings

A plane of projection is an imaginary transparent plane located between the object being viewed and the observer. This plane of projection is always perpendicular to the line of sight. Think of this plane as a clear sheet of glass or plastic positioned a short distance away from the object, Fig. 4-7. In our ex-

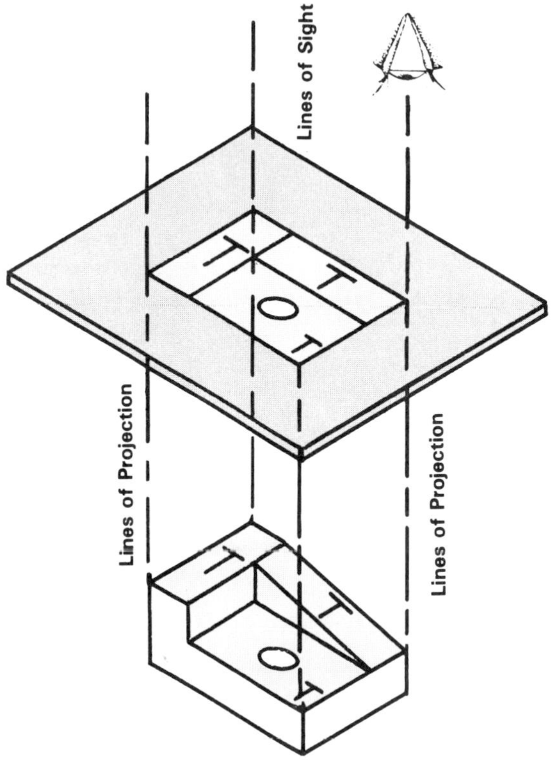

Fig. 4-7. When a line of sight passes through or pierces a plane of projection, the lines of sight are called lines of projection.

ample, the plane of projection is placed over the top of an object. When the observer looks down at the object, his or her **lines of sight** pass through or ''pierce'' the plane of projection. On the other side from the observer, the lines of sight are referred to as the **lines of projection** and they trace out or record the shape and size of the object as they pierce the plane of projection. The three dimensional object is transformed into a two-dimensional image on the plane of projection using this technique. As the observer's eye traces the outline and features of the object, each of the piercing points captures the true shape and size of the object on the plane of projection placed parallel to the object.

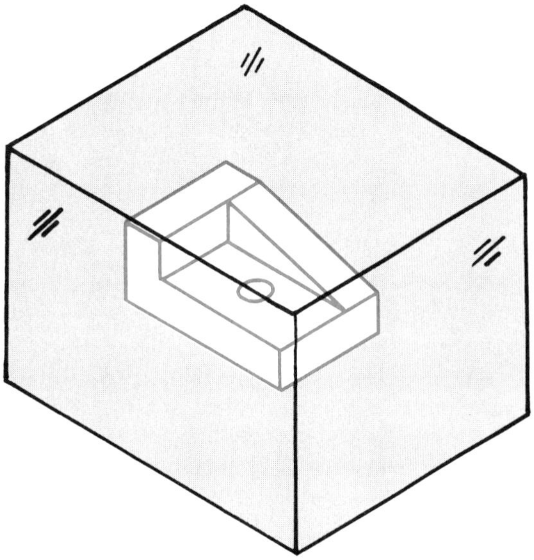

Fig. 4-8. The object surrounded by three transparent planes in the glass box technique.

Visualizing Multiviews Using the Glass Box Technique

The glass box technique described here provides a three-dimensional model for visualizing images. The glass box is made of three transparent planes: horizontal, frontal, and profile planes of projection, Fig. 4-8. Imagine the object inside the box. The horizontal plane is located above the object and records the top view, Fig. 4-7. The frontal plane is vertical and records the front view, Fig. 4-9. The profile plane is also vertical, located to the right side of the object, and records the right side view, Fig. 4-10. All of the views may be projected onto the sides of the glass box, Fig. 4-11.

Arranging Views of a Multiview Drawing in Third-Angle Projection

A common way to visualize the arrangement of the views is to fold out the panes of the glass box, Fig. 4-12. The frontal plane remains stationary, while the horizontal plane folds upward, Fig. 4-13, and the profile plane folds out to the right, Fig. 4-14. The three views are then revolved, Fig. 4-15, into the multiview arrangement, Fig. 4-16.

The arrangement of the top, front, and side views of a product is critical. The top view MUST appear directly above the front view! The right side view MUST appear directly to the right of the front view! Similarly, a left side view MUST appear directly to

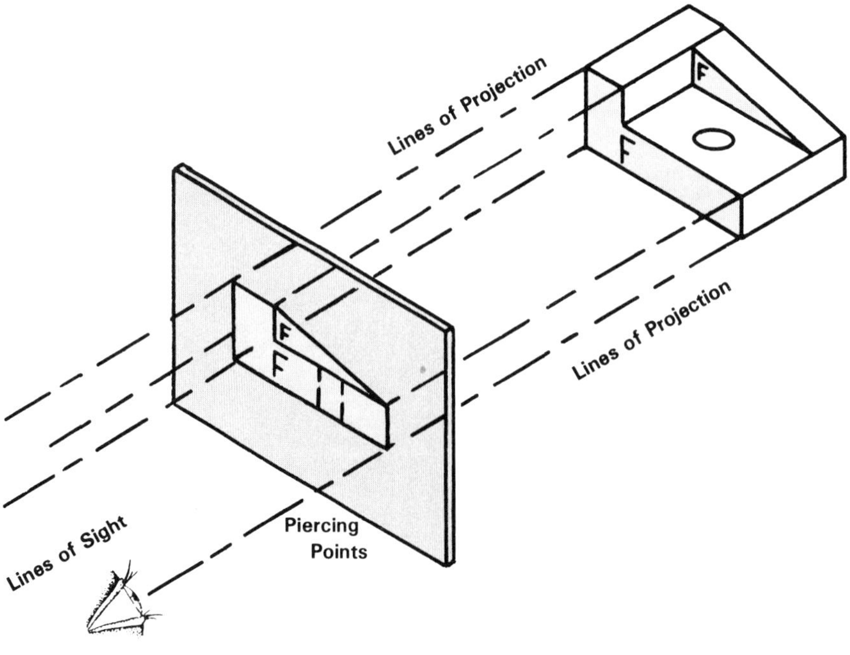

Fig. 4-9. The front view of the object as seen on the plane of projection.

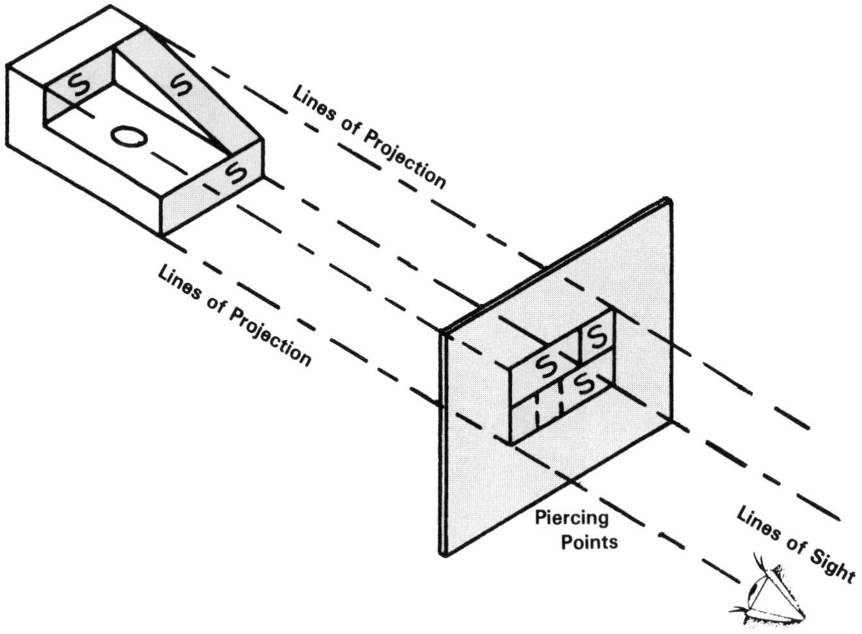

Fig. 4-10. The side view of the object as seen on the plane of projection.

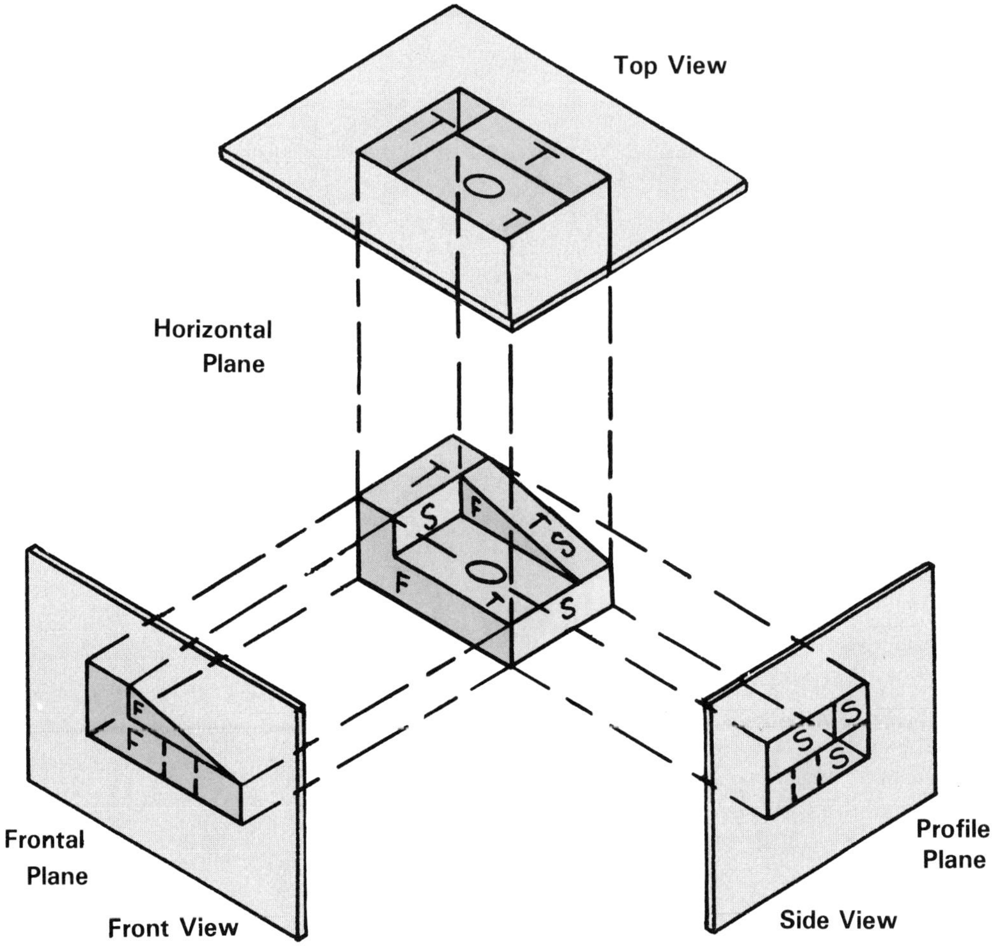

Fig. 4-11. Combining the top, front, and right planes of projection.

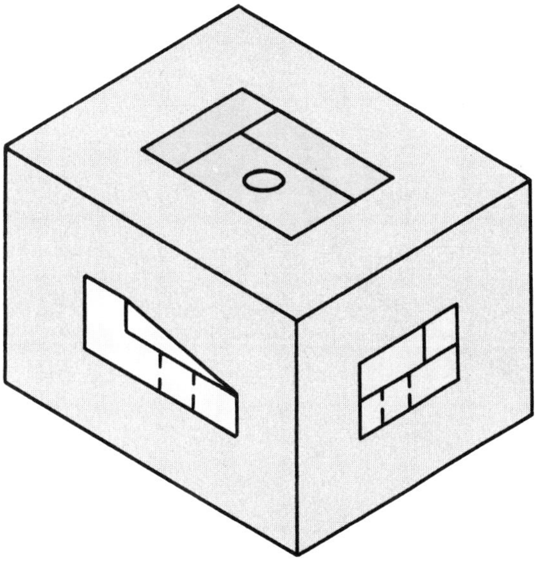

Fig. 4-12. The glass box technique shows three views.

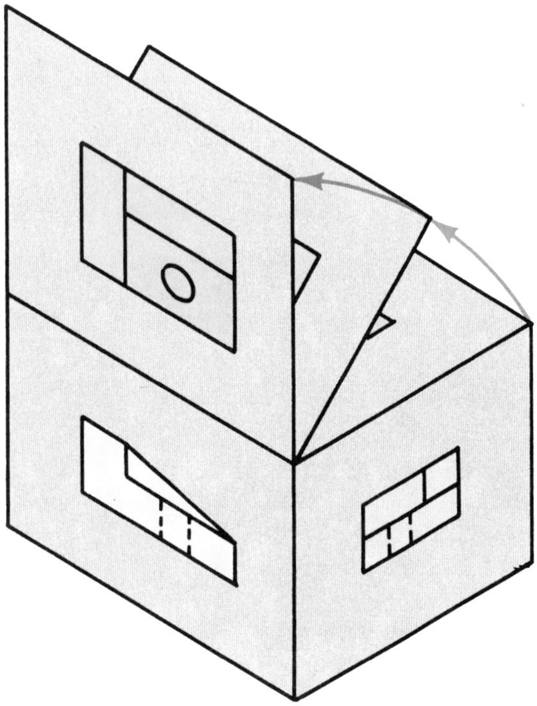

Fig. 4-13. Unfolding the top view of the glass box to put the drawing in the same plane as the front view.

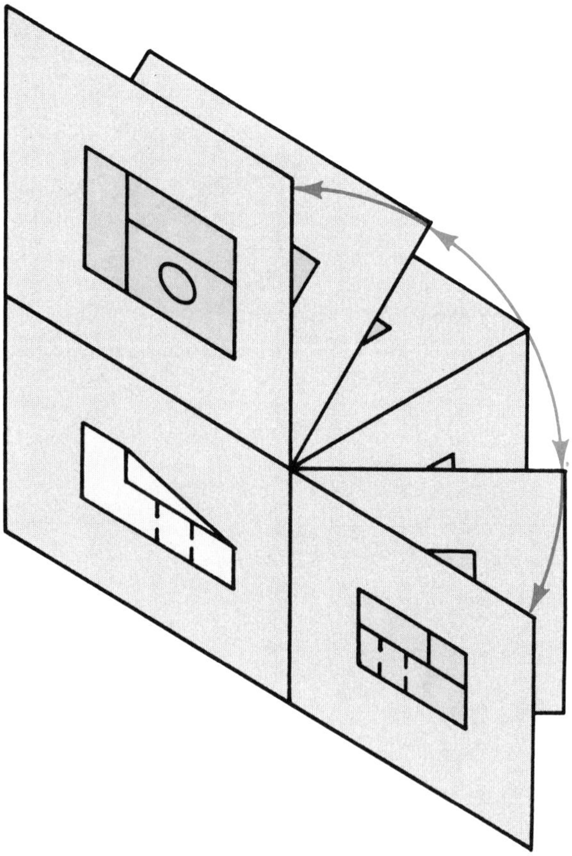

Fig. 4-14. Unfolding the side view of the glass box to put the drawing in the same plane as the front view.

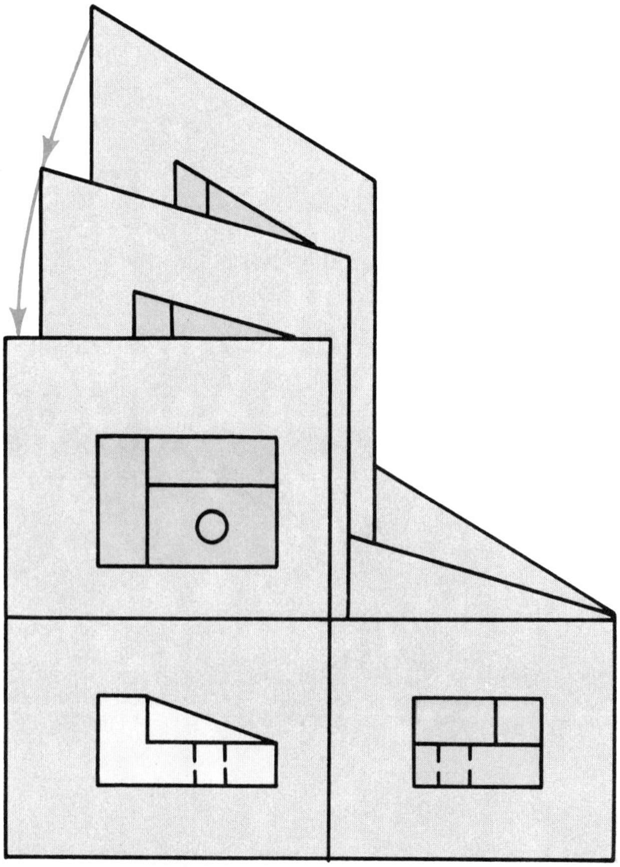

Fig. 4-15. Revolving the entire drawing made up of the top, front, and side views from the isometric.

the left of the front view! If needed, a bottom view would be located below the front view, Fig. 4-17. A back view could be located to the right of the right side view or to the left of the left side view. When the glass box is removed mentally, folding plane lines may be used to mark the position of the panes of glass.

Laying-Out Multiview Drawings in Third-Angle Projection

The layout of a multiview drawing involves several questions. First, how many views are need-

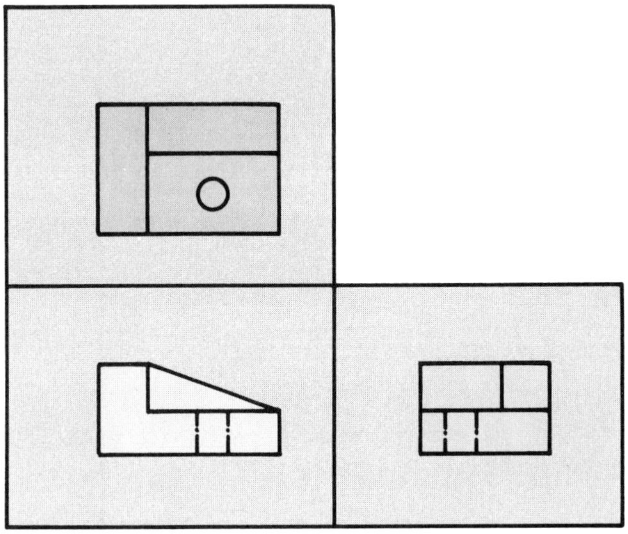

Fig. 4-16. The multiview arrangement as seen from straight-on.

ed to completely describe the product? If the top, front, and right side views are needed, the front view will be placed in the lower left area of the drawing. The top view will be directly above, and the right side view will be directly to the right of the front view.

Secondly, how does the product size compare to the available paper size? When using an ''A'' size sheet horizontally, the drawing space inside the border lines and title block will be about 7.7 in. high and 10.6 in. wide, Fig. 4-18. For products that are 4 in. long, 2 in. tall, and 3 in. deep or smaller, a full scale drawing can be made on an ''A'' size sheet. For larger products, use larger paper or choose a smaller scale.

For example, vertical layout of a 1.5 in. tall and 1 in. deep product requires 2.5 in. of space for the views. This would leave 5.2 in. of space on an ''A'' sheet to be distributed in the three areas, V1, V2, and V3, Fig. 4-19. Horizontal layout of the 3 in. long and 1 in. deep product on the ''A'' size sheet requires 4 in. of space for the views. The remaining 6.6 in. would be left for the three areas, H1, H2, and H3, Fig. 4-19, between the views and borders.

Third, how much space will be needed between views for dimensions and notes? In this example, leave 2 in. of space between the views and split the remainder evenly between the views and borders. Vertical and horizontal lines can be lightly drawn to ''block in'' the top, front, and right side views. The finished layout looks like Fig. 4-20.

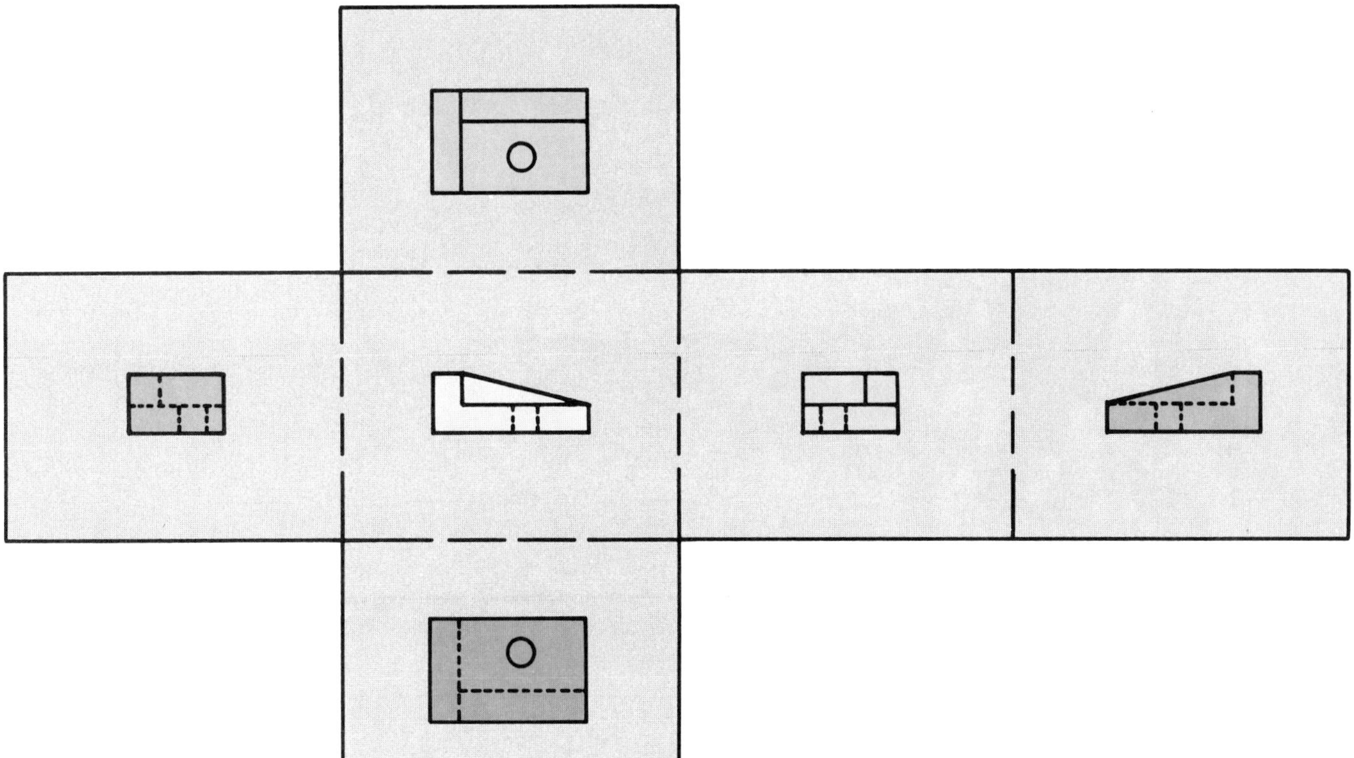

Fig. 4-17. When completely unfolded, the glass box technique reveals six different views of an object. The three extra multiview drawings represent the bottom view, the left side view, and the back view.

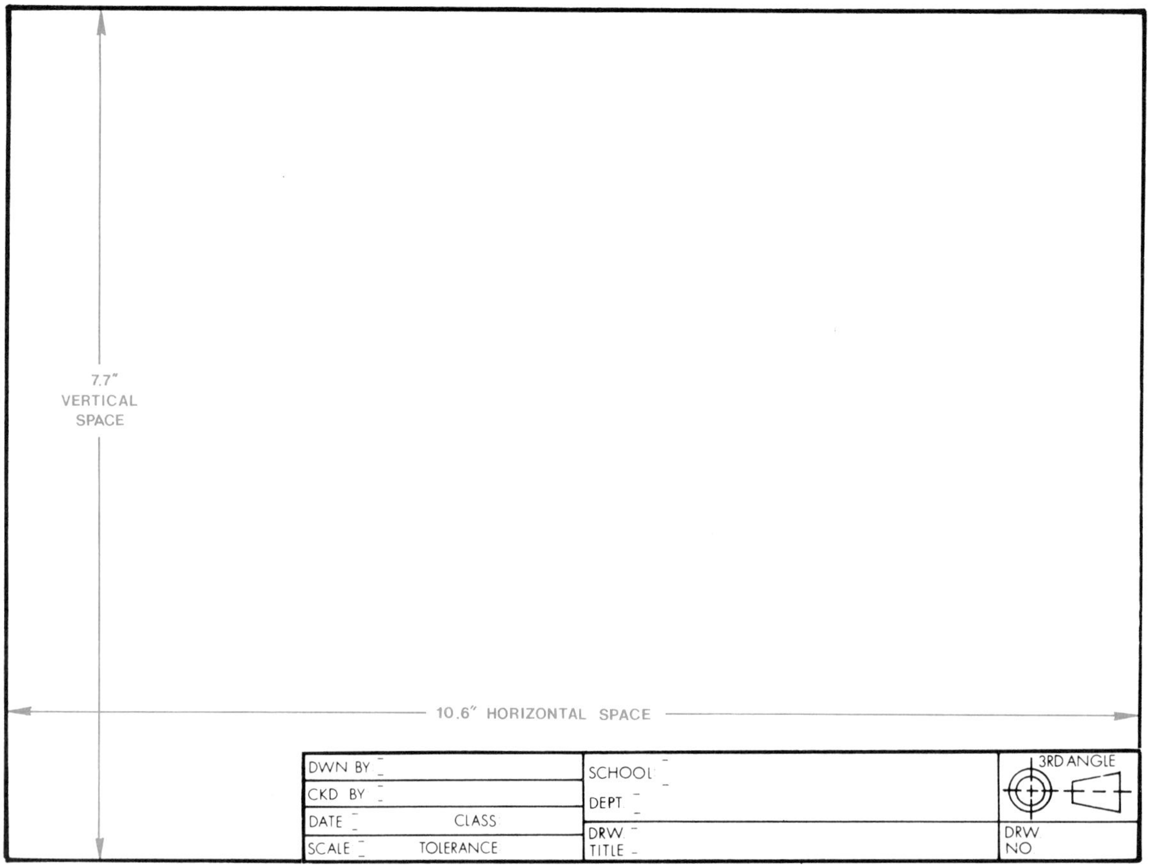

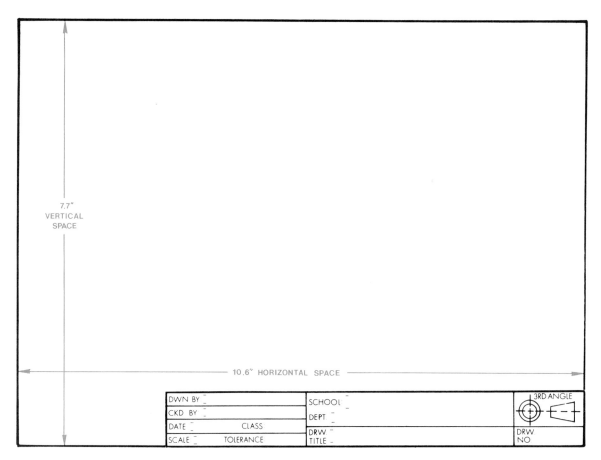

Fig. 4-18. Note the usable space in an "A" size drawing sheet.

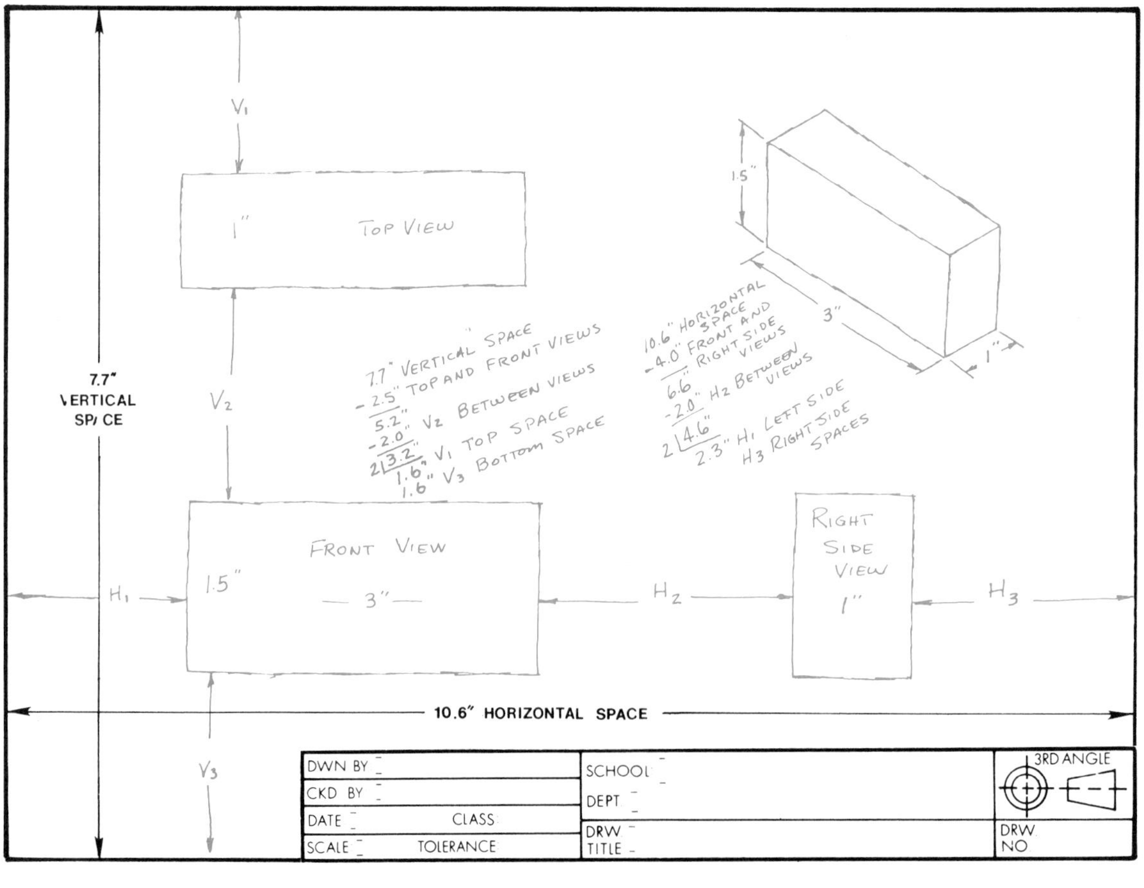

Fig. 4-19. Dividing the horizontal and vertical space when laying out the distance between the borders of the drawing sheet and the views of the object.

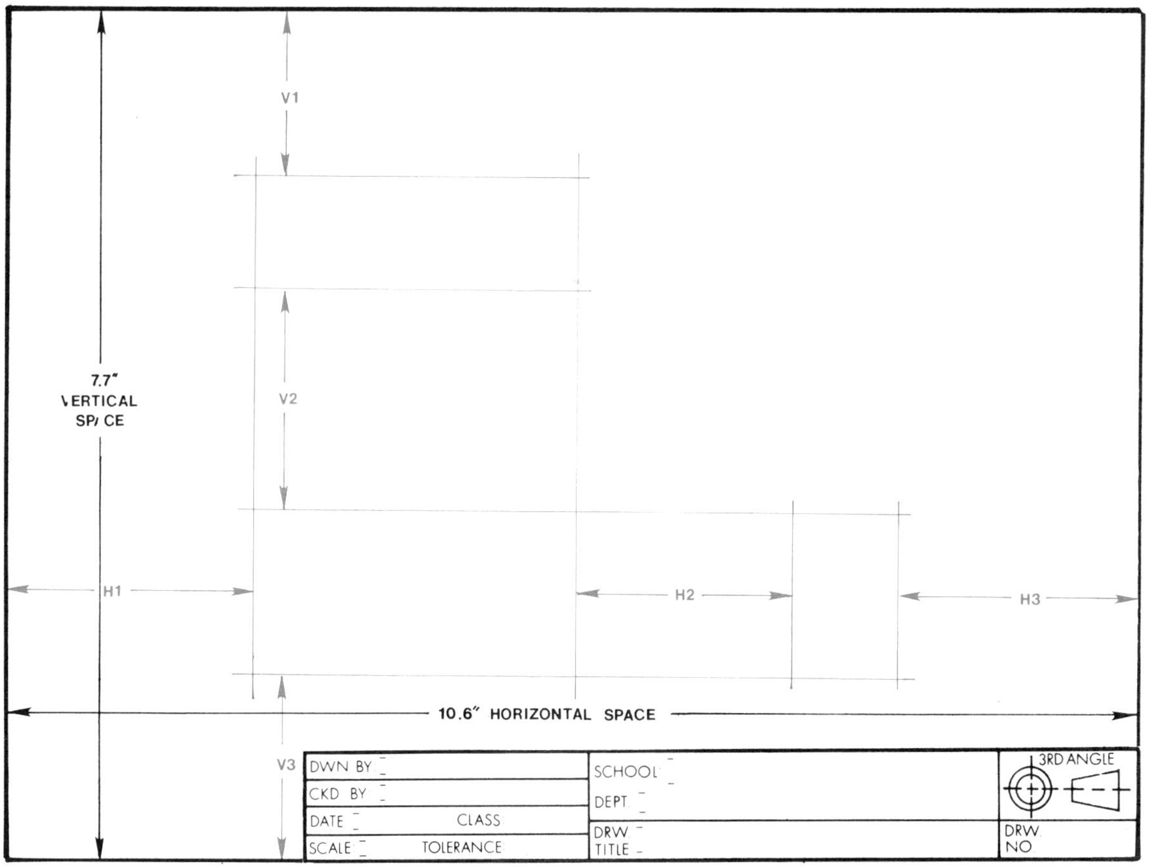

Fig. 4-20. Position the views as shown.

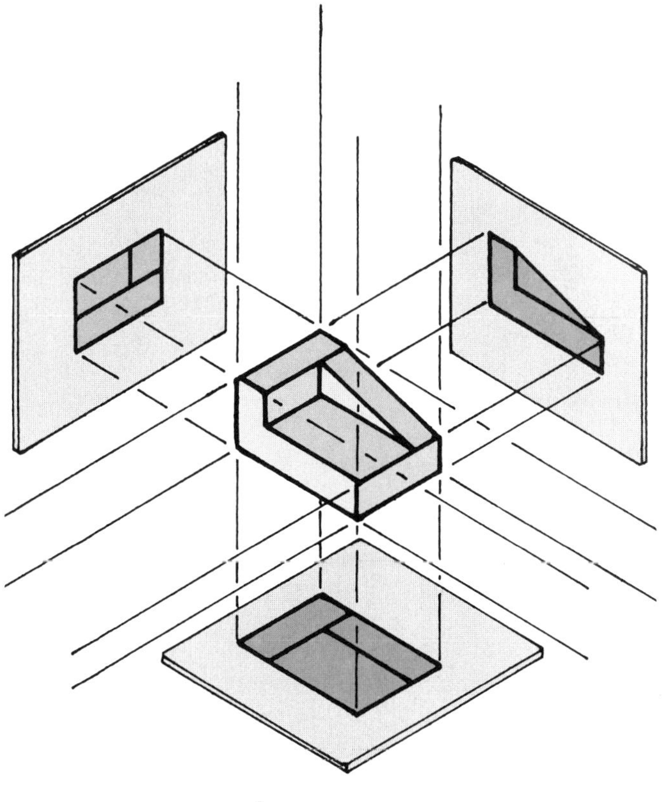

Fig. 4-21. Images or views appear as "shadows" in first-angle projection.

Comparing Third-Angle and First-Angle Projection

In the United State and Canada, drafters draw what they see from the top of an object, and position the top view above the front view as you have learned. Similarly, the right side view appears to the right of the front view, and the left side view appears to the left of the front view. This is the third-angle projection which you have studied.

In all other countries, drafters use **first-angle projection** and draw the views of what they see in a "shadow" position. The top view is positioned below the front view, Fig. 4-21. The right side view is positioned to the left of the front view, Fig. 4-21. The left side view is positioned to the right of the front view, Fig. 4-21. Use the unfolding box technique to visualize the views as they move from the isometric, Fig. 4-22, to the multiview positions, Figs. 4-23 and 4-24. In first-angle projection, visualize a light shining through the object to project a shadow on the plane for each view. The planes are then unfolded. Remember, the views in both the first and third angle projections are the same, but are arranged differently.

The cone, shown in Fig. 4-25, is used in the title block of industrial drawings to indicate first-angle or third-angle projections.

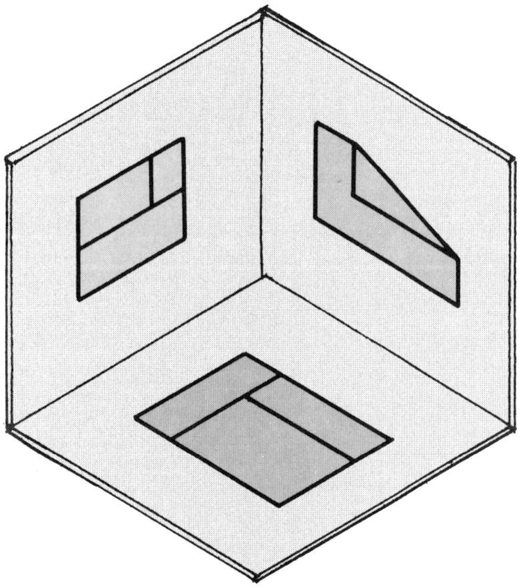

Fig. 4-22. Example of how the views would appear in the glass box for a first-angle projection.

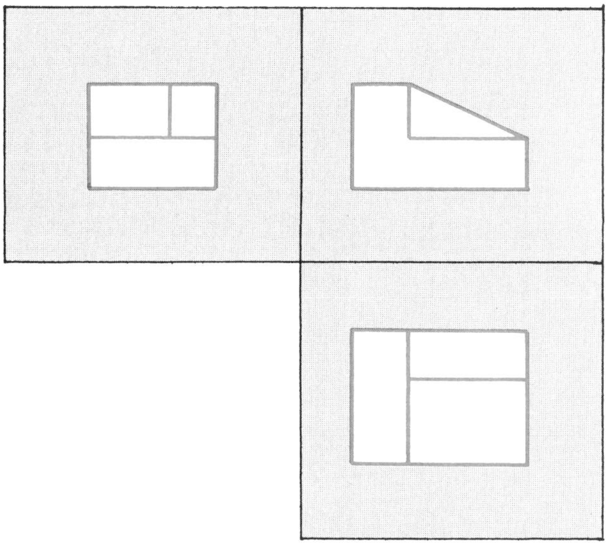

Fig. 4-24. Multiview arrangement as seen from the straight-on position in first-angle projection.

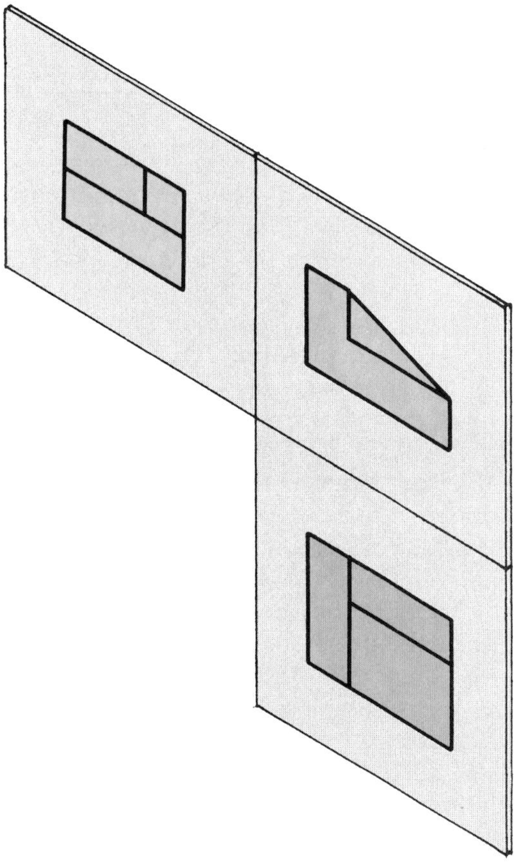

Fig. 4-23. Unfolding the glass box images into a flat position around the front view.

DEVELOPING A FIRST AUXILIARY VIEW

Many objects contain slanted surfaces. Since slanted surfaces are not parallel to any of the six planes of the glass box, their true size and true shape are distorted in the planes of projection. **Auxiliary views** show true size and shape of slanted surfaces.

To develop an auxiliary view of a slanted surface, the observer must move to a new position perpendicular to the slanted surface. Lines of sight will then pierce a new projection plane, parallel to the slanted surface, and create an image representing true size and shape, Fig. 4-26.

To complete an auxiliary view, collect ''true size and shape'' information from more than one view. In this example, true depth appears in the right side view. True length appears as a line in the front view for our example. This line is called an **edge view.** The right side view in this situation is called the **adjacent view.** Combining this true size and shape information provides the data necessary to complete an auxiliary view.

After visualizing the true size planes in the exploded positions, shown in Fig. 4-26, collapse the planes as shown in Fig. 4-27. The auxiliary plane is then folded ''upward'' and the right side view is folded ''outward'' into a single isometric plane as in Fig. 4-28. Next, revolve the three views ''downward'' into a multiview arrangement, Fig. 4-29. Thus, Fig. 4-30 shows the multiview projection of the front, right side, and auxiliary views.

Constructing True Size and Shape of a Rectangular Surface

Follow this example to construct an auxiliary view. With two or more views of the object given,

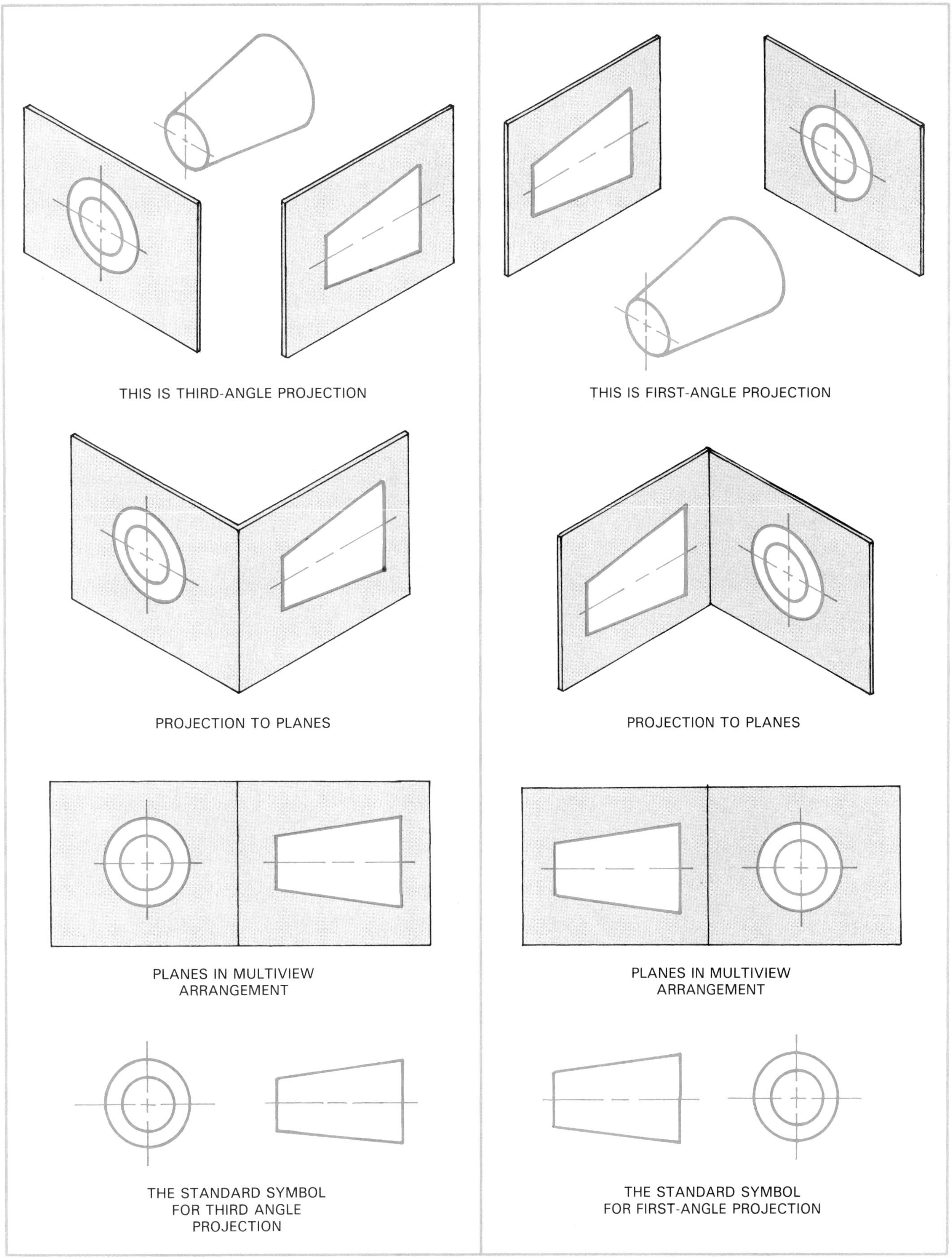

Fig. 4-25. Schematic showing the comparison of third-angle projection and first-angle projection.

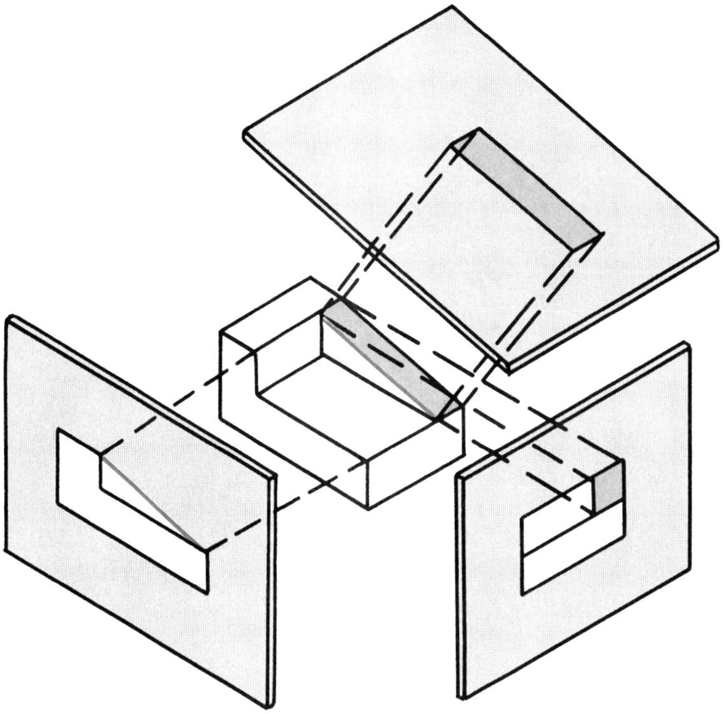

Fig. 4-26. The true size and shape of a slanted surface will appear on a plane of projection which is parallel to the slanted surface.

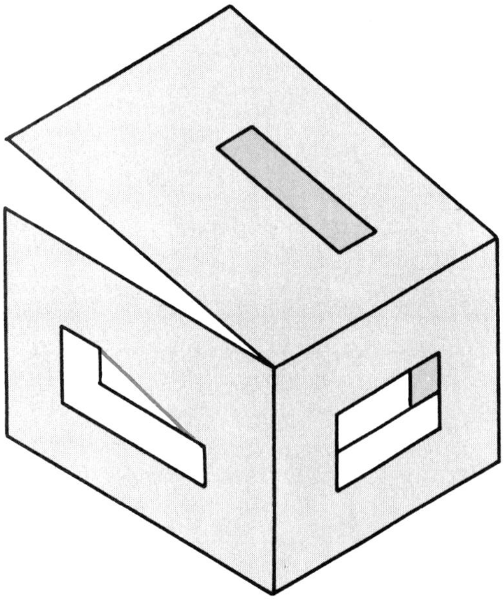

Fig. 4-27. Using the glass box arrangement to show the front, side, and auxiliary views.

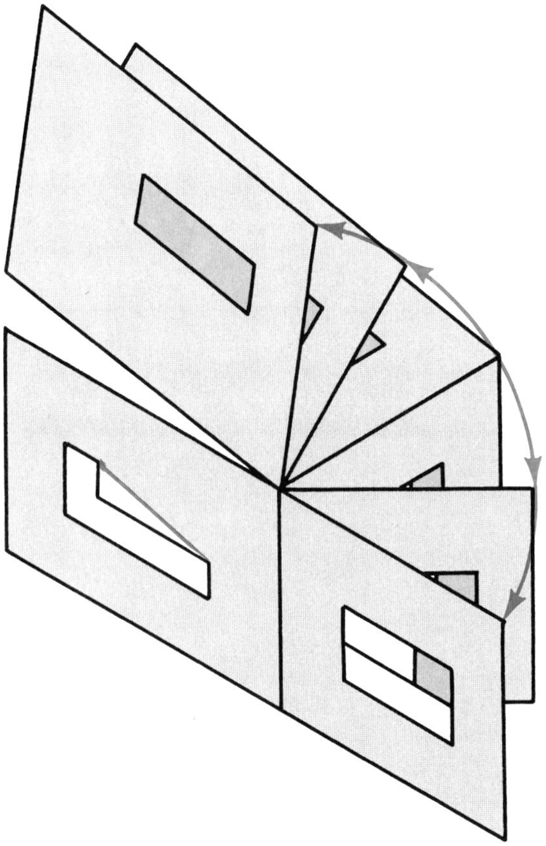

Fig. 4-28. Folding out the auxiliary view and the side view to place all surfaces into one plane.

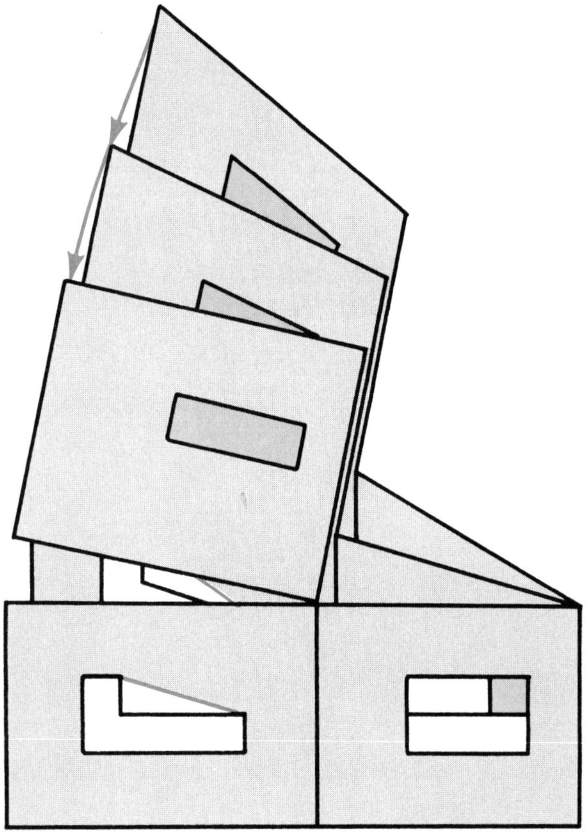

Fig. 4-29. Rotating the single plane forward to position the views in a multiview arrangement.

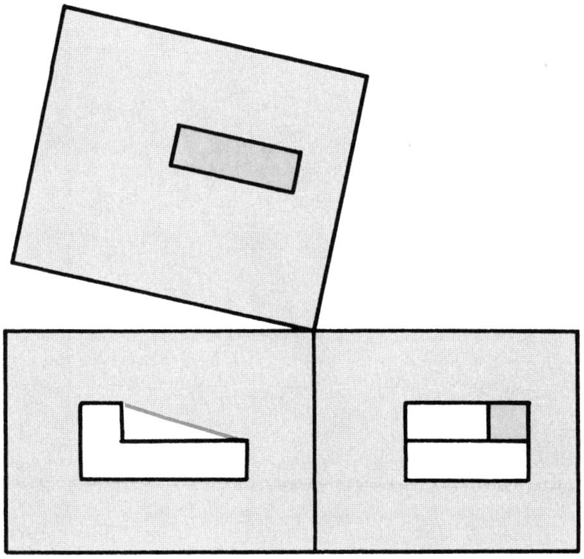

Fig. 4-30. The front view, the side view, and the auxiliary view in multiview arrangement showing the slanted surface of the object in true size and true shape.

Fig. 4-31, apply the following steps:

1. Sketch a pictorial view of the problem, Fig. 4-32.
2. Identify and label the auxiliary surface in all views, including the pictorial, Fig. 4-33.

Fig. 4-31. When solving an auxiliary problem, the front view may provide the true length of the slanted surface.

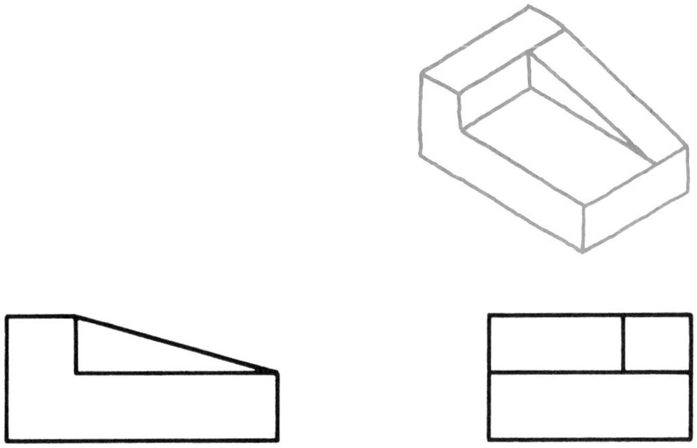

Fig. 4-32. As a starting point, sketch an isometric view of the problem. This will help you visualize the inclined surface.

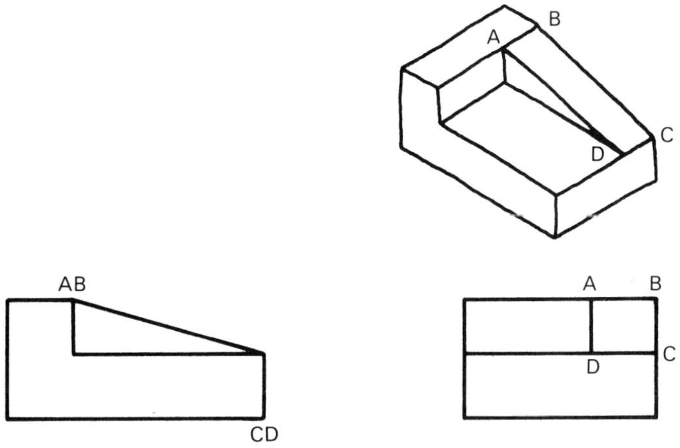

Fig. 4-33. Labeling the points on the auxiliary surface makes transferring the information easier.

3. Locate and label the edge view, Fig. 4-34.
4. Construct projection lines perpendicular to the edge view, Fig. 4-35.
5. Construct a folding line (G) parallel to the edge view. This folding line may be constructed on or near the edge view, Fig. 4-36.
6. Construct a second folding line (F) between the two given views. This may be drawn on or near the auxiliary surface and must be parallel to its edge, Fig. 4-37.
7. Use a divider to transfer distances "folding line to A and folding line to D" from the side view to the auxiliary view, Fig. 4-38.

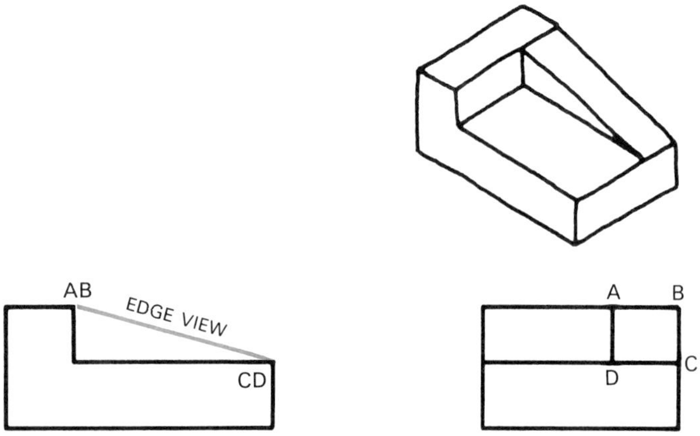

Fig. 4-34. The auxiliary surface appears as a line in the edge view.

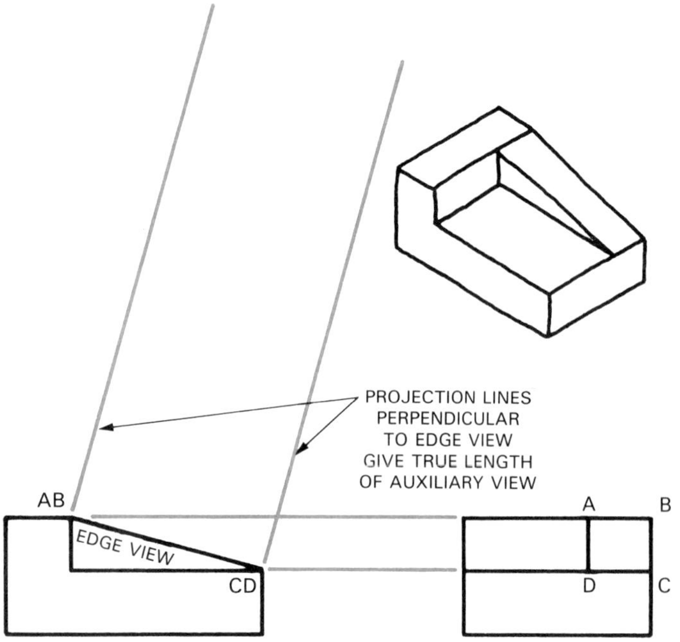

Fig. 4-35. Extend projection lines at a 90 degree angle or perpendicular from the edge view.

8. Similarly, transfer distances "folding line to B and C" from the side view to the auxiliary view, Fig. 4-39.
9. Draw the auxiliary surface and label its true size and shape, (TS&S), Fig. 4-40.

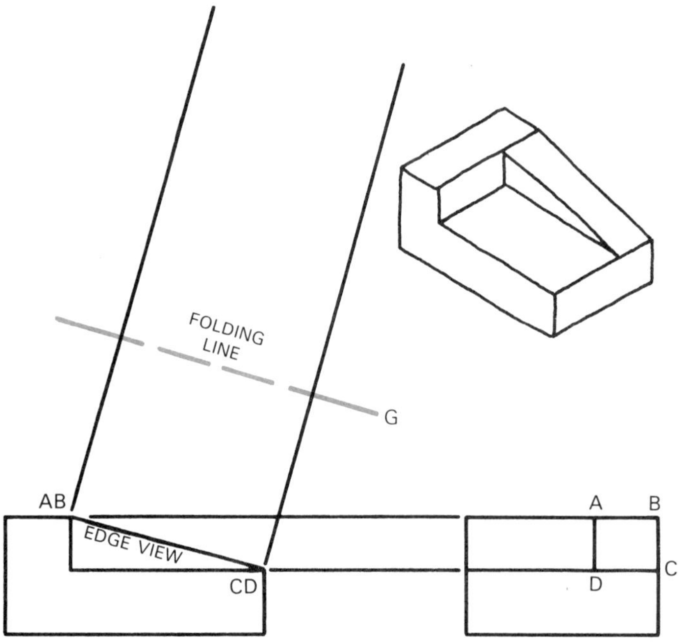

Fig. 4-36. Construct a folding line G parallel to the edge view.

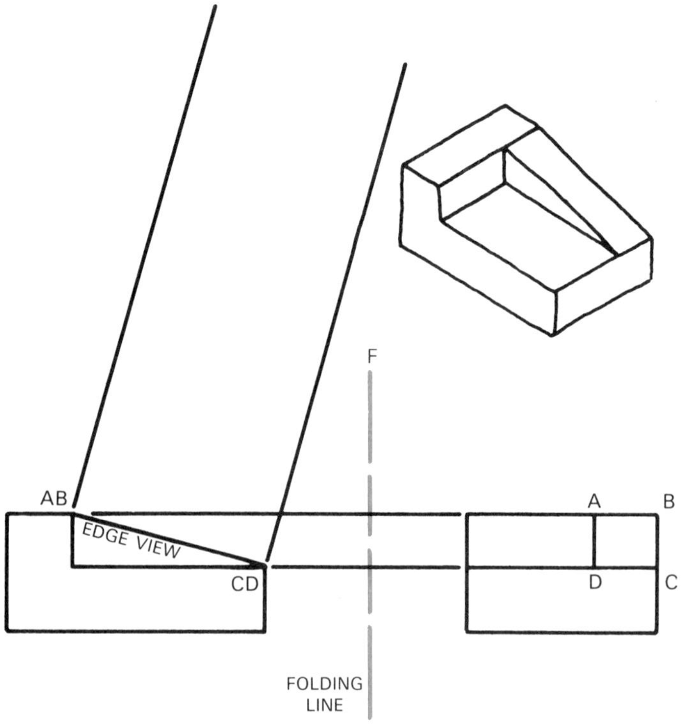

Fig. 4-37. Construct a folding line F between the front view and the side view.

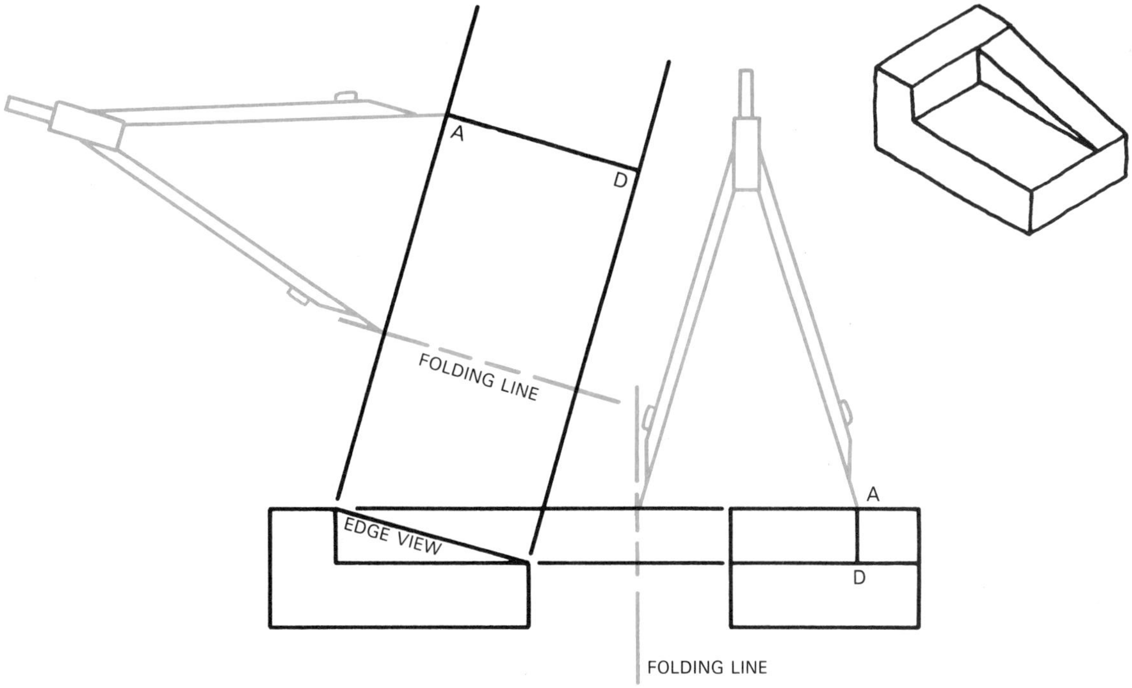

Fig. 4-38. Using dividers, transfer distances from the folding line to points A and D to the auxiliary view.

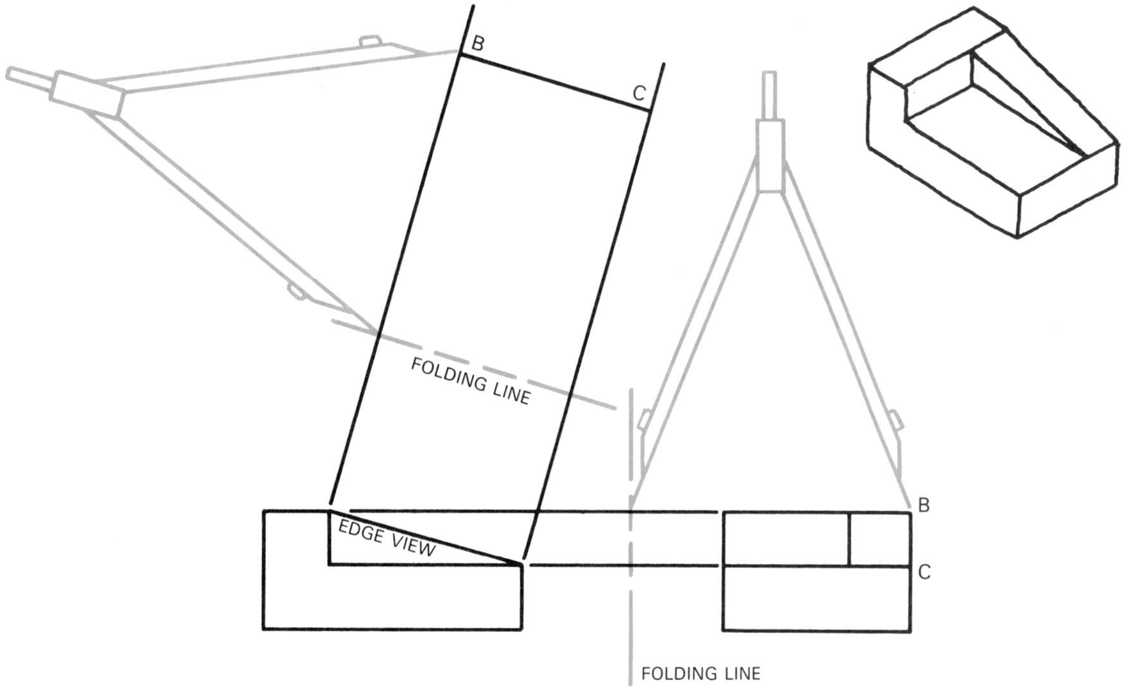

Fig. 4-39. Transfer distances from the folding line to points B and C to the auxiliary view using dividers.

Creating an Auxiliary of a Circular Shape

Steps 1-9 listed above may also apply to circular shapes.

In addition to these steps, the circle in the front view must be divided into parts as shown in Fig. 4-41. These parts are located by using the 30 x 60 x 90 degree triangle.

Place the vertical folding line through the center of the circle in the front view. A center folding line makes the transfer of distances much easier. The

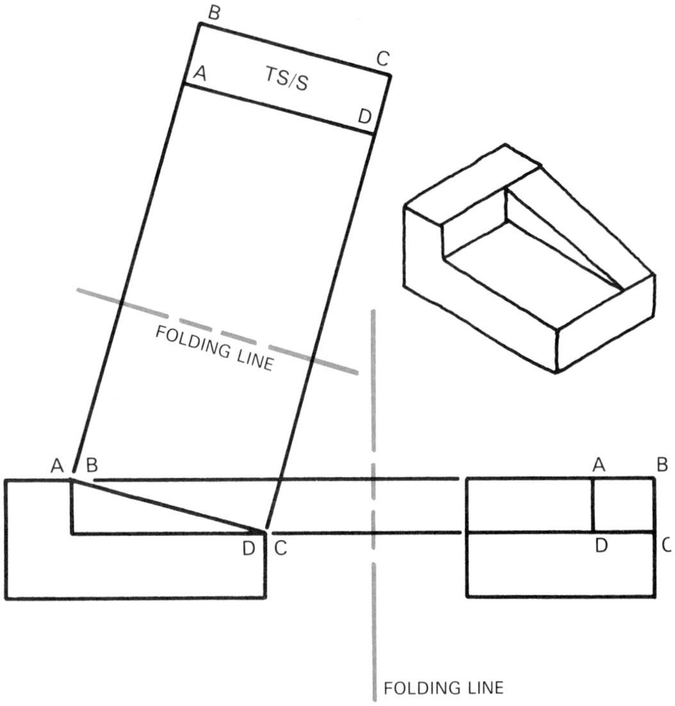

Fig. 4-40. Draw the auxiliary view in true shape and size.

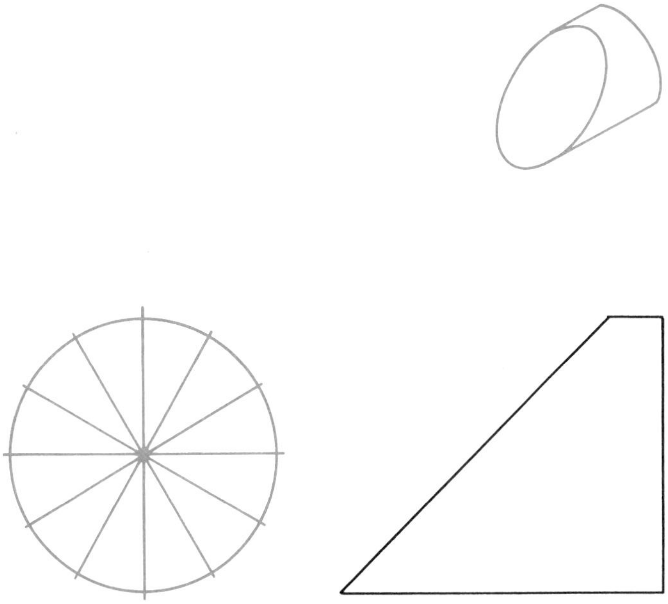

Fig. 4-41. In creating an auxiliary of a circular shape, first divide the circle into 12 equal parts. The diameter of the circle is the same as the height of the object. Refer to the isometric view to visualize this object.

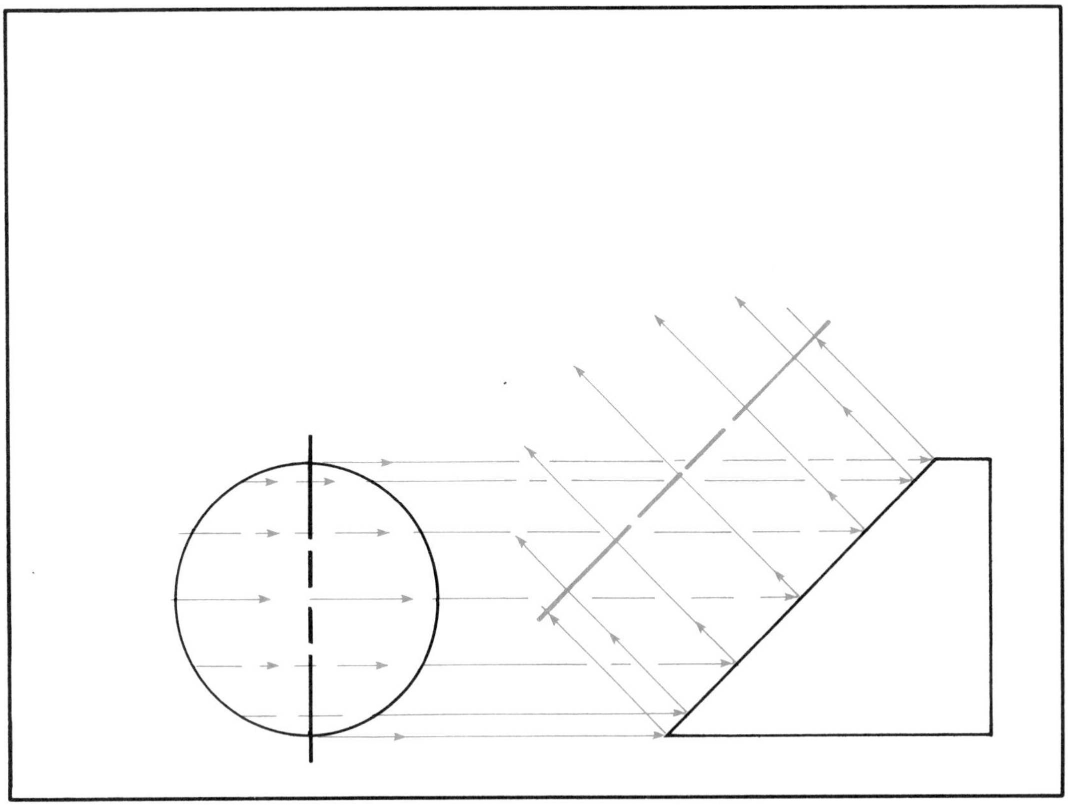

Fig. 4-42. Constructing a folding line through the center of the circle simplifies the transfer of distances.

second folding line, as indicated in step 6 is located parallel to the edge view. Draw the other folding line parallel to the edge view in a location which allows adequate space for transferring distances from the front view, Fig. 4-42.

Project the lines from the front view toward the edge view at a right angle to its folding line. These projection lines "bounce off" the edge view at a

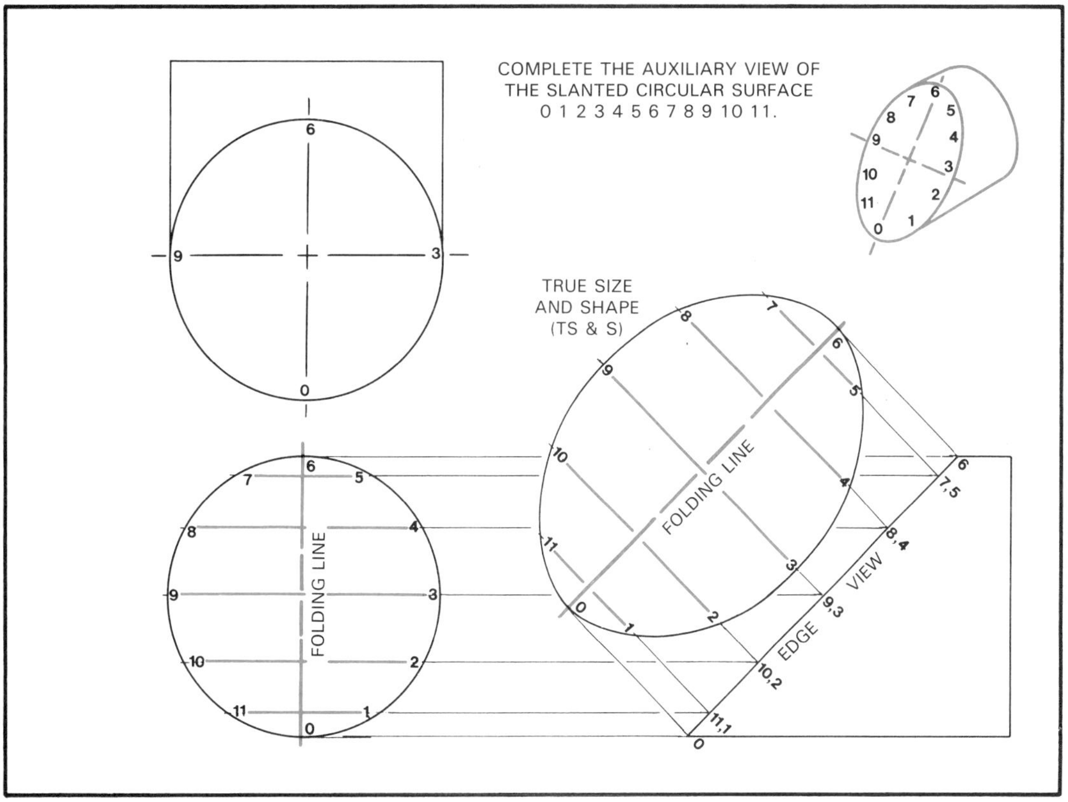

Fig. 4-43. The distances are transferred from the front view and marked on both sides of the folding line for symmetrical surfaces. Connect the points in a smooth line.

right angle through its folding line. Distances are then transferred from the front to the auxiliary view, Fig. 4-43. Connect the points in a smooth curve to create the auxiliary view. The true size and shape of the object is then complete.

DEVELOPING A SURFACE LAYOUT

A surface layout shows all surfaces of an object in a two-dimensional drawing. It can then be folded into its three-dimensional form. Paper containers are common examples of surface layouts, Fig. 4-44. Each container is designed for a specific application. Innovative layout minimizes waste and provides easy use of the product.

Surface developments are also used in heating and air conditioning duct work. Standard heating and cooling ducts are produced from previously developed patterns. However, jobs requiring unique sections are developed by using surface layout procedures.

Surface development problems require layout and construction of a three-dimensional model. Surface layout utilizes various geometric construction skills and may include auxiliary views to develop true sizes and shapes.

Developing the Surfaces of a Rectangular Container

The first step in developing any container or duct work is to sketch an isometric view of the finished product. Next, lay out horizontal and vertical lines to represent the top, front, and side views. Length, depth, and height are transferred from these views. Complete the layout by projecting the additional side, back, and bottom views of the object. Finally, label all corners to ensure propoer layout and add tabs where surfaces are fastened together. A typical surface layout is illustrated in Fig. 4-45.

Fig. 4-44. Most common containers and packages were originally created as surface layouts.

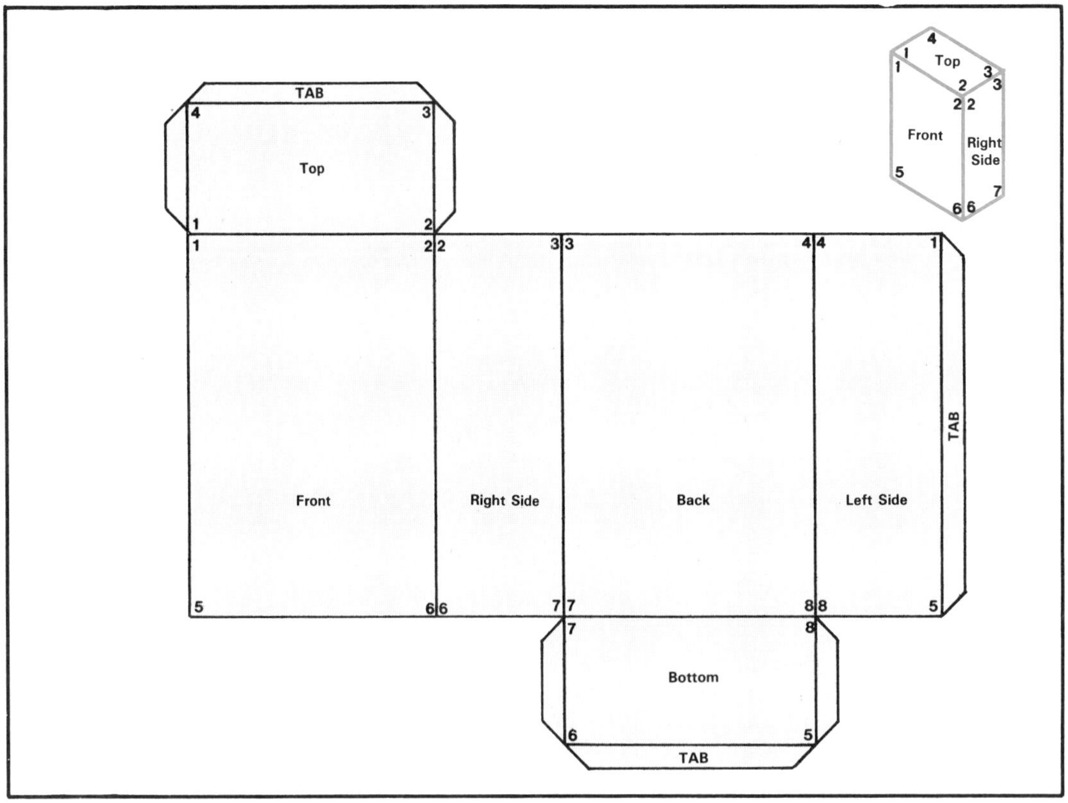

Fig. 4-45. Surface layout for a typical rectangular container. Note the tabs used to fasten the surfaces.

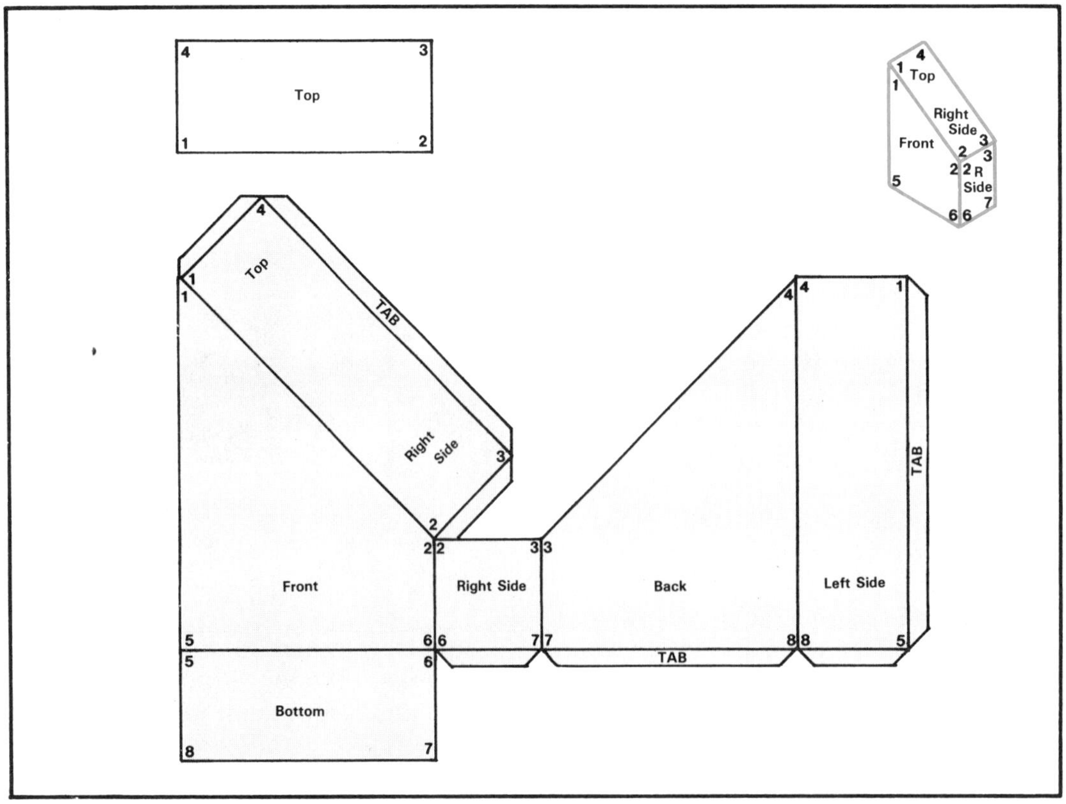

Fig. 4-46. Surface layout for a modified rectangular container. Note how the slanted surface adjoins the front view.

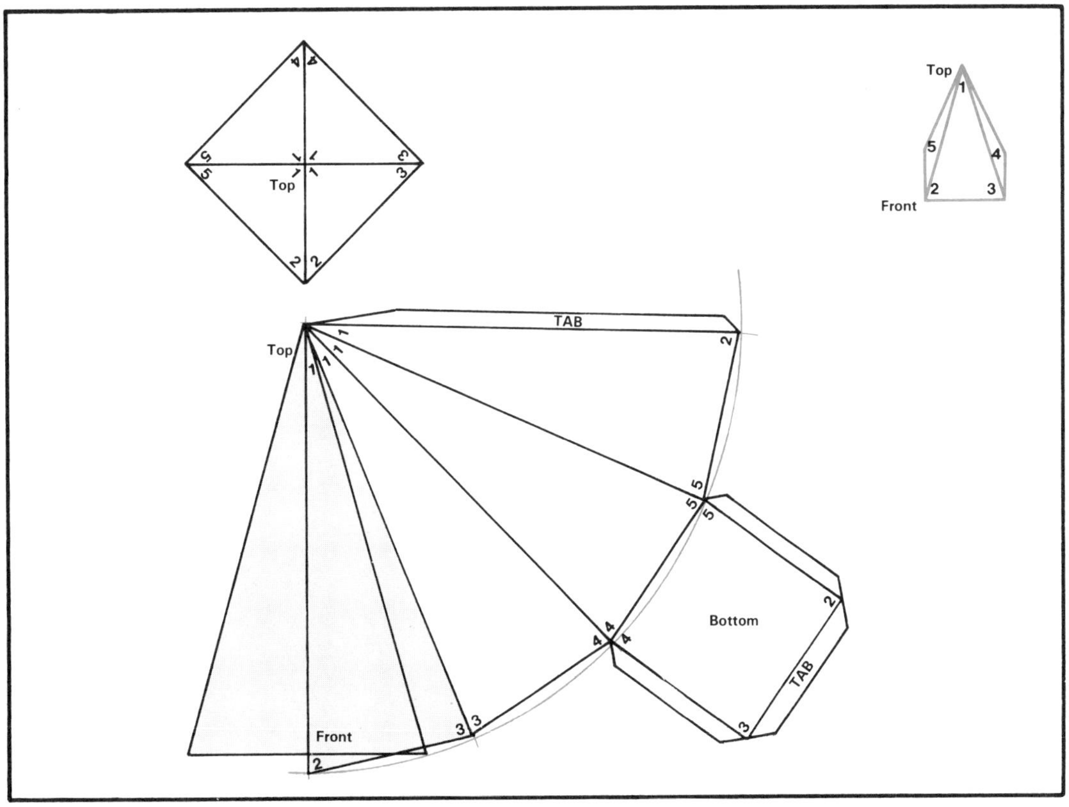

Fig. 4-47. When developing a surface layout for a pyramid, the true length must be collected from several views.

Developing a Rectangular Container with a Slanted Surface

The top surface of the example shown in Fig. 4-46 is slanted and must be drawn in true size and shape. The slanted line in the front view is an edge view. It provides true length. The slanted surface is hinged away from its edge view at a right angle. The depth can be transferred from an adjacent view. This procedure is similar to drawing an auxiliary view with the folding line on the edge view.

Developing a Pyramid

A pyramid is an example of a shape with multiple slanted surfaces, Fig. 4-47. Its development includes a combination of true length data collected from more than one view. The top view provides true length and depth of the base. The front view repeats the length of the base and adds true height of the pyramid.

The slanted lines on the left and right side of the front view are true length since they are parallel to the frontal plane.

Construct the pyramid following these steps:

1. Draw an arc with 1 as the center and 1-3 as the radius, Fig. 4-48, counterclockwise from a 6 o'clock to a 3 o'clock position.
2. Using the top view, adjust your compass to the length of the base, shown in Fig. 4-47. Starting at point 2, mark distances 2-3, 3-4, 4-5, and 5-2 on the arc, Fig. 4-48.
3. Draw lines 1-2, 1-3, 1-4, 1-5, and 1-2 at the 3 o'clock position, followed by 2-3, 3-4, 4-5, and 5-2 to identify the true size and shape of the pyramid sides, Fig. 4-49.
4. Using the top view, construct the base hinged from 4-5 or one of the other base edges, Fig. 4-49.
5. Label all corners in all views and add tabs where necessary, Fig. 4-49.

Developing a Cylinder

Cylindrical containers are used daily for food products. Accurate pattern layout is important because it affects the volume of the container. The surface layout of a cylinder includes a circular top and bottom and a rectangle. The rectangle's height is the same as the height of the cylinder. The rectangle's length is equal to the circumference of the cylinder.

To develop a cylinder follow these steps and refer to Fig. 4-50.

1. Lay out the height of the rectangular by projecting horizontal lines from the top and the

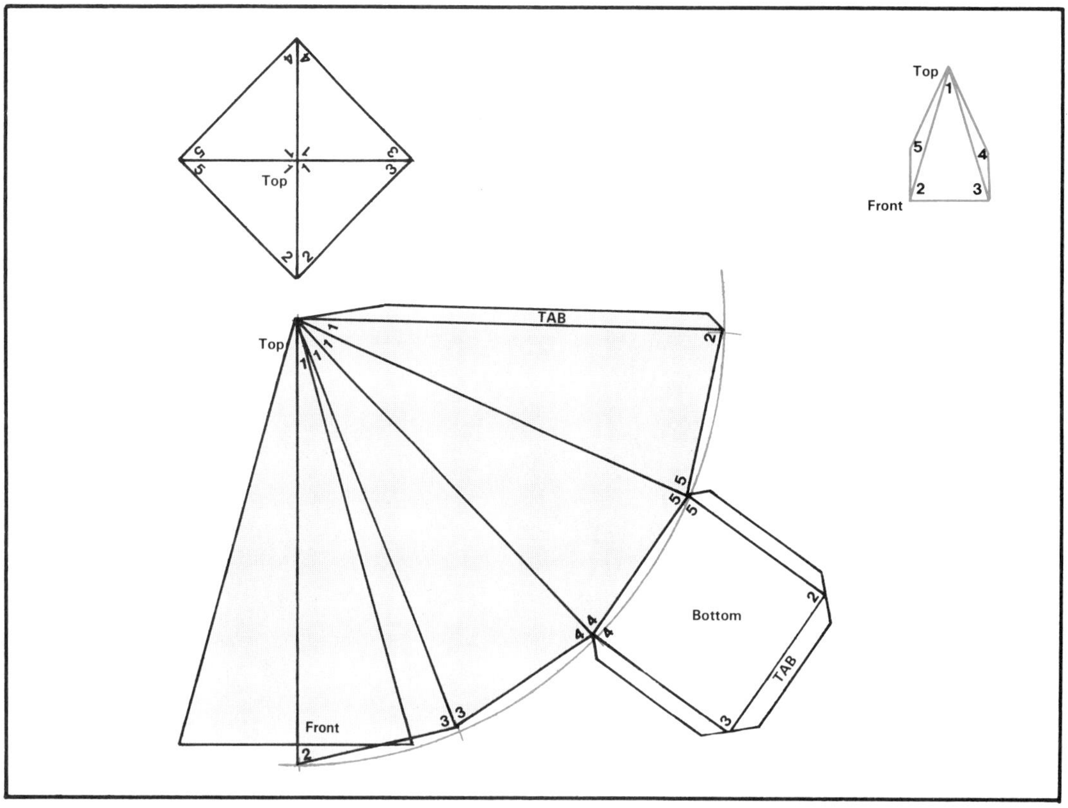

Fig. 4-48. Construct an arc with a radius equal to the length on the side of the pyramid.

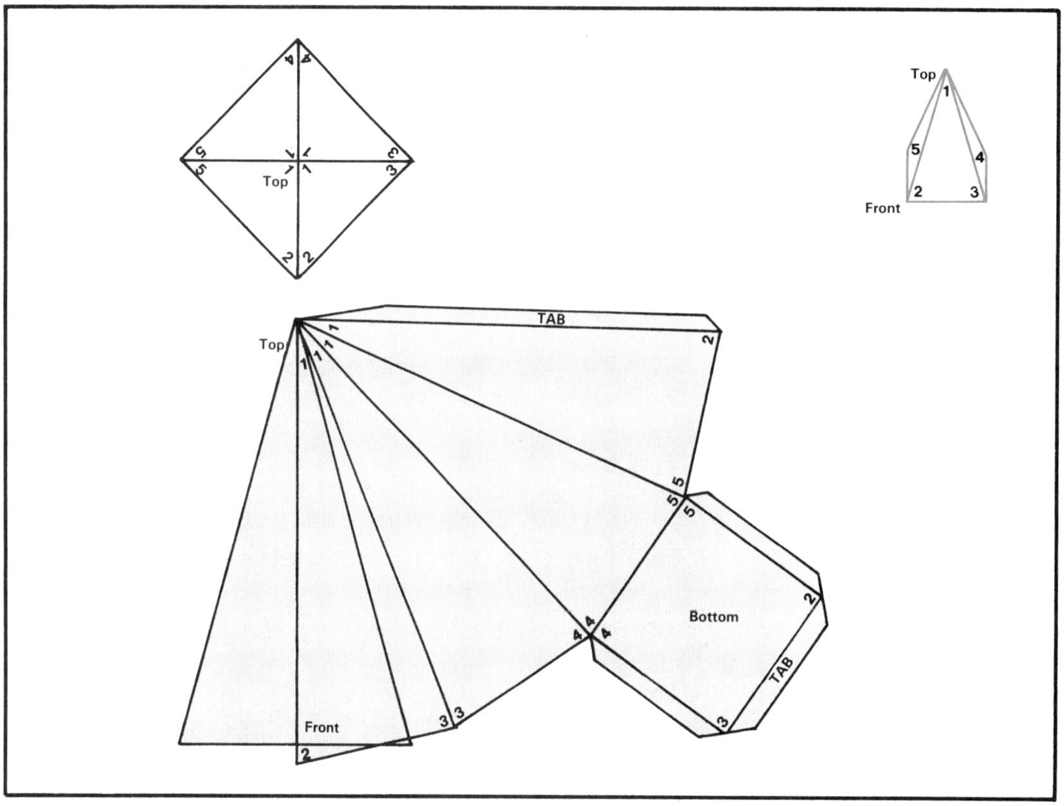

Fig. 4-49. The base of the pyramid is added adjoining one of the sides.

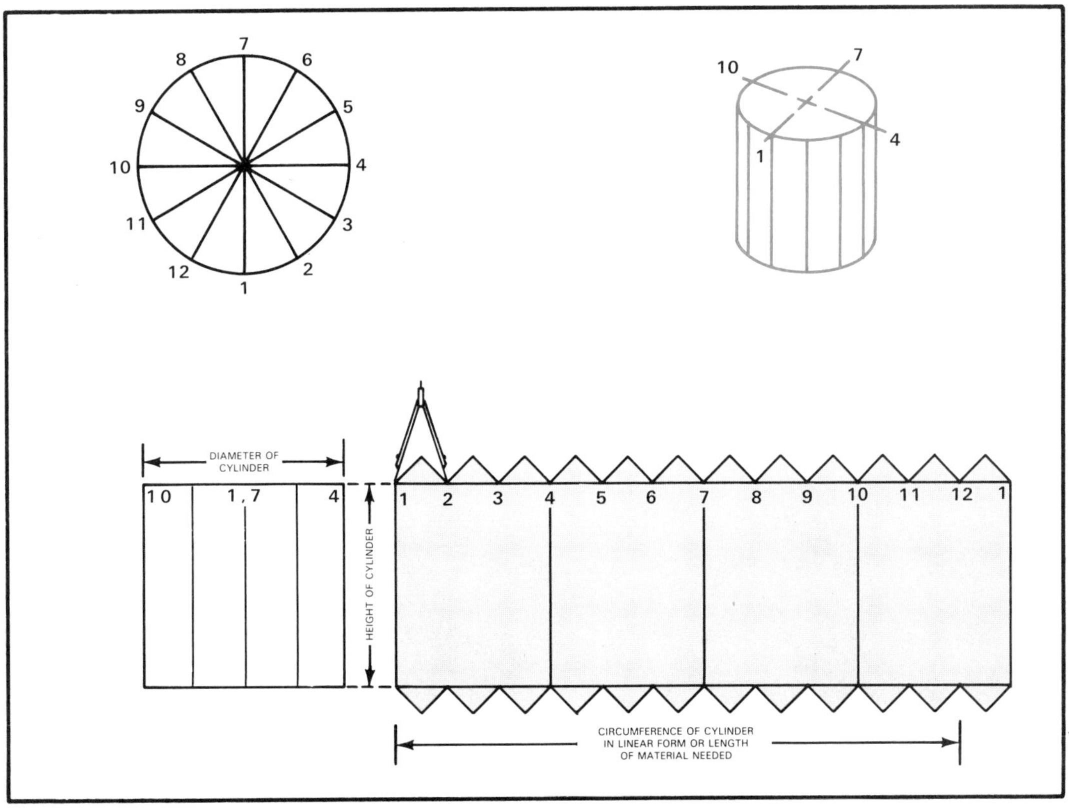

Fig. 4-50. In developing the surface layout for a cylinder, the circumference of the cylinder determines the length of the material needed. The height of the cylinder is the same as the height of the layout. The length of the layout is equal to the diameter times 3.14 (π). The length may also be found by chord lengths from the divisions of the circle to the rectangle. A third method is to construct a 60 degree angle to the 3 o'clock position from a horizontal base line and use four times this measurement as the length of the layout.

bottom of the cylinder.

2. Lay out the length of the rectangle equal to the circumference of the circle.

   Determine the circumference of the cylinder by one of three methods.

   Method I. Multiply the diameter of the cylinder times π. Thus $C = \pi D$. ($\pi = 3.14$, D = diameter.)

   Method II: Divide the circle as shown in the top view into 12 equal parts using the 30 x 60 x 90 degree triangle. Transfer each part onto a straight line. More segments produce smaller parts. Smaller parts improve the accuracy of equating the curved arc length to the straight chord length.

   Method III: Draw a horizontal line tangent T to the bottom of the circle in the top view. Construct a line from the 3 o'clock position downward at a 60 degree angle to the horizontal line X. Distance TX is 1/4 of the circumference. Transfer distance TX four times to construct the length of the rectangle.

3. Draw the top and bottom circles and connect them to the rectangle by using tabs.

Developing a Cone

Laying out a pattern for a cone uses information and techniques similar to developing a pyramid or a cylinder. The key part in laying out a cone is in transferring its circumference onto a curved line. Method II above can also be used to transfer distances onto an arc, Fig. 4-51.

The basic reason for laying out the length of the curved line recognizes that the length of the curved line must be equal to the length of the circumference on the circular base.

Developing a Cylinder With an Angled Top

The development of a cylinder has three parts. The bottom is a circle, the top is an ellipse, and the side has a straight base and a wave-shaped top, Fig. 4-52. The circle in the top view becomes the bottom. The elliptical shape is developed as an auxiliary as described earlier in this chapter.

The side is rolled out to be the same length as the circumference of the base. Lay out the length and divide it into 12 equal parts as in Methods II or III. The wave-shaped top is developed by projecting positions 1-12 down from the circular view and

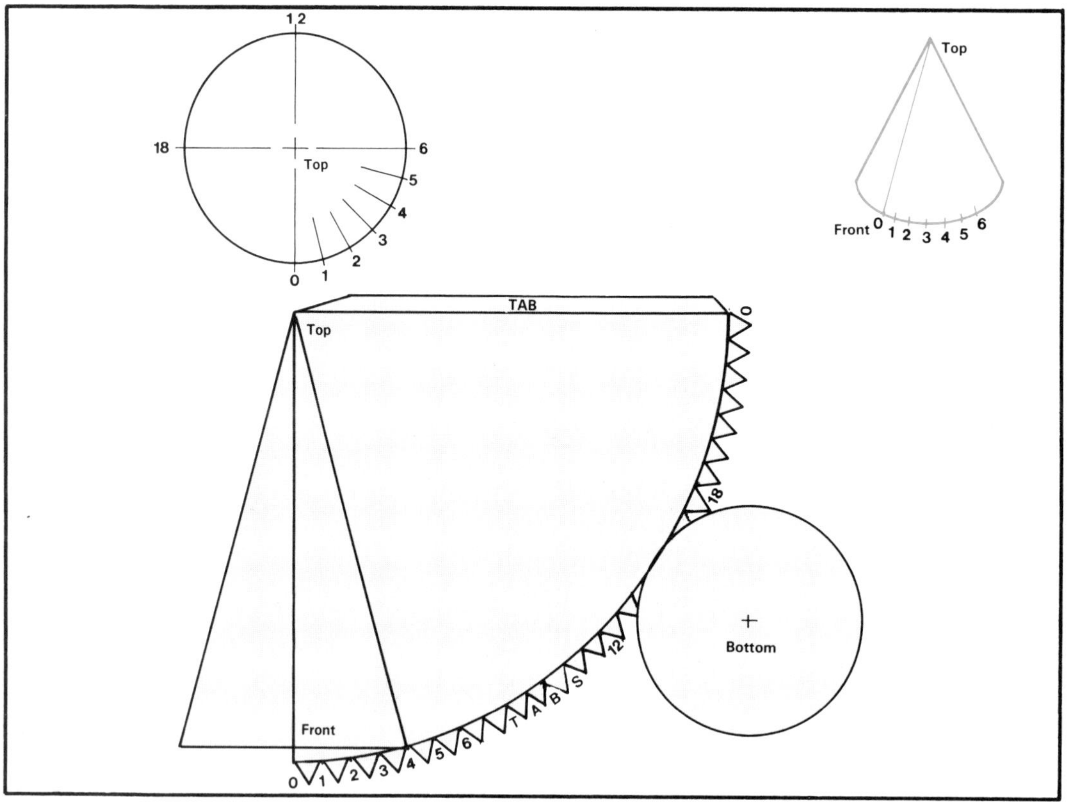

Fig. 4-51. Developing a pattern for a cone. As in the cylinder, the circular base may be developed in a number of methods. The distance from the top of the cone to the base is the length used for the layout of the pattern. Use the numbered points for reference when constructing the pattern.

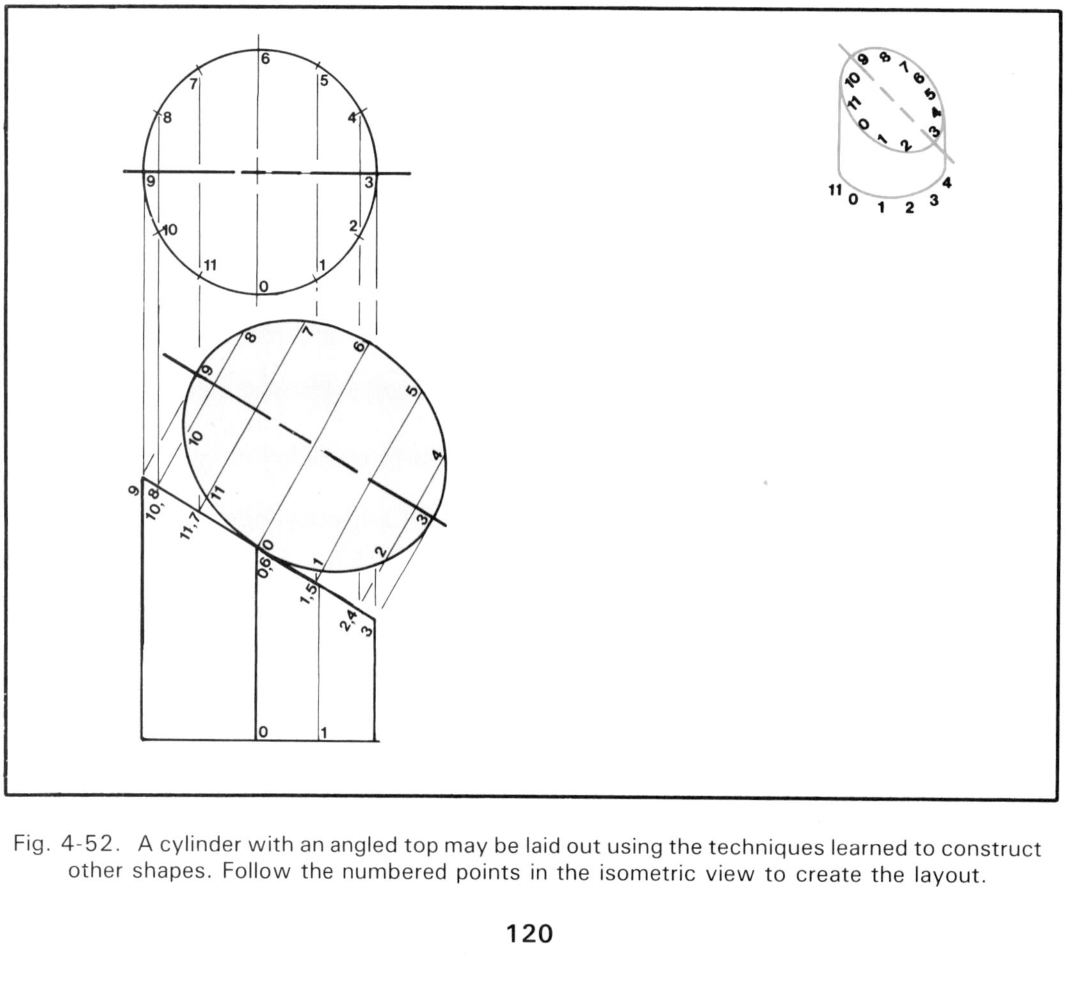

Fig. 4-52. A cylinder with an angled top may be laid out using the techniques learned to construct other shapes. Follow the numbered points in the isometric view to create the layout.

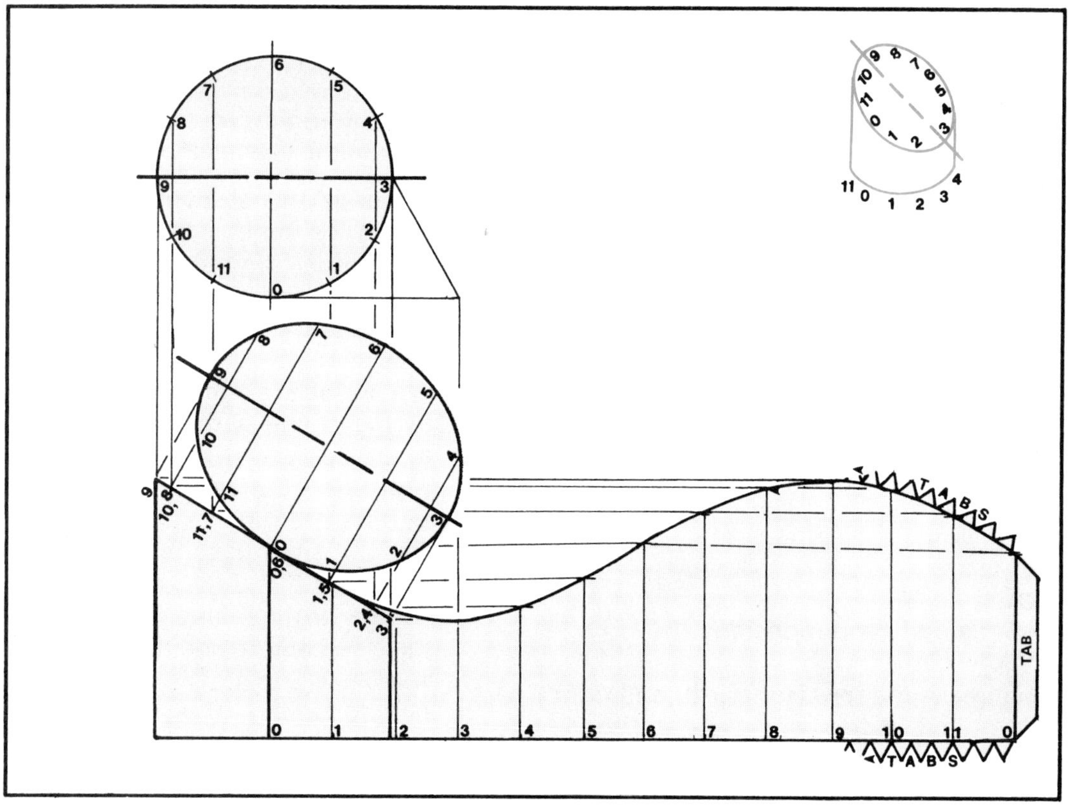

Fig. 4-53. Completed pattern for a cylinder with an angled top.

"bouncing" them off the edge view horizontally. These horizontal projection lines intersect with the 12 equal parts projected up from the base, Fig. 4-53. The wave shape is drawn by connecting the intersections 1-1 through 12-12 with a smooth curve.

SUMMARY

The concepts described and illustrated within this chapter provide you with the basic fundamentals for visualizing multiview and isometric drawings. The problems you complete will help you become familiar with common relationships between views.

You may want to concentrate on a few difficult problems or you may choose to complete more drawings. Different problems will provide you appropriate levels of experience to develop drafting skills.

The following list of criteria may be used as a self-evaluation in comparing your results to professional standards.

1. Demonstrate consistency in line quality.
2. Construct accurate horizontal and vertical projections between views.
3. Apply dashed lines properly.
4. Use centerlines consistently.
5. Sketch correct isometric images to verify multiview drawings.
6. Draw correct multiview drawings from isometric views.
7. Draw isometric views properly.
8. Project and measure accurately.
9. Keep your work neat and accurate.

Chapter 4—PROJECTING IMAGES
Review What You Have Learned

Write your answers on a separate sheet of paper. Do not write in this textbook.

Essay:

1. Write a concise explanation of the "glass box" technique used to demonstrate how images may be projected.
2. Write a descriptive paragraph covering the steps taken in moving a mental image to a finished drawing.

Multiple Choice: Carefully read the statements below and write the letter of the best answer for each of the items on your answer sheet.

3. In the U.S., what angle projection is used?
   a. First.
   b. Second.
   c. Third.
   d. Fourth.
   e. None of the above.

4. The height of an object can be seen in which view(s)?
   a. Top.
   b. Front.
   c. Side.
   d. Top and side.
   e. Side and front.
5. A multiview projection includes at least how many views?
   a. One.
   b. Two.
   c. Three.
   d. Four.
   e. Five.
6. When laying out a multiview projection, consideration must be given to:
   a. Product size.
   b. Sheet size.
   c. Scale.
   d. Space needed for dimensions.
   e. All of the above.
7. When laying out the top, front, left, and right sides of a multiview drawing, horizontal space is allocated in how many areas?
   a. Two.
   b. Three.
   c. Four.
   d. Five.
   e. Six.

True or False: Carefully read the statements below. Write a "T" on your answer sheet for the statements which are true. For the statements which are false, write an "F." Rewrite each false statement so it becomes true.

8. A multiview drawing is formed by folding out a glass box. True or False?
9. As the horizontal plane is folded up to position the top view above the front view, the folding line is vertical. True or False?
10. The side view in a multiview projection is always directly beside the bottom view. True or False?
11. Vertical space layout is distributed above, below, and between the views. True or False?
12. In third-angle projection, the picture plane is between the viewer and the object. True or False?
13. In first-angle projection, the picture plane is behind the viewer and the object. True or False?

Completion: After studying this chapter, read the incomplete sentences below. Write the missing word or words on your answer sheet.

14. Isometric views are __________ to interpret than multiview drawings and __________ to produce.
15. In a surface of a multiview drawing, when your eye is in line with the surface, it appears as a __________.
16. Multiview drawing involves __________, __________, and __________ views.
17. Lines of sight pass through a picture plane as __________ __________ to the object.
18. As the profile plane is folded out to position the side view beside the front view, the folding line is __________.
19. The top view of a multiview projection is always directly __________ the front view.

Matching: When comparing multiview positions in first and third-angle projection, match the views in column A with the correct position of the view in column B relative to the front view. Write your answers on a separate answer sheet.

Column A	Column B
20. Top third angle.	a. Above.
21. Right side third angle.	b. Below.
22. Left side third angle.	c. To the right.
23. Top first angle.	d. To the left.
24. Right side first angle.	e. Behind or in front.
25. Left side first angle.	

Practice What You Have Learned: On a fresh sheet of 8 1/2 x 11 inch drawing paper, carefully and neatly draw isometric views of the following:

A desk drawer (be sure to include all of the fine points of construction).

A school locker including shelves and any other permanent additions.

A soda pop can with the pop top still un-opened.

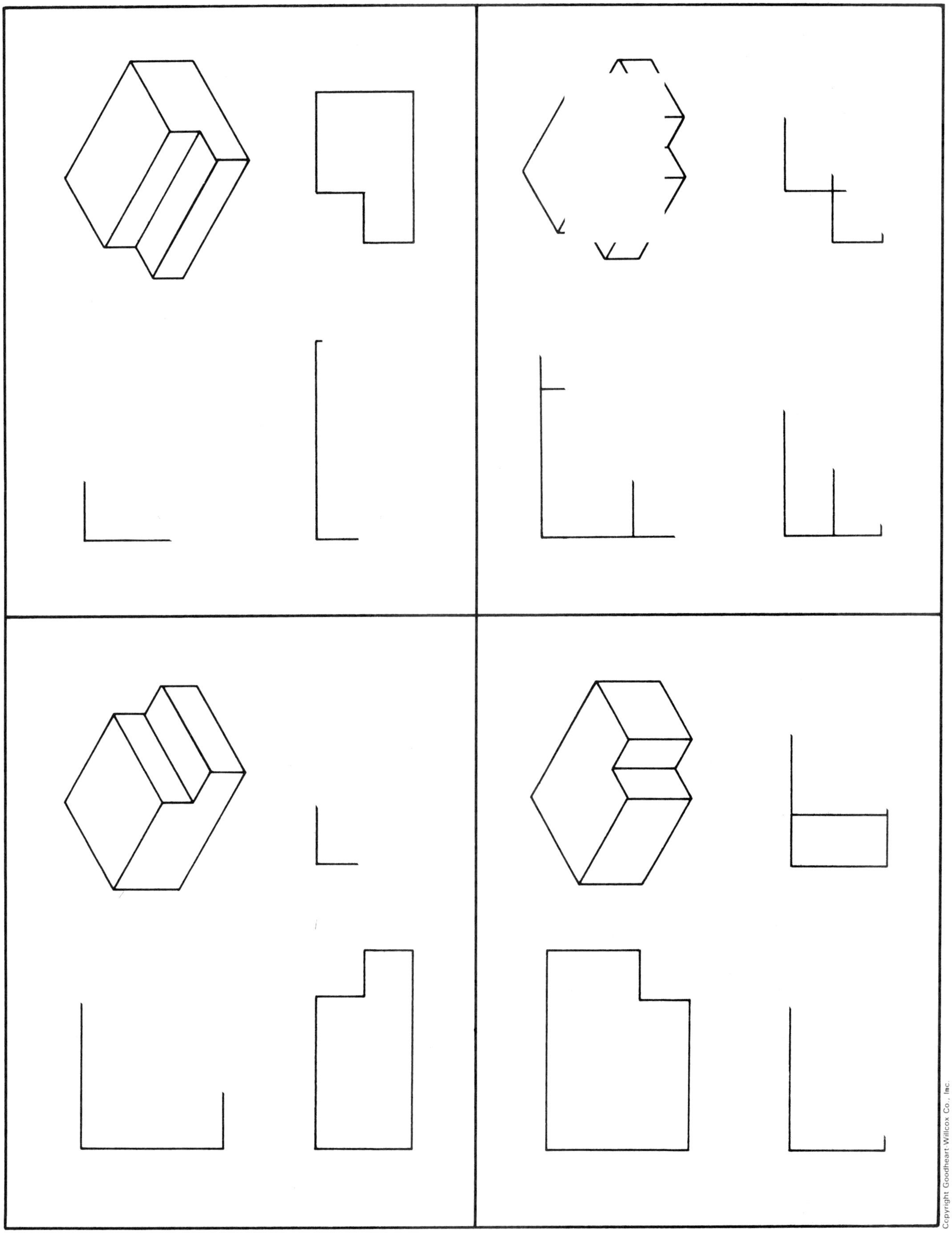

4-1 MULTIVIEW AND ISOMETRIC DRAWINGS OF RECTANGULAR OBJECTS. On a separate sheet of paper, add the missing lines to complete the front, top, and side views of the multiview drawings. Complete the missing lines in the isometric view of the object.

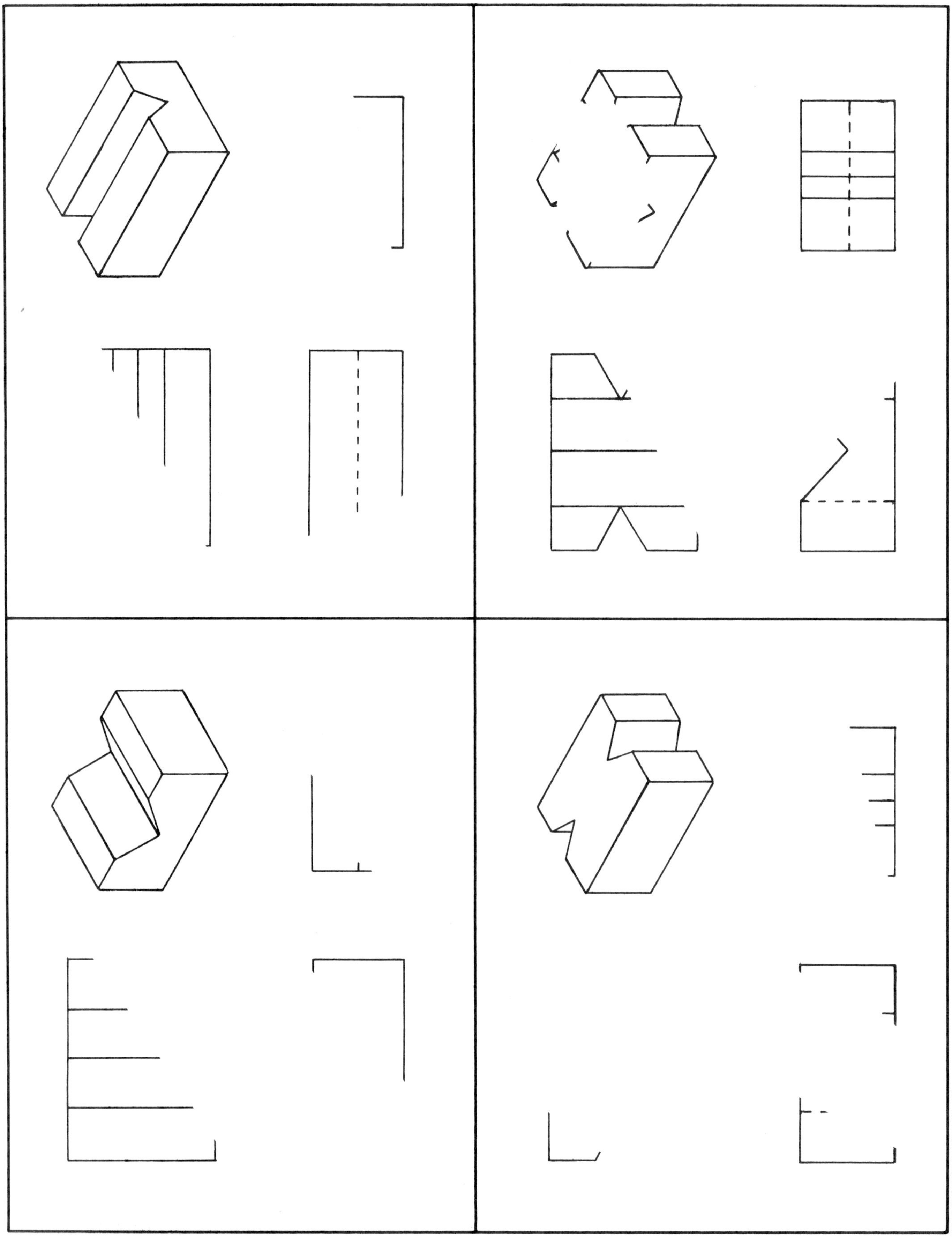

4-2 MULTIVIEW AND ISOMETRIC DRAWINGS OF OBJECTS WITH SLANTED LINES. Add the missing lines to complete the front, top, and side views of the multiview drawings. Complete the missing lines in the isometric view for the object.

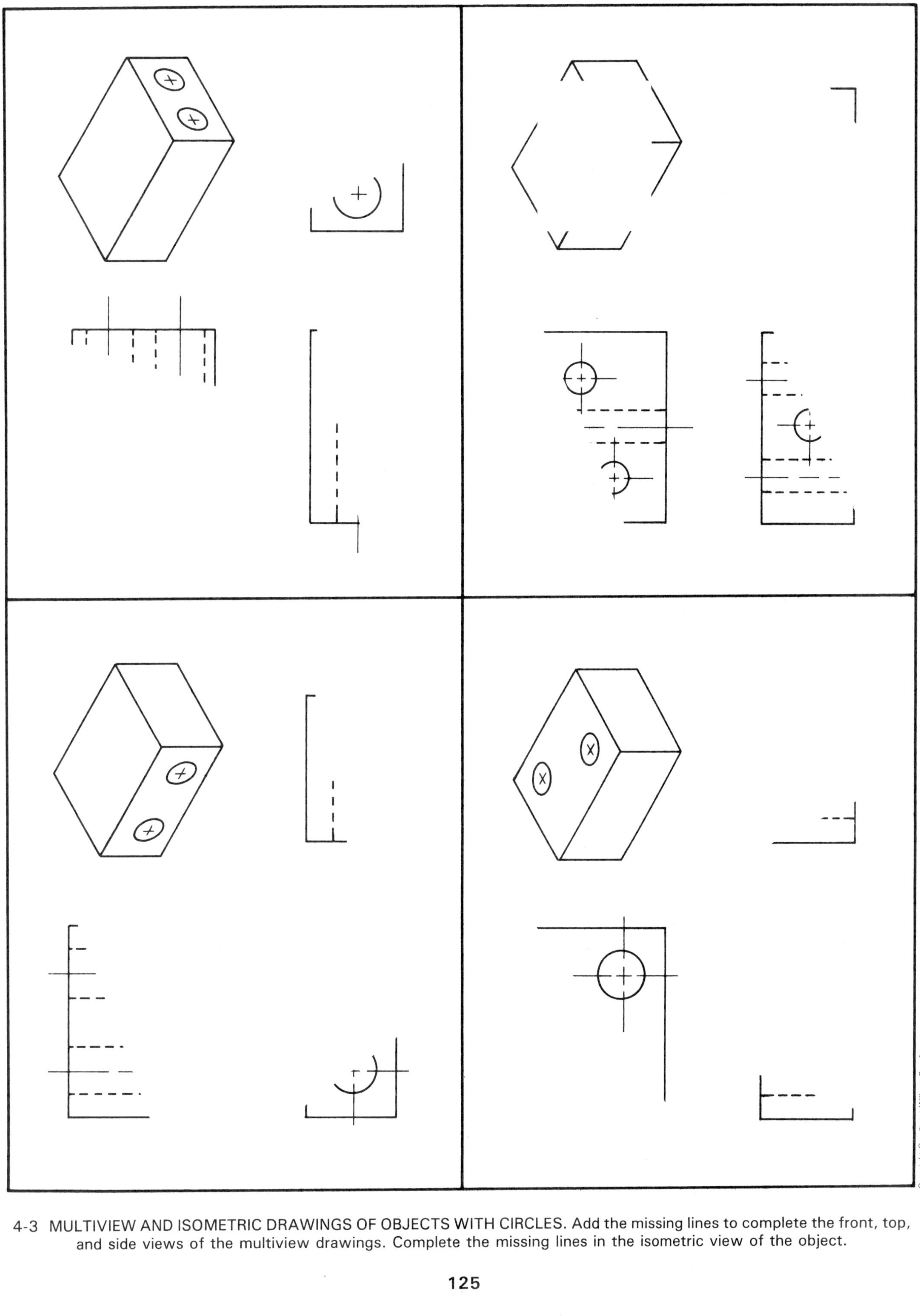

4-3 MULTIVIEW AND ISOMETRIC DRAWINGS OF OBJECTS WITH CIRCLES. Add the missing lines to complete the front, top, and side views of the multiview drawings. Complete the missing lines in the isometric view of the object.

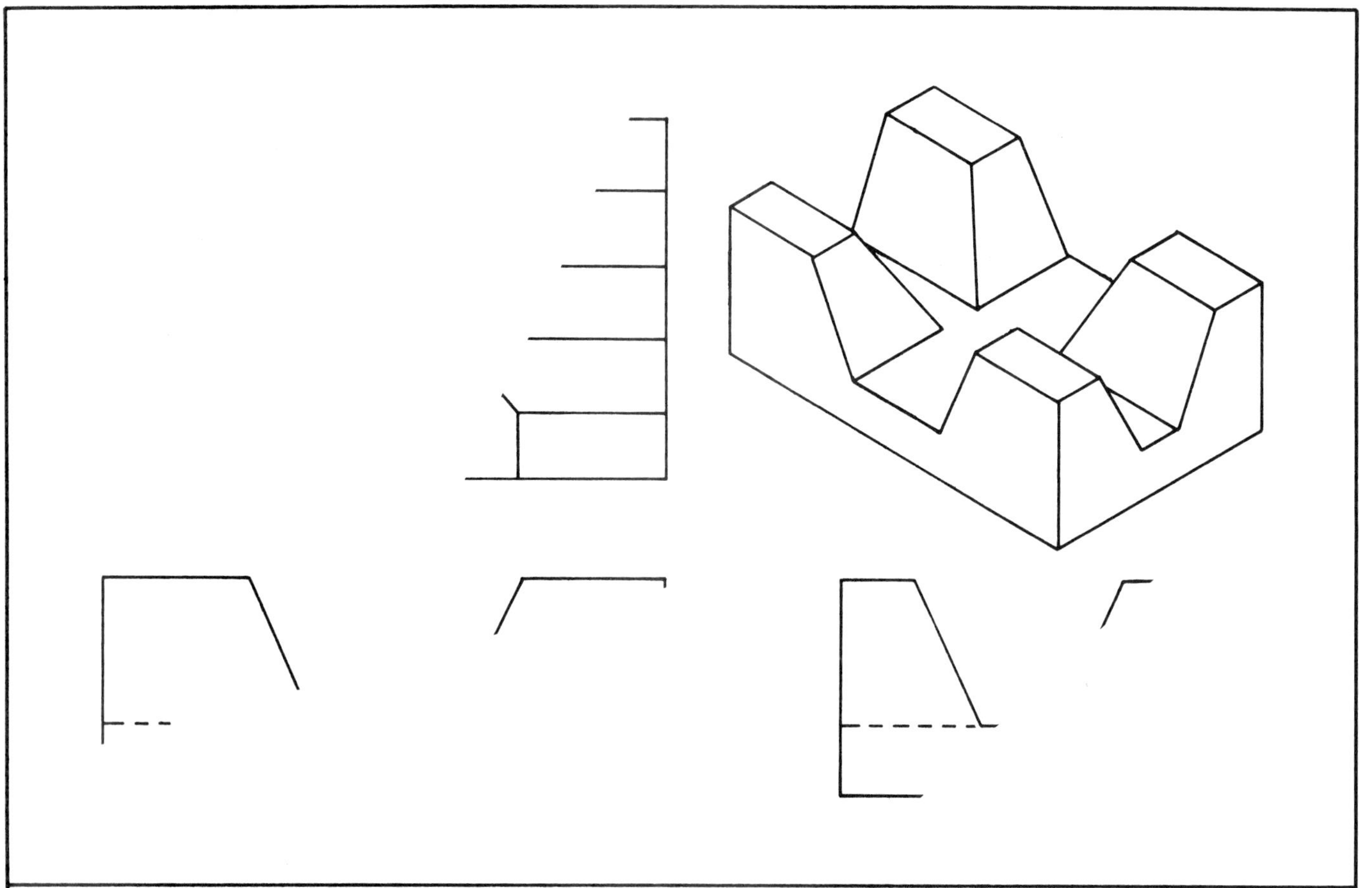

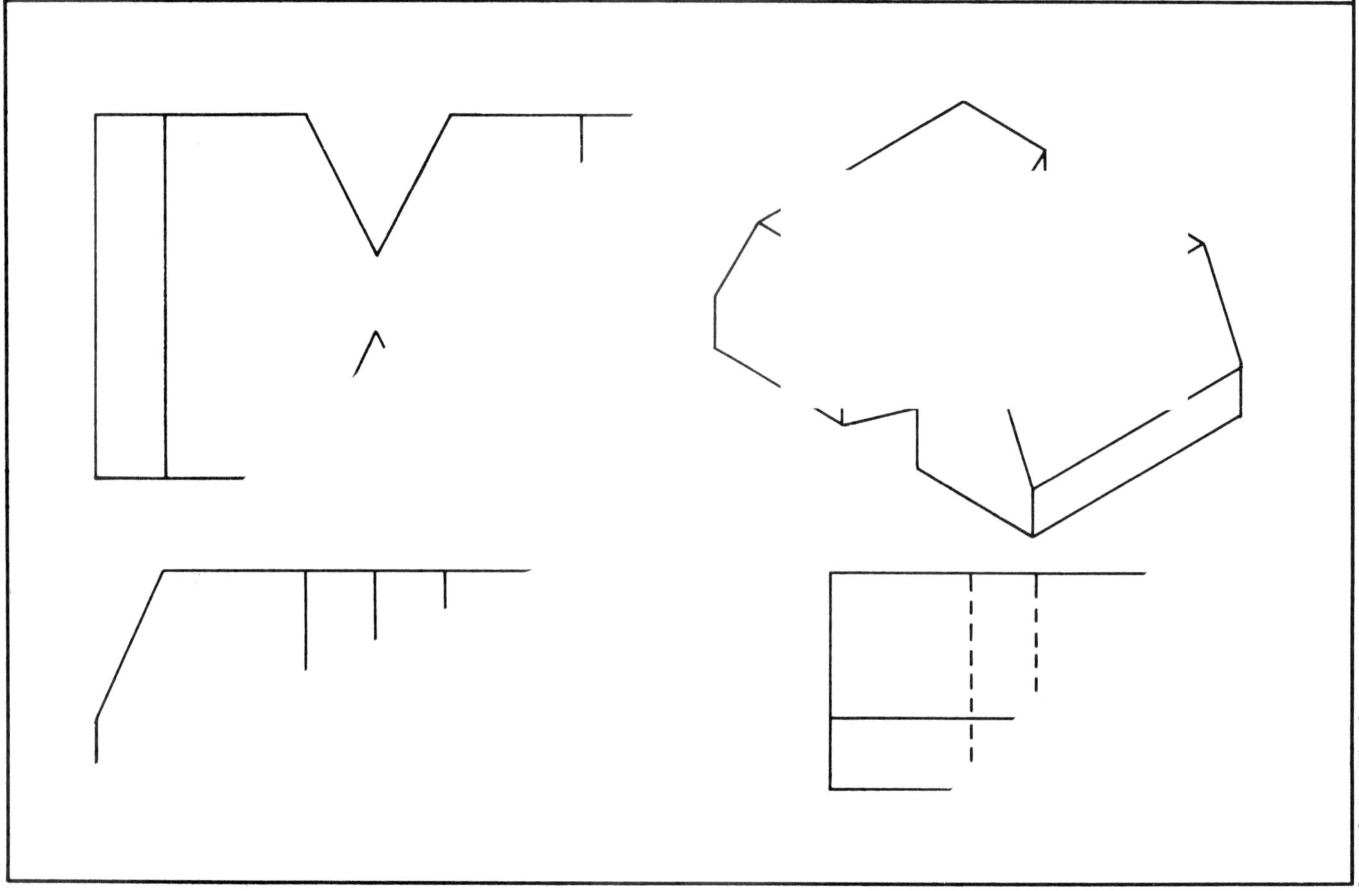

4-4 MULTIVIEW AND ISOMETRIC DRAWINGS OF OBJECTS WITH ANGLES. Add the missing lines to complete the front, top, and side views of the multiview drawings. Complete the missing lines in the isometric view of the object.

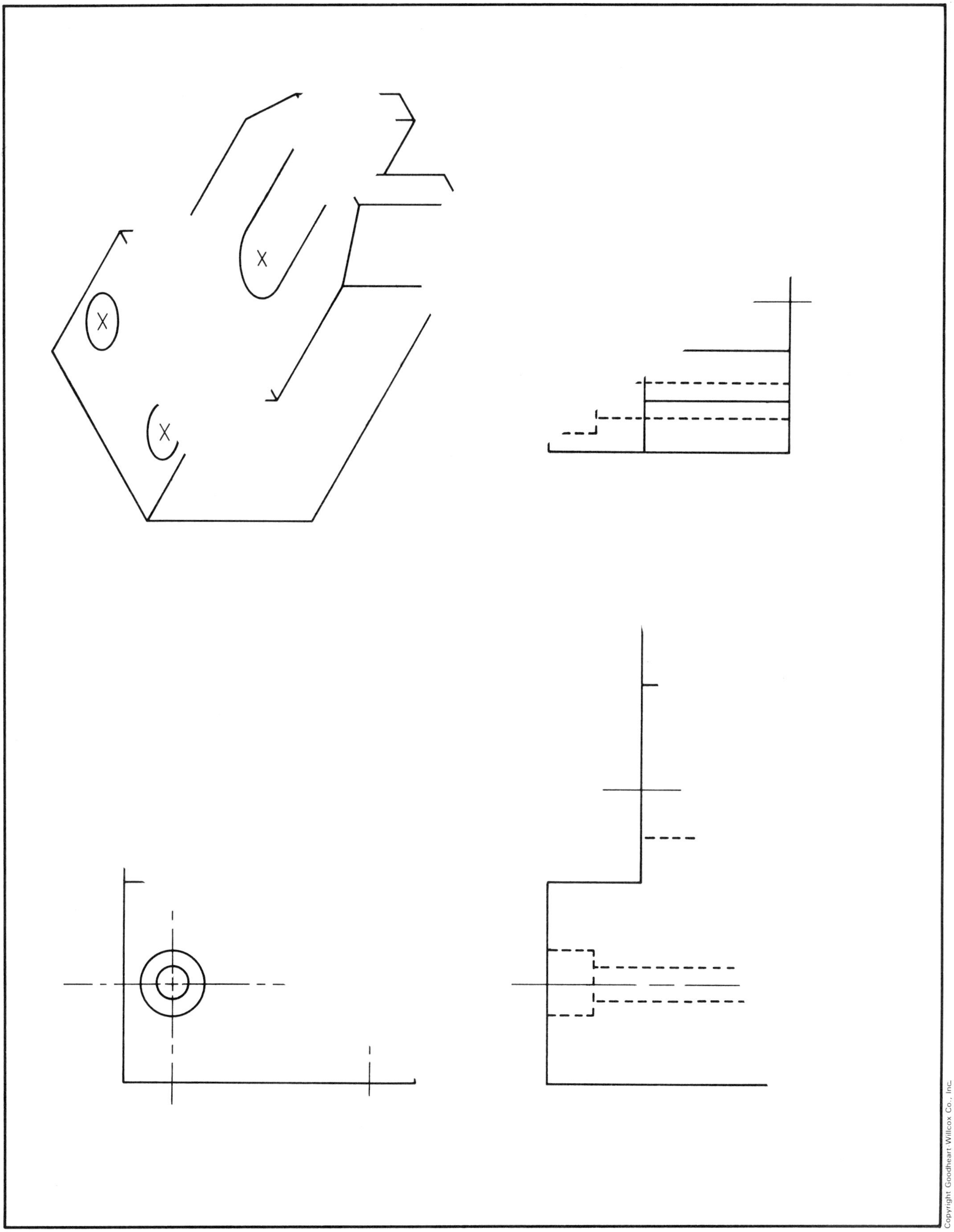

4-5 MULTIVIEW AND ISOMETIC DRAWINGS OF SLIDE BRACKET. Add the missing lines to complete the front, top, and side views. Complete the isometric drawing.

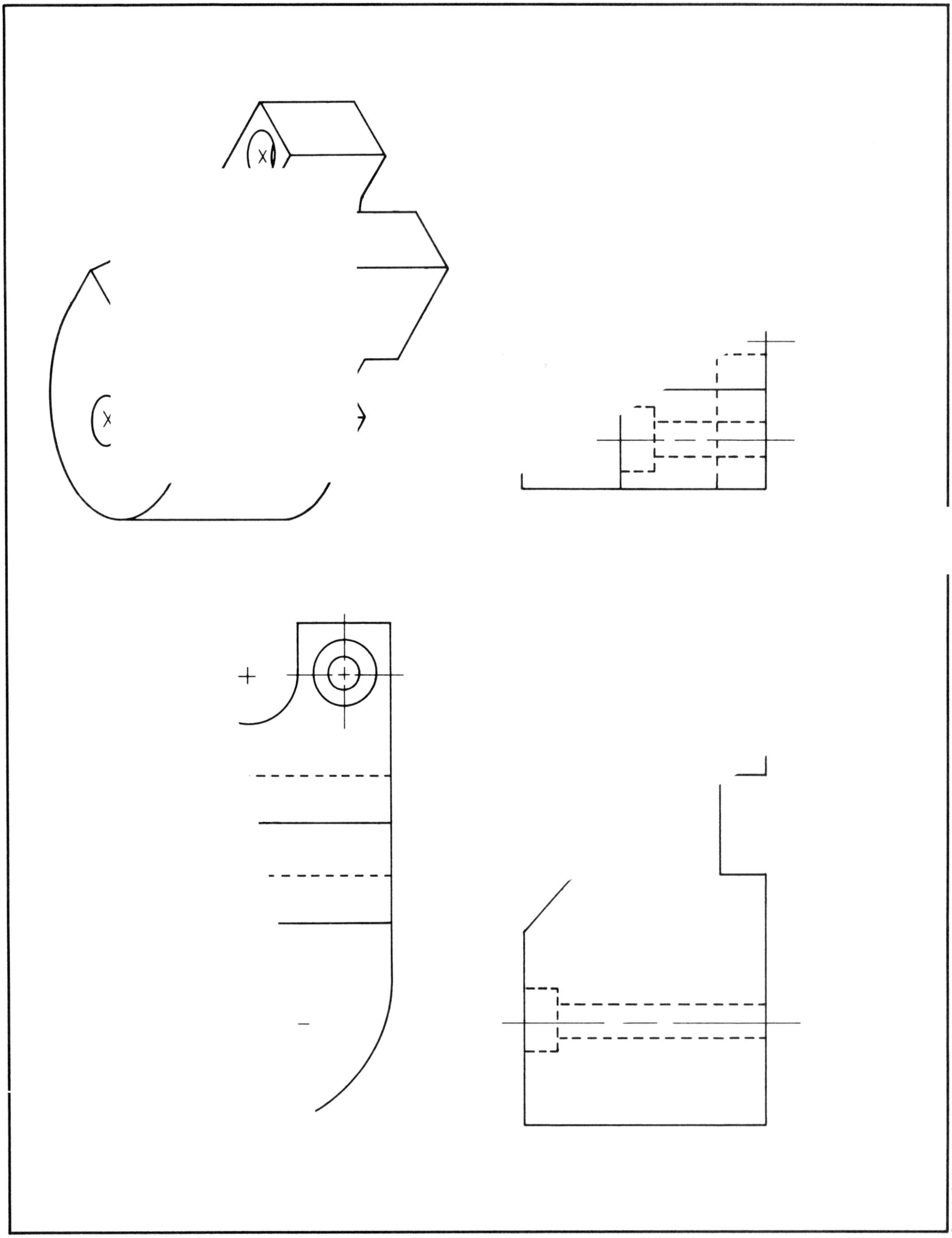

4-6 MULTIVIEW AND ISOMETRIC DRAWING OF SLANT BRACKET. Add the missing lines to complete the front, top and side views. Complete the isometric drawing.

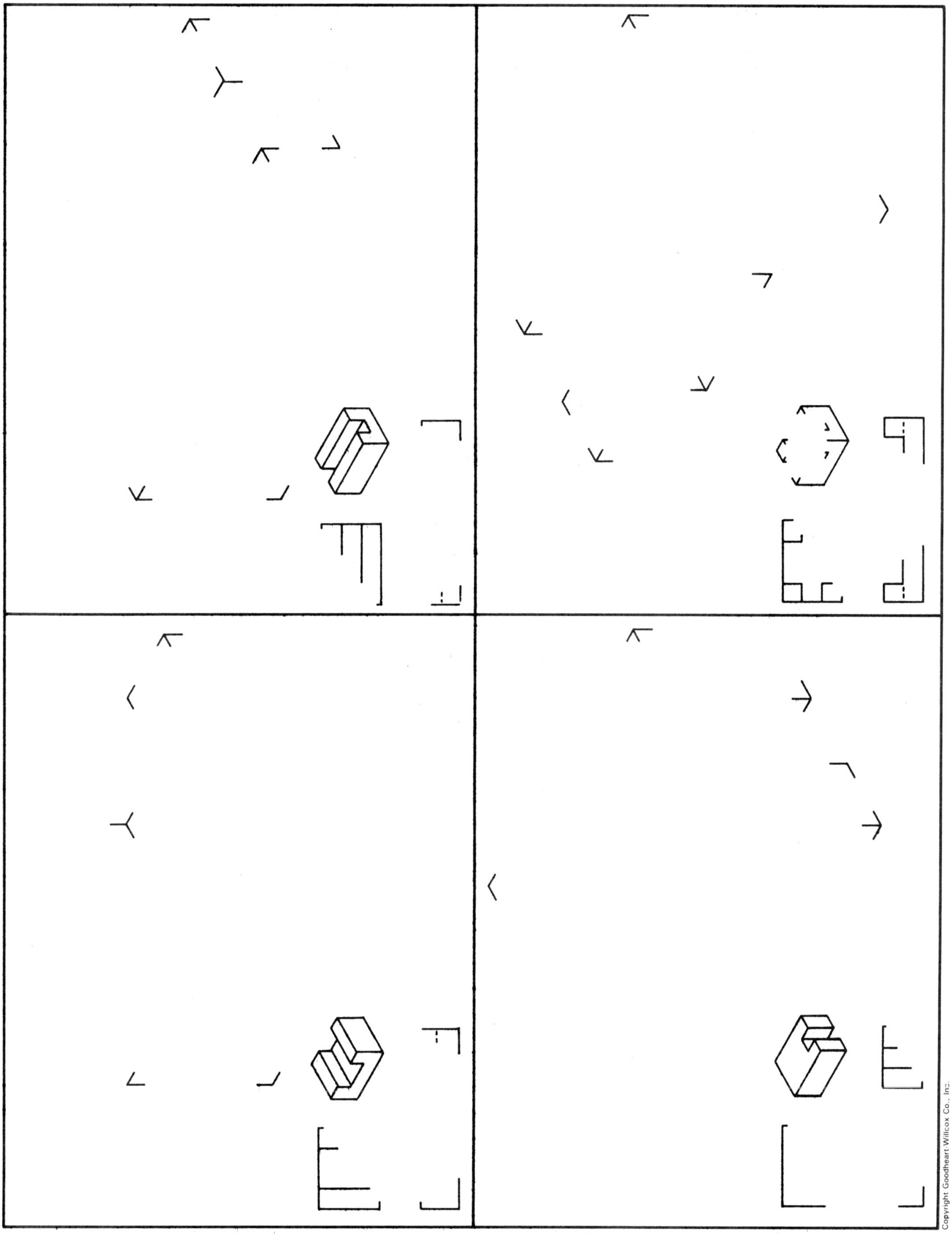

4-7 ISOMETRIC AND MULTIVIEW DRAWINGS OF RECTANGULAR OBJECTS. Add the missing lines to complete the front, top, and side views of the multiview drawing. Complete the isometric drawing.

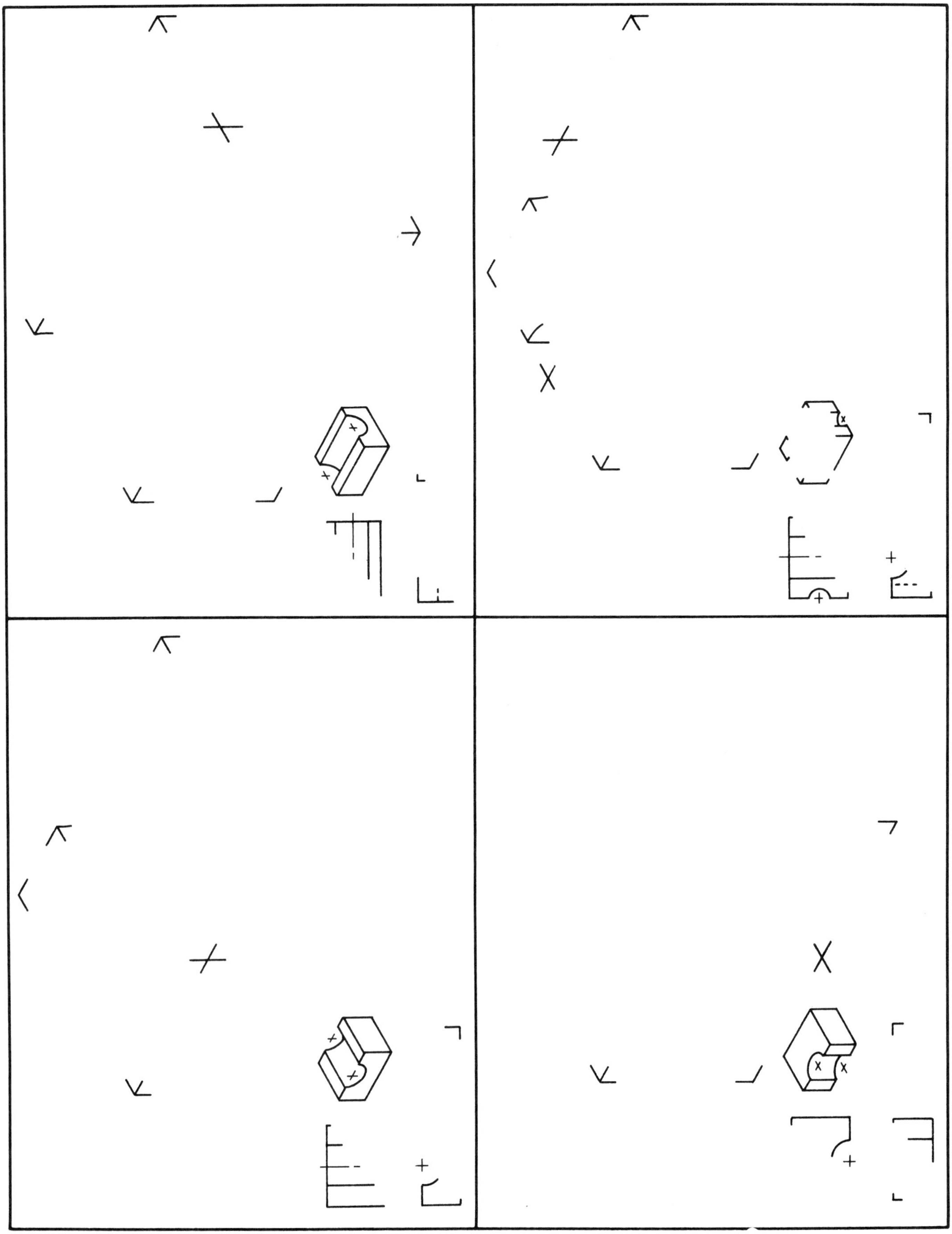

4-8 ISOMETRIC AND MULTIVIEW DRAWINGS OF OBJECTS WITH CURVES. Add the missing lines to complete the front, top, and side views of the multiview drawings. Complete the isometric drawings.

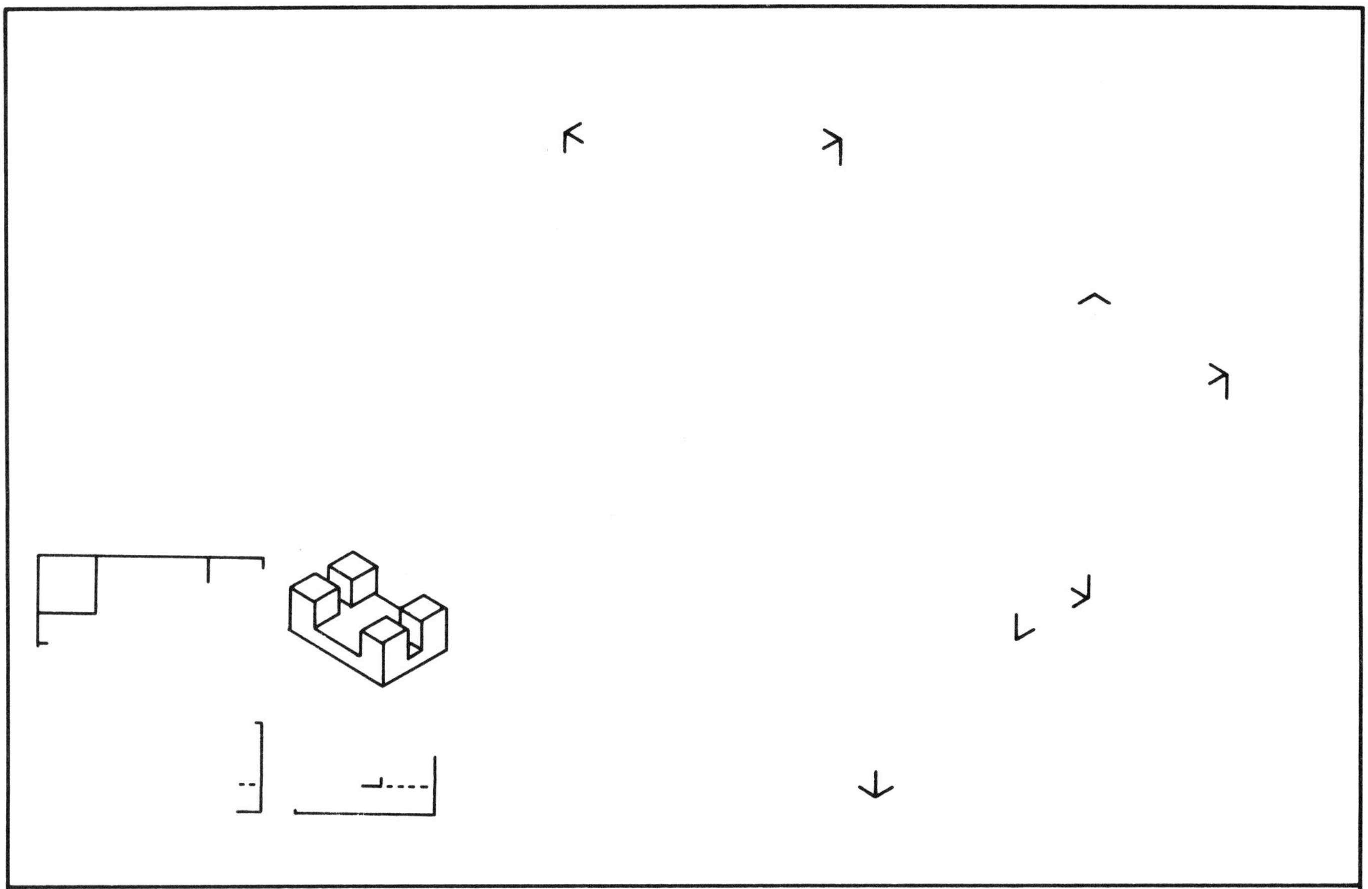

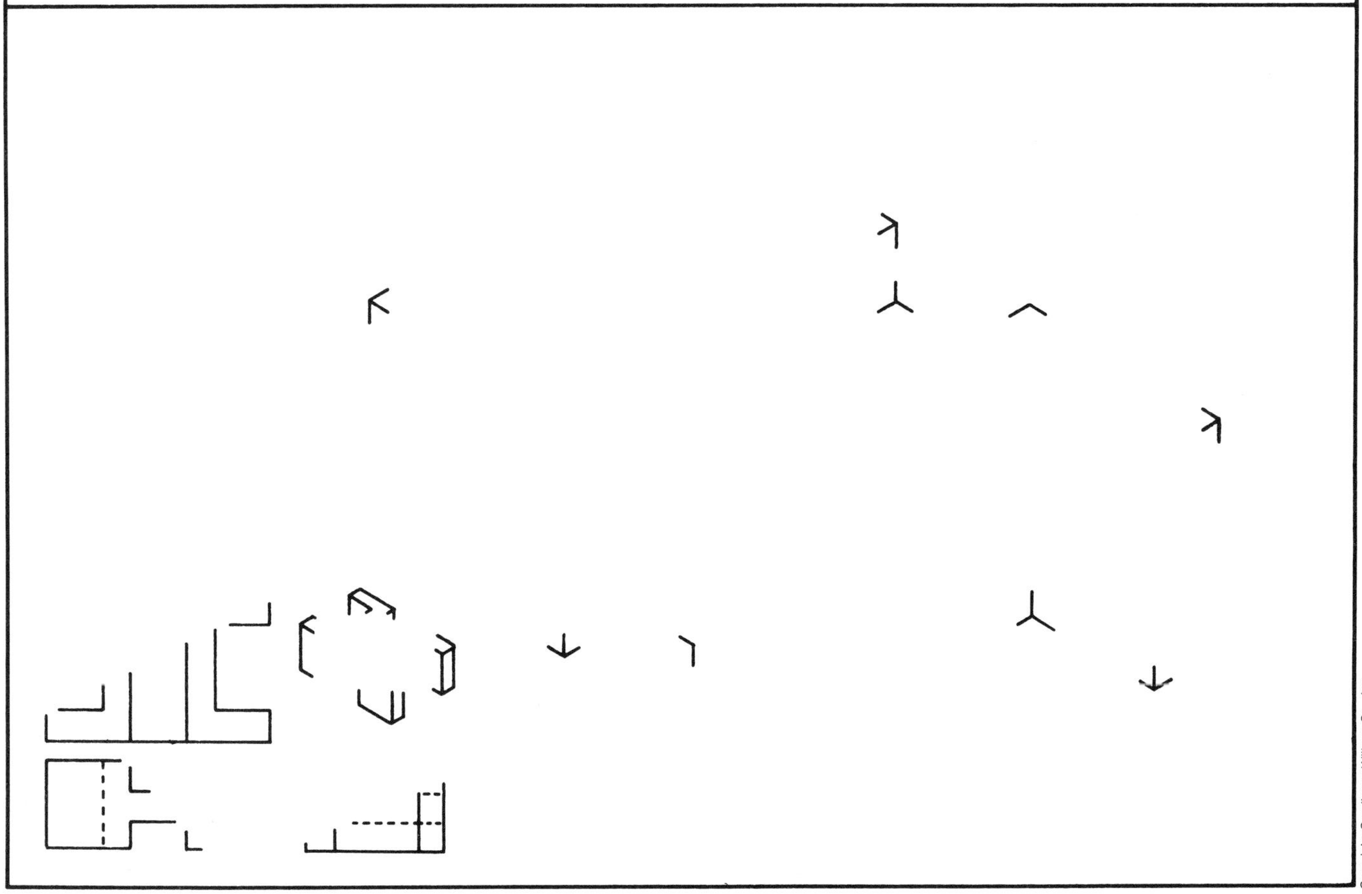

4-9 ISOMETRIC AND MULTIVIEW DRAWINGS OF BLOCKS. Add the missing lines to complete the multiview and isometric drawings.

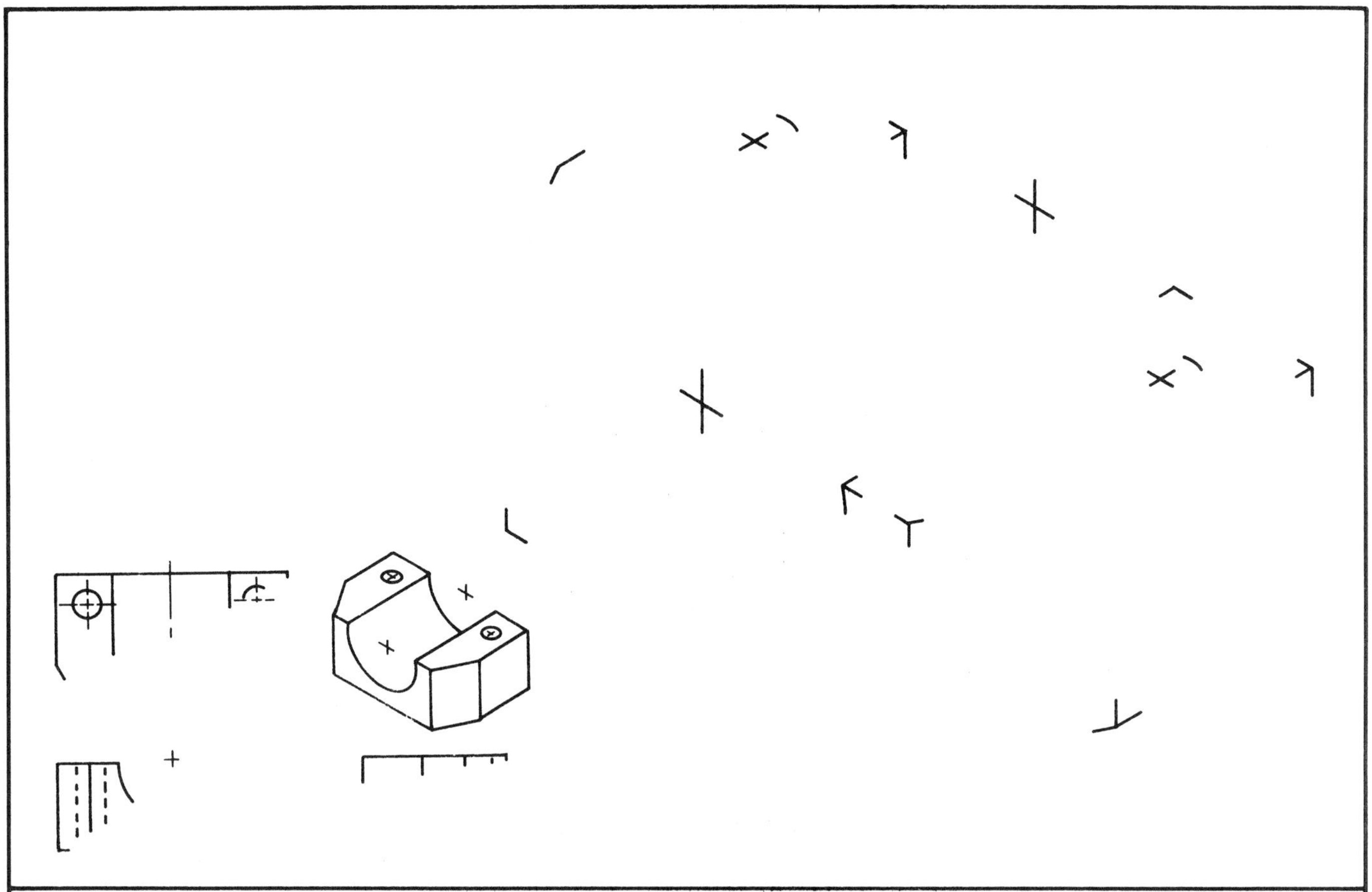

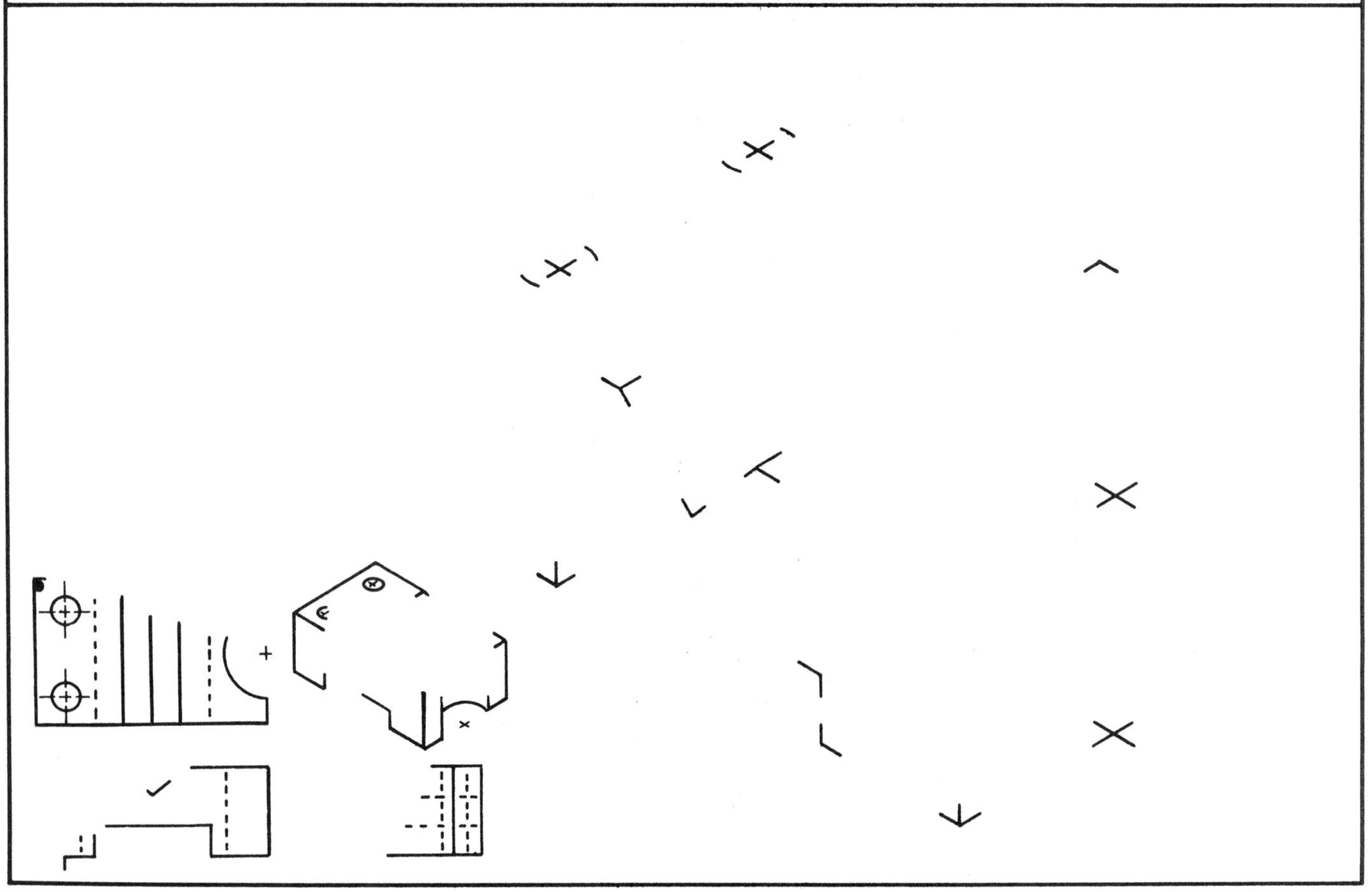

4-10 ISOMETRIC AND MULTIVIEW DRAWINGS WITH CIRCULAR SHAPES. Add the missing lines to complete the multiview and isometric drawings.

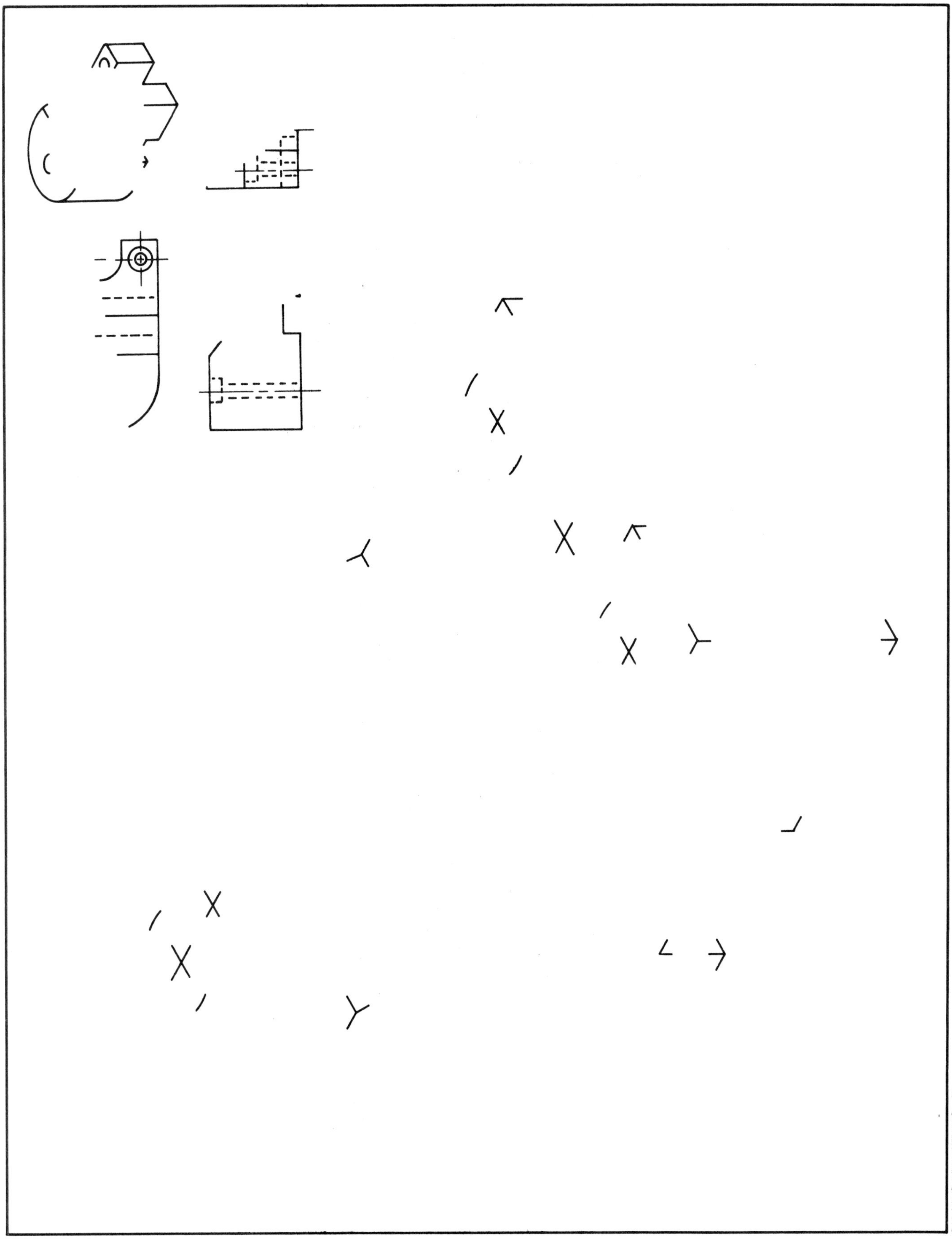

4-11 ISOMETRIC AND MULTIVIEW DRAWINGS OF BRACKET. Add the missing lines to complete the multiview and the isometric drawing.

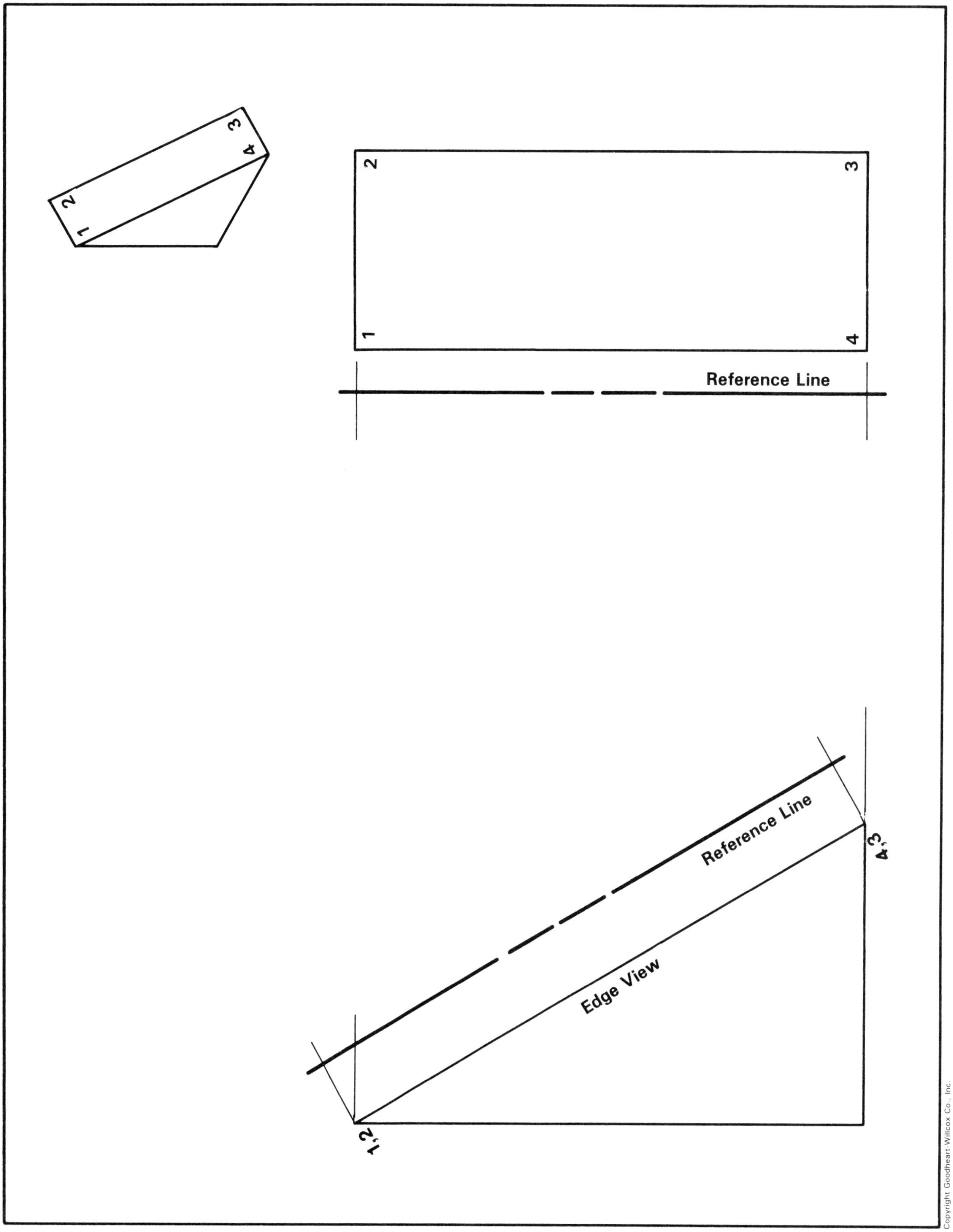

4-12 AUXILIARY VIEW OF RECTANGULAR SURFACE. After studying the examples in the textbook, complete the auxiliary view.

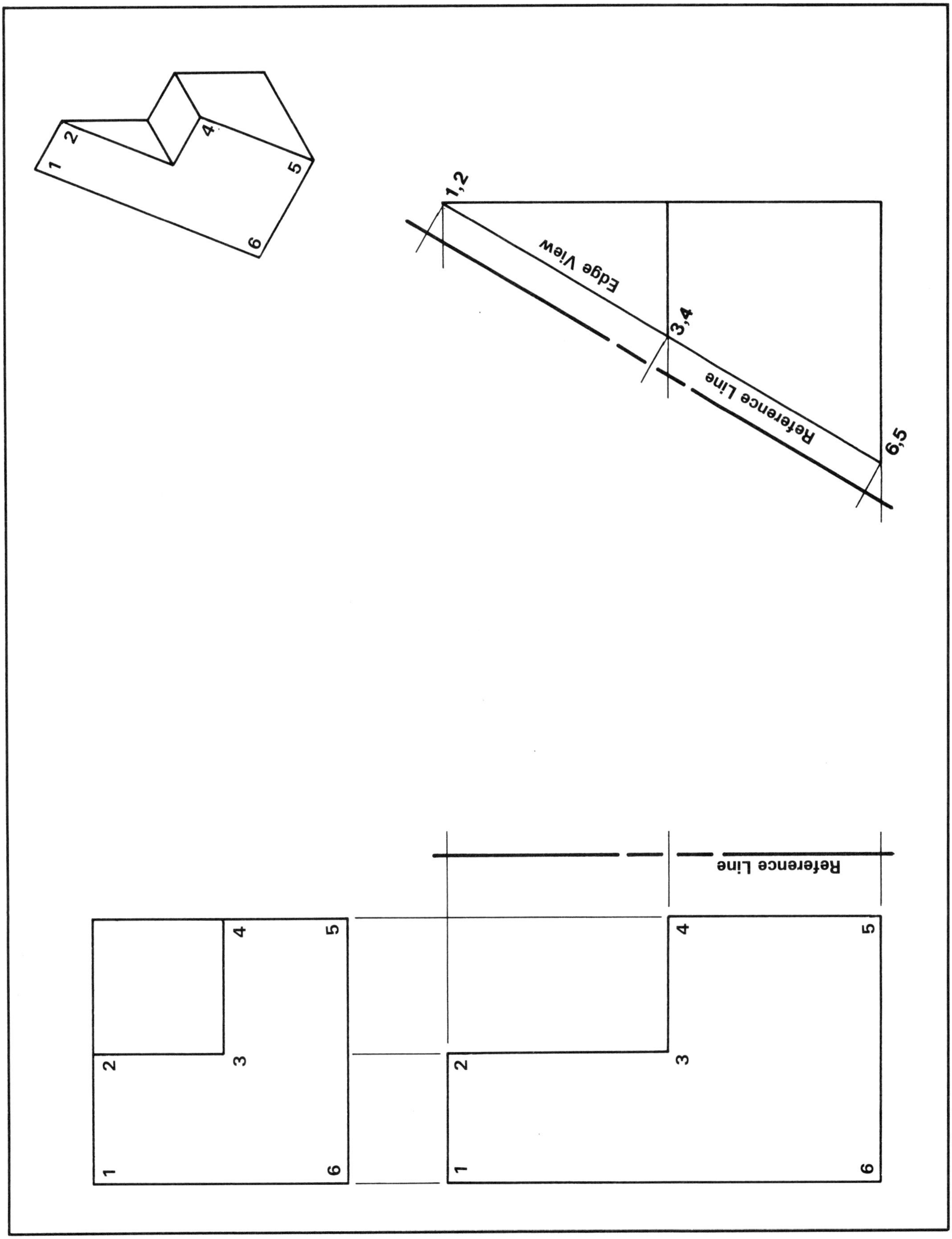

4-13 AUXILIARY VIEW OF "L" SHAPED SURFACE. After carefully examining the three views provided, construct the auxiliary view.

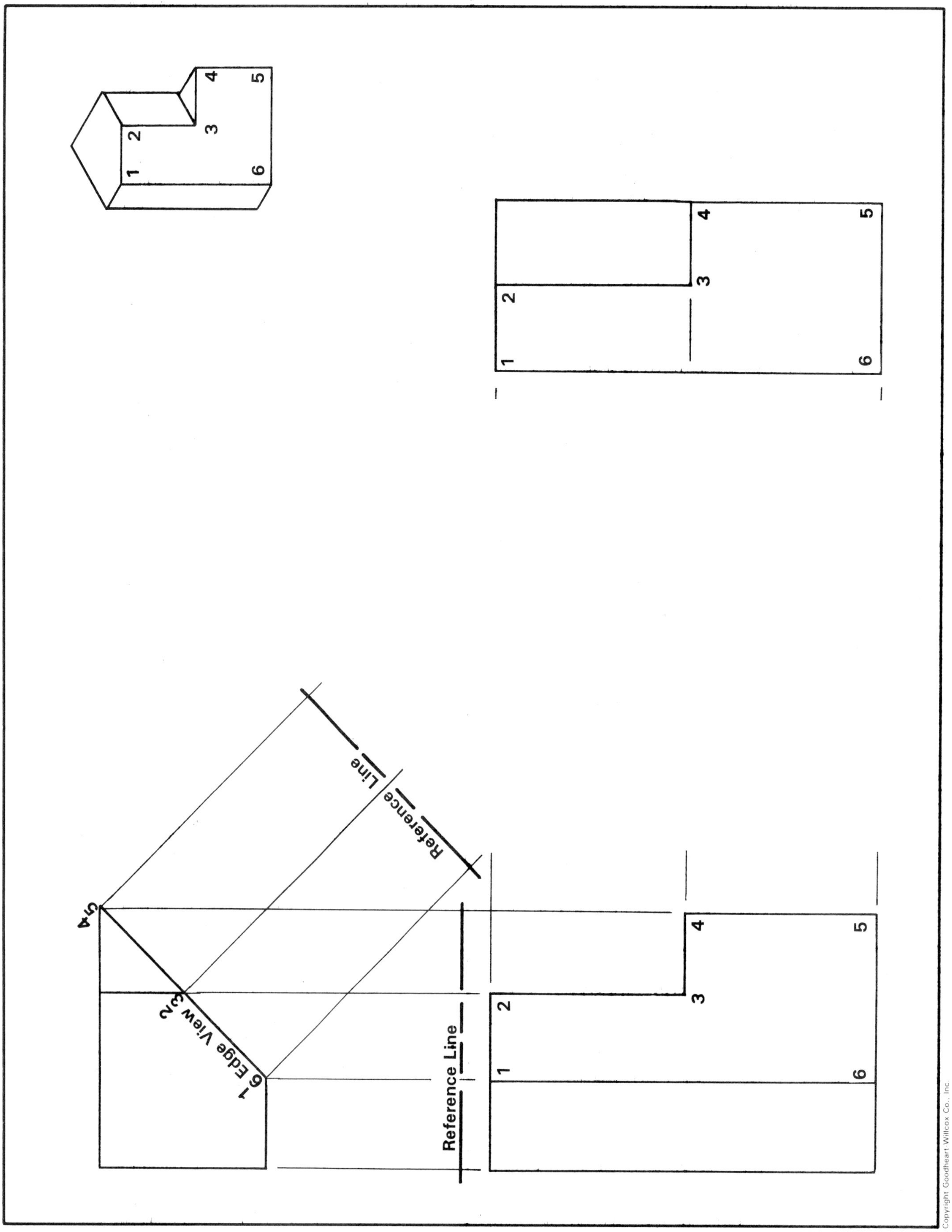

4-14 AUXILIARY VIEW OF "L" SURFACE. Carefully construct the "L" shaped auxiliary view of this object.

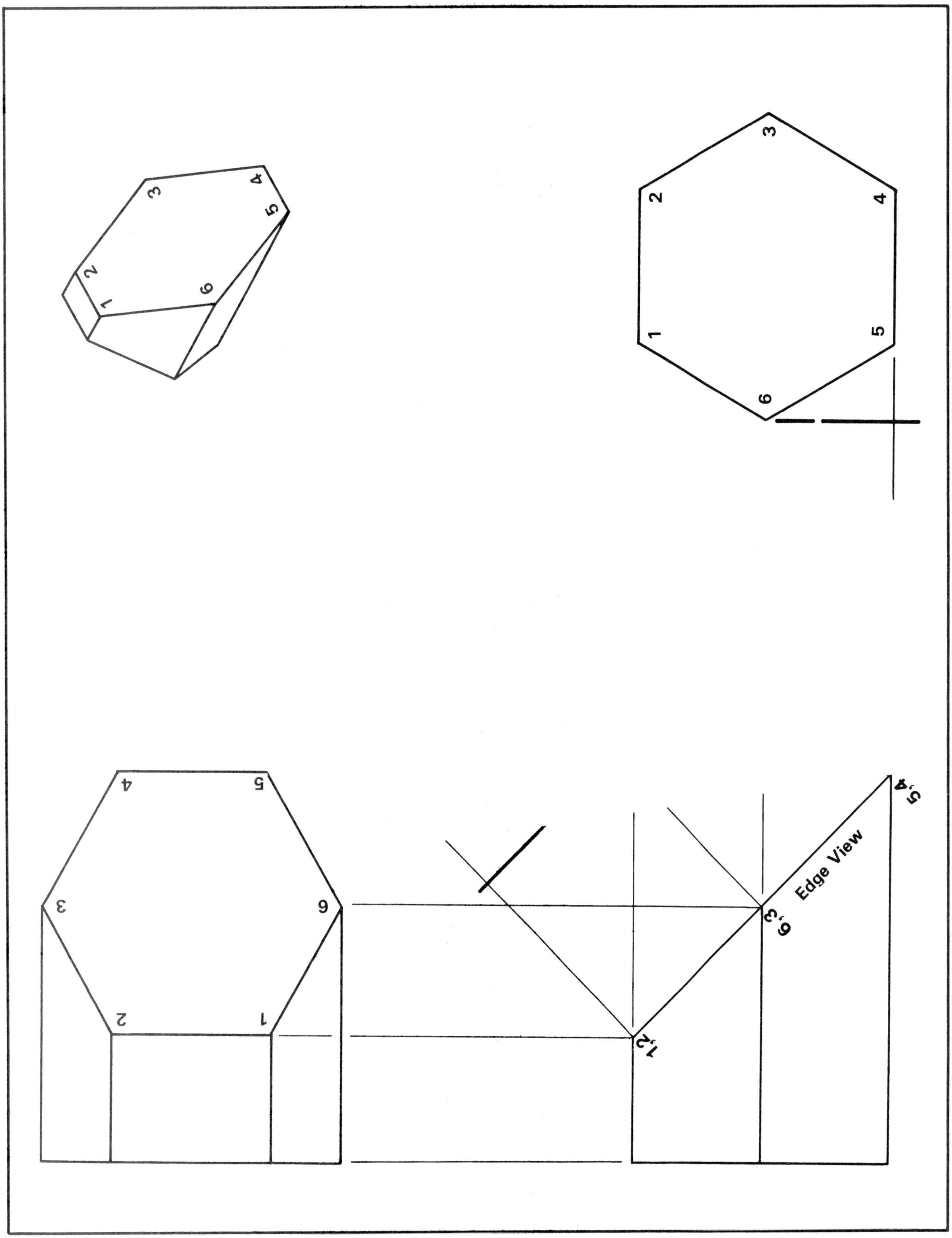

4-15 AUXILIARY VIEW OF HEXAGONAL SURFACE. Using the information provided on this exercise, construct the auxiliary view.

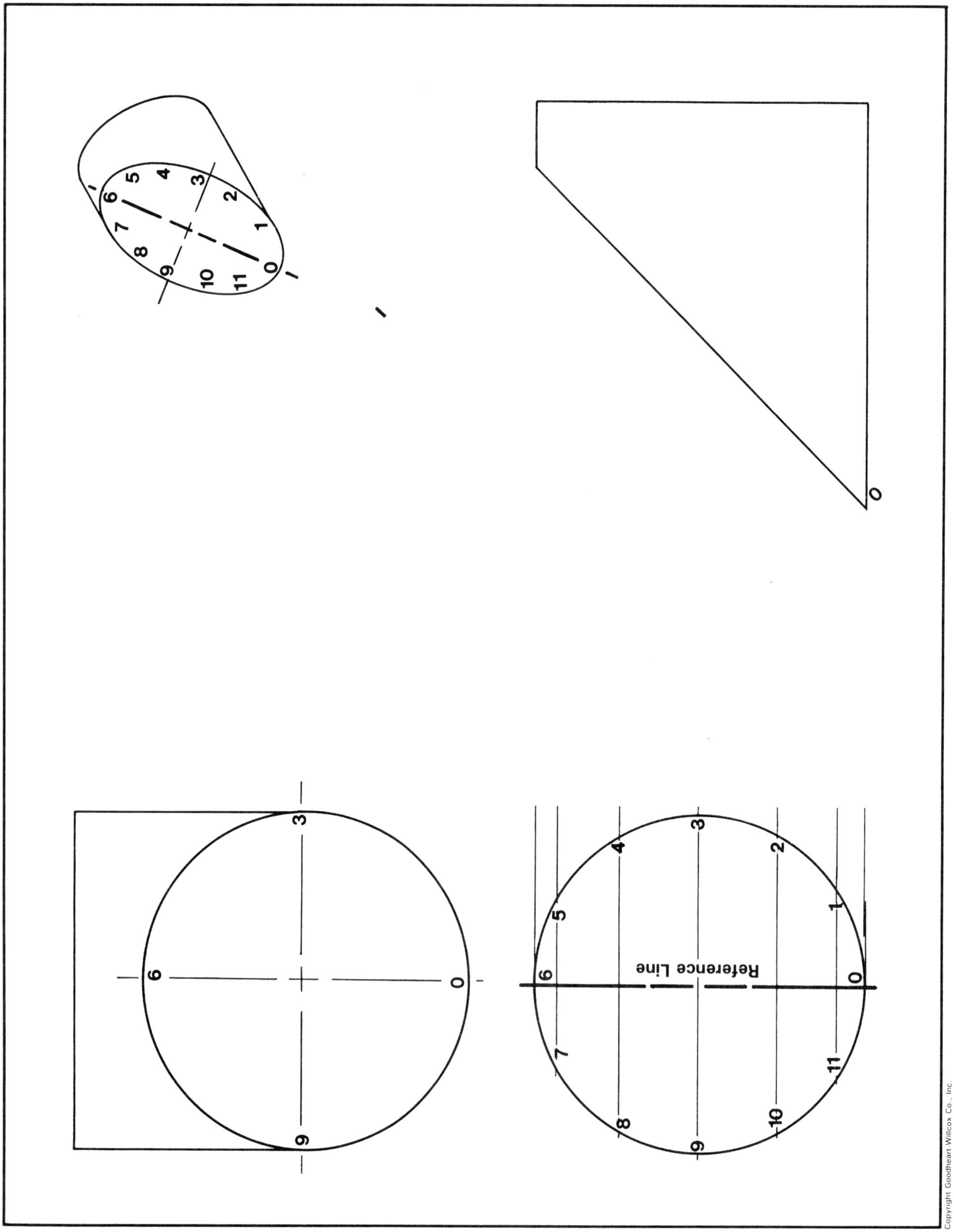

4-16 AUXILILARY VIEW OF CIRCULAR SURFACE. Study the drawing and then construct the auxiliary view of the slanted circular surface.

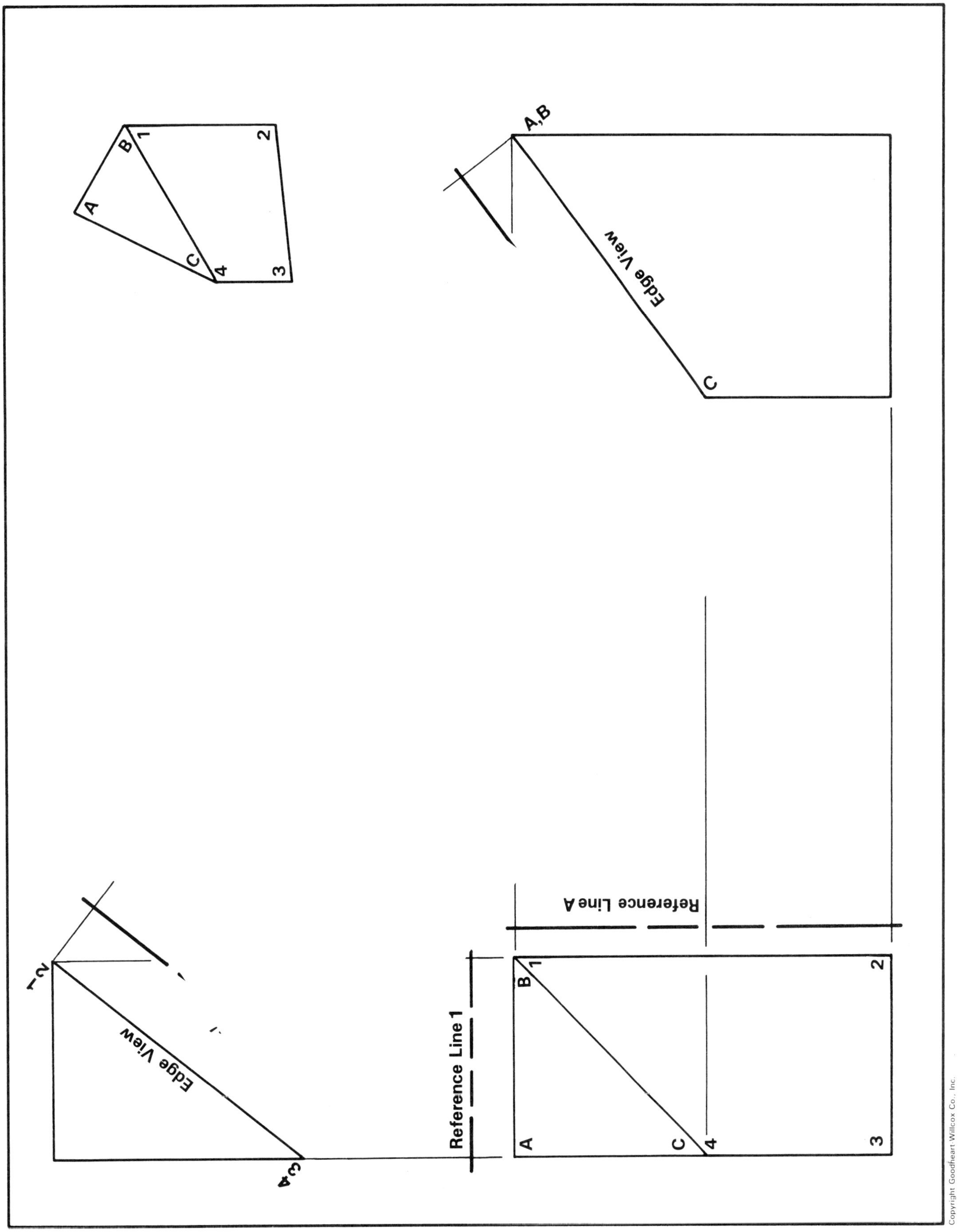

4-17 AUXILIARY VIEWS OF TWO SLANTED SURFACES. Review the object drawn below and construct the auxiliary views for ABC and 1234.

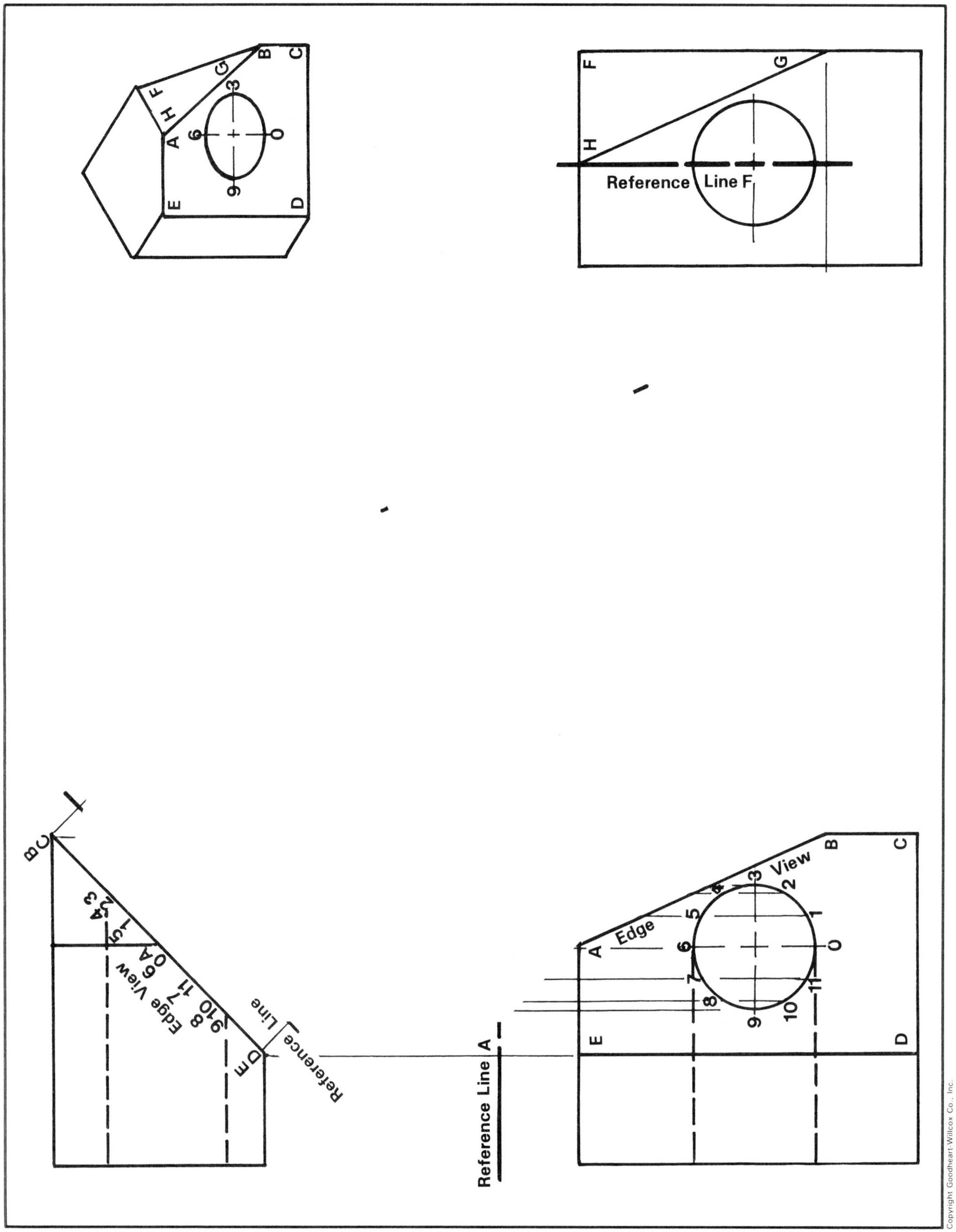

4-18 AUXILIARY VIEW OF MODIFIED WEDGE. Carefully study the views of the object pictured on this page. Construct the auxiliary views for surfaces ABCDE and FGH in the space provided.

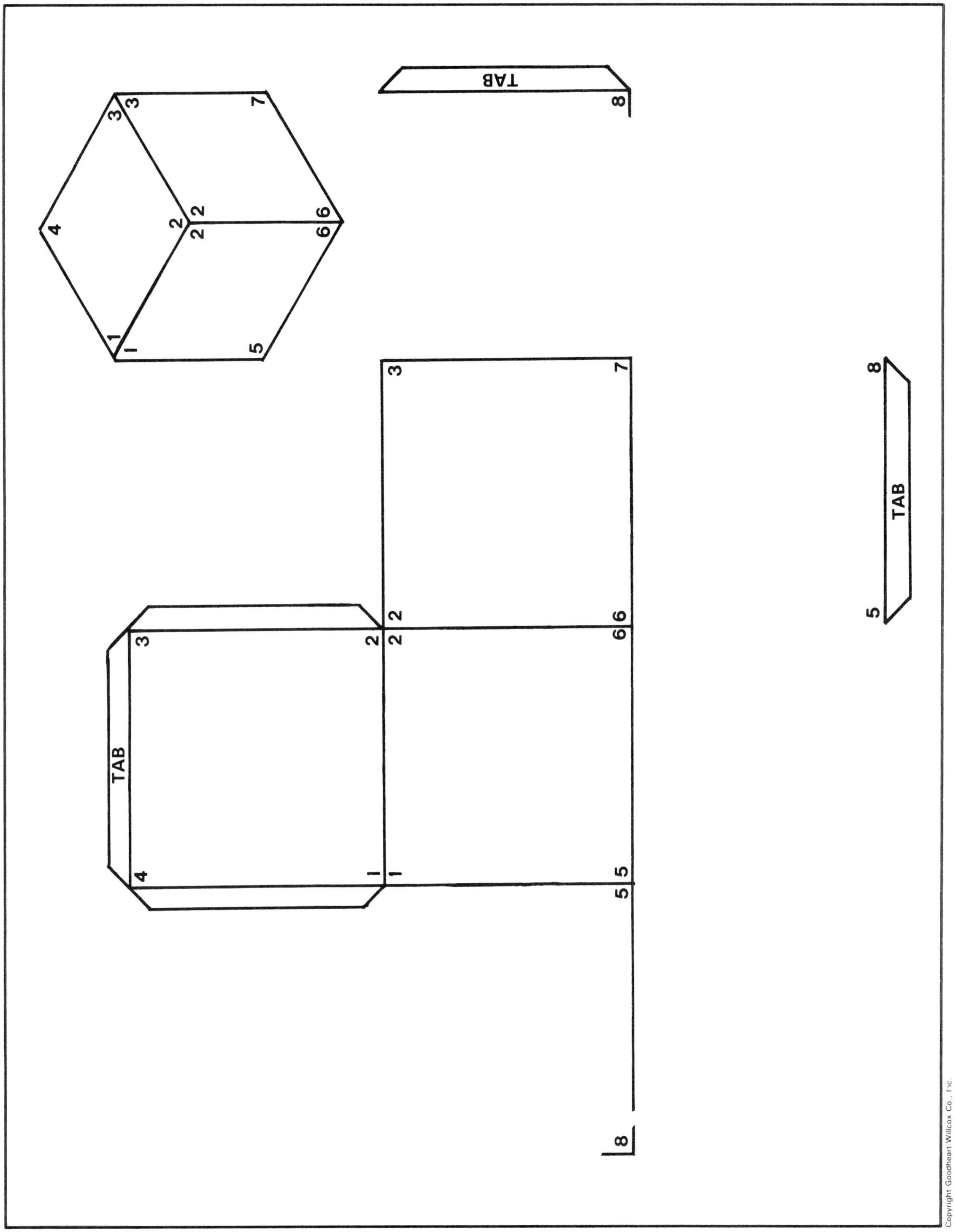

4-19 LAYOUT OF A CUBE. Layout the cube shown on this page. Label the six sides as shown. Cut out the pattern, fold over the tabs, and assemble the cube.

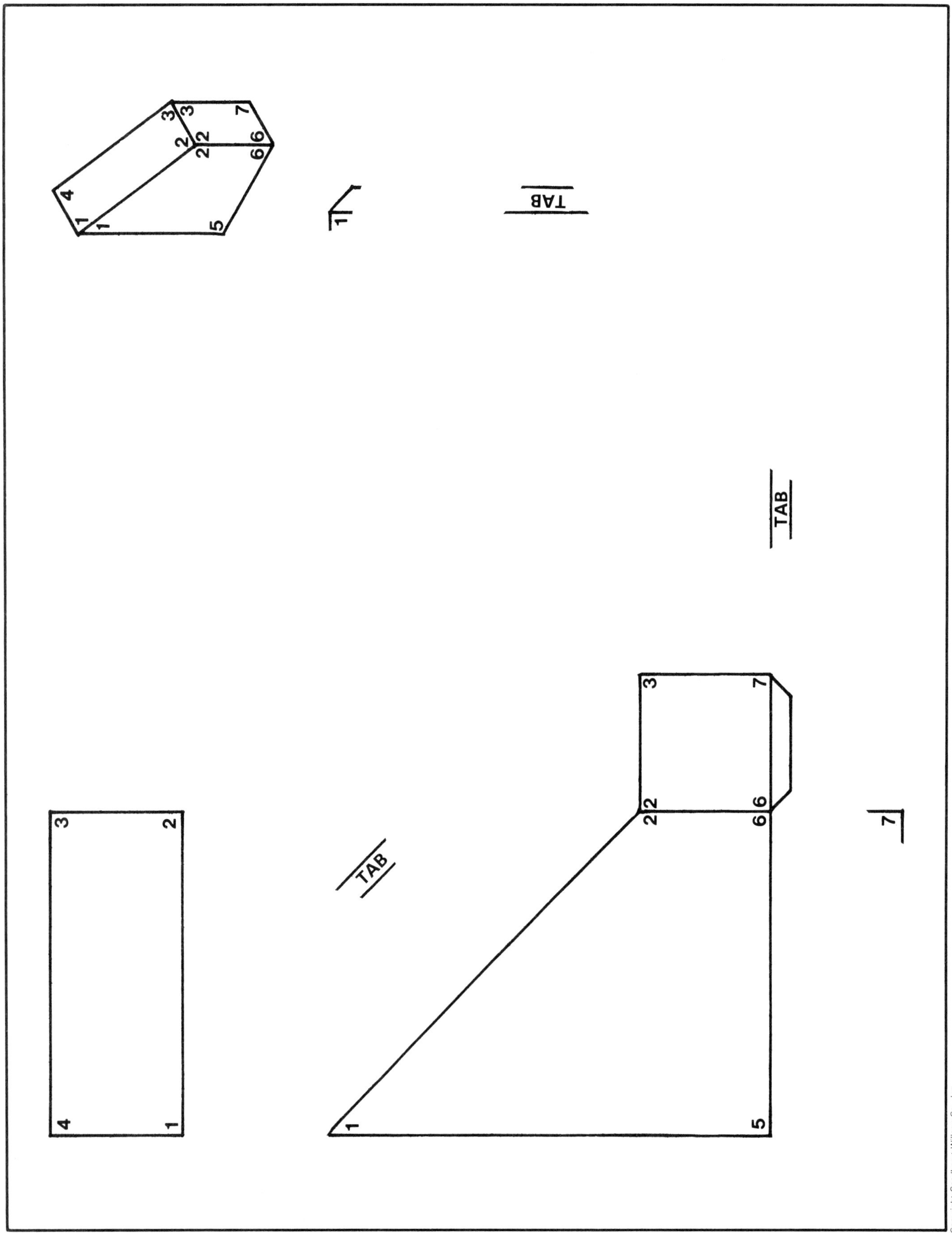

4-20 LAYOUT OF RECTANGULAR BOX WITH A SLANTED TOP. On a separate sheet of stiff paper, layout the object shown. Label the corners of the rectangle and the slanted top. Cut out and assemble to check your work.

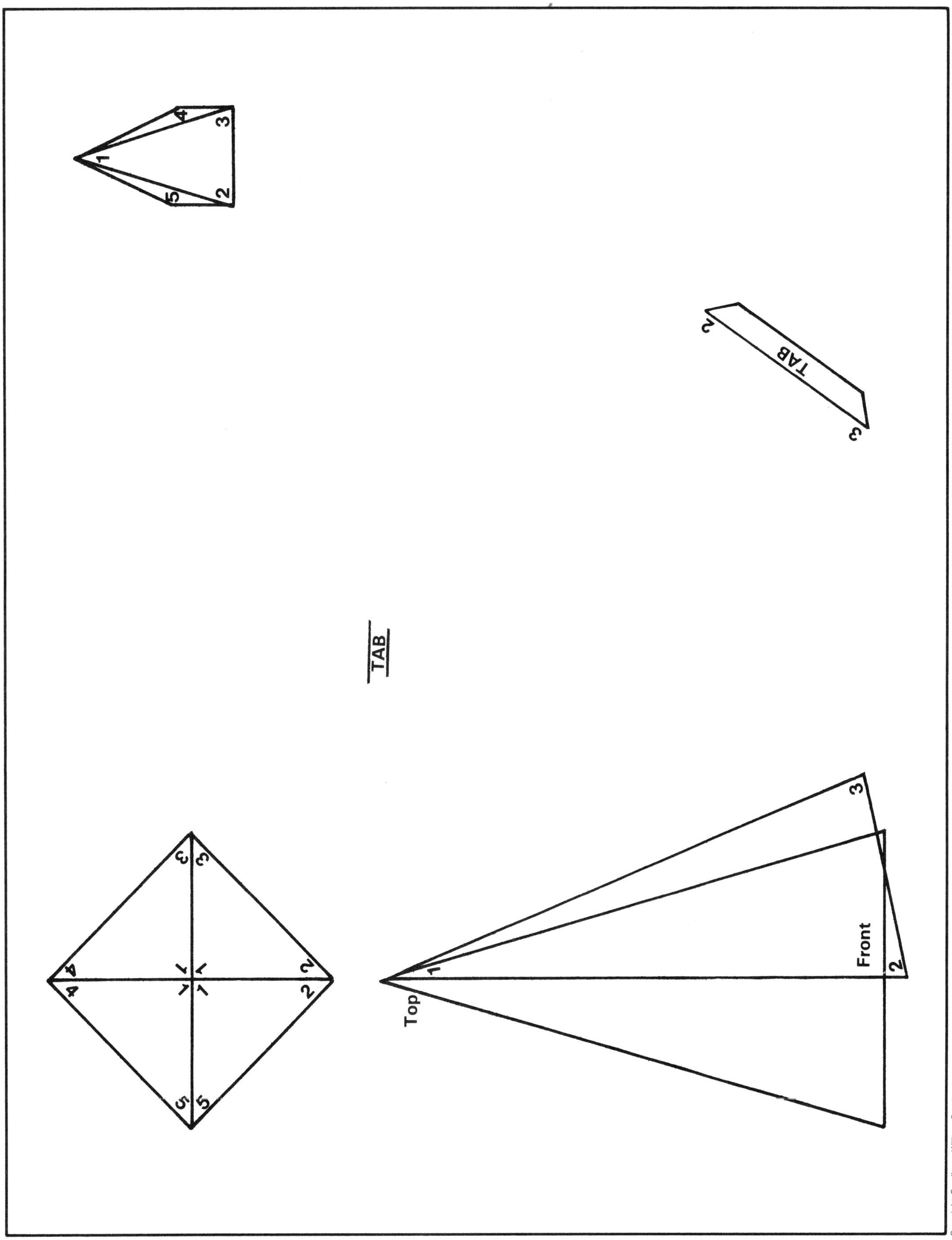

4-21 LAYOUT OF A PYRAMID. Layout the pyramid as shown in the drawing. Label the corners. Cut out and assemble to check your layout.

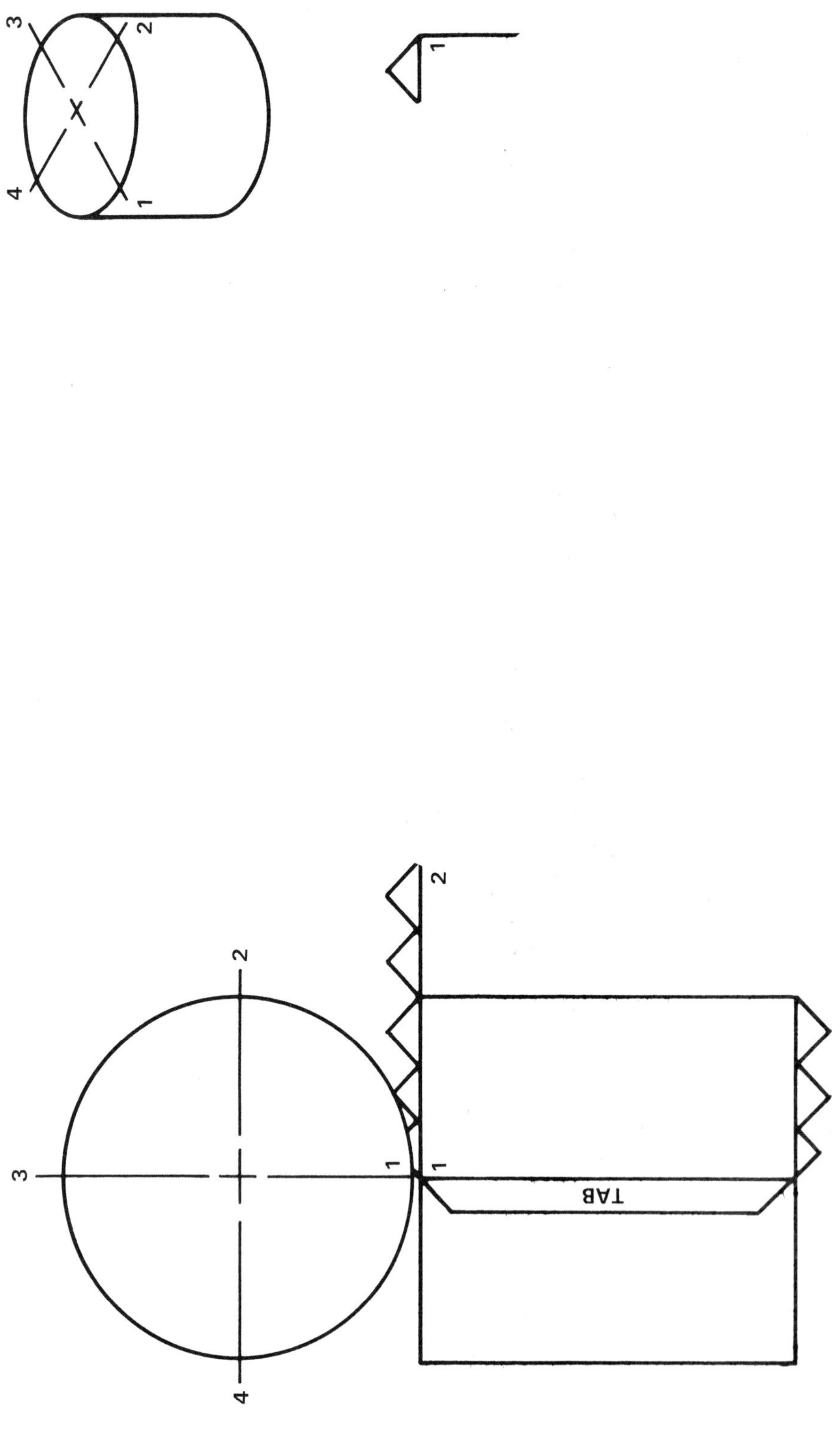

4-22 LAYOUT OF A CYLINDER. On a separate sheet of stiff paper, layout the cylinder shown in this exercise. Cut out the pattern and assemble to check your accuracy.

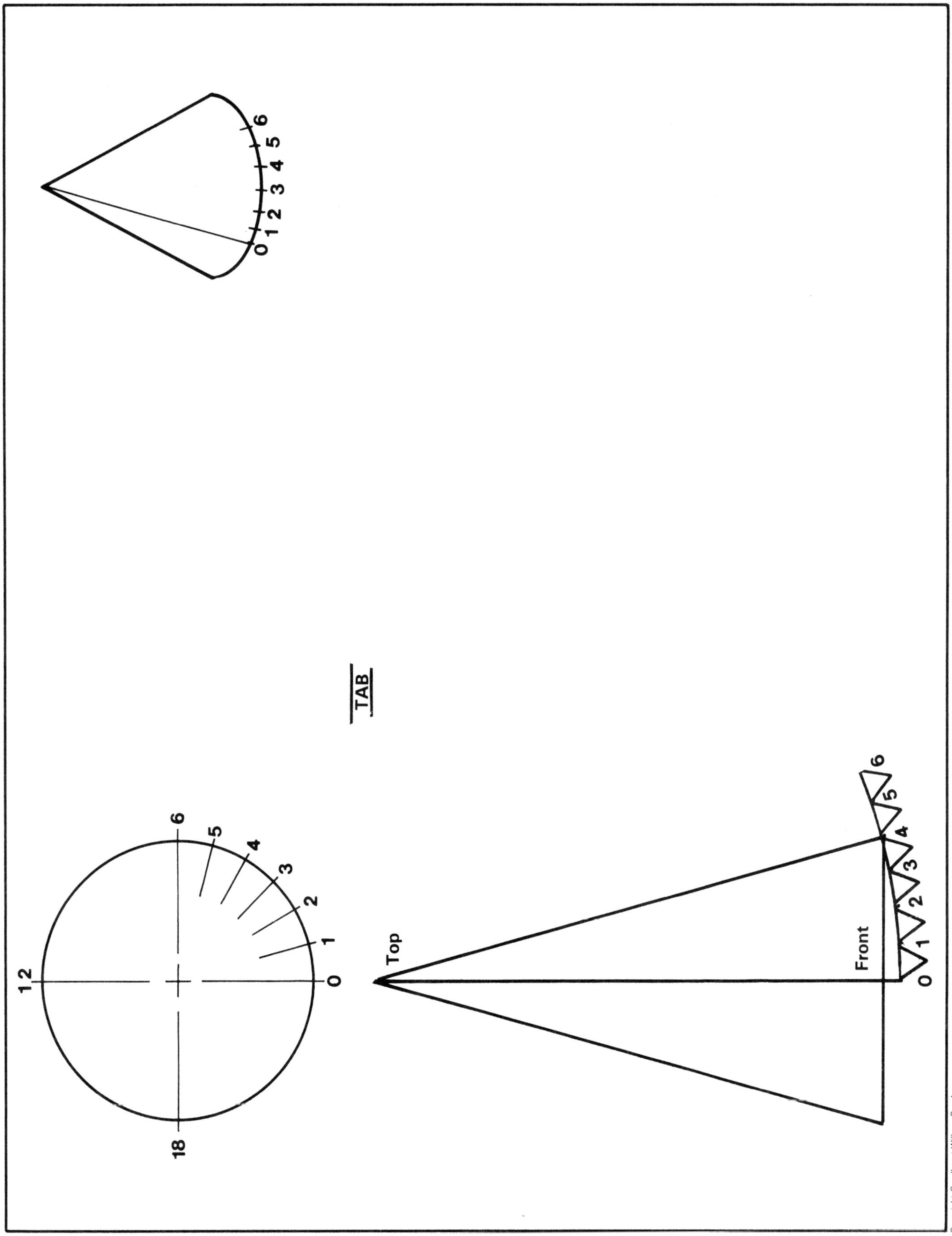

4-23 LAYOUT OF A CONE. Layout the cone shown here. Be sure to add tabs for assembly. Cut out the pattern and assemble.

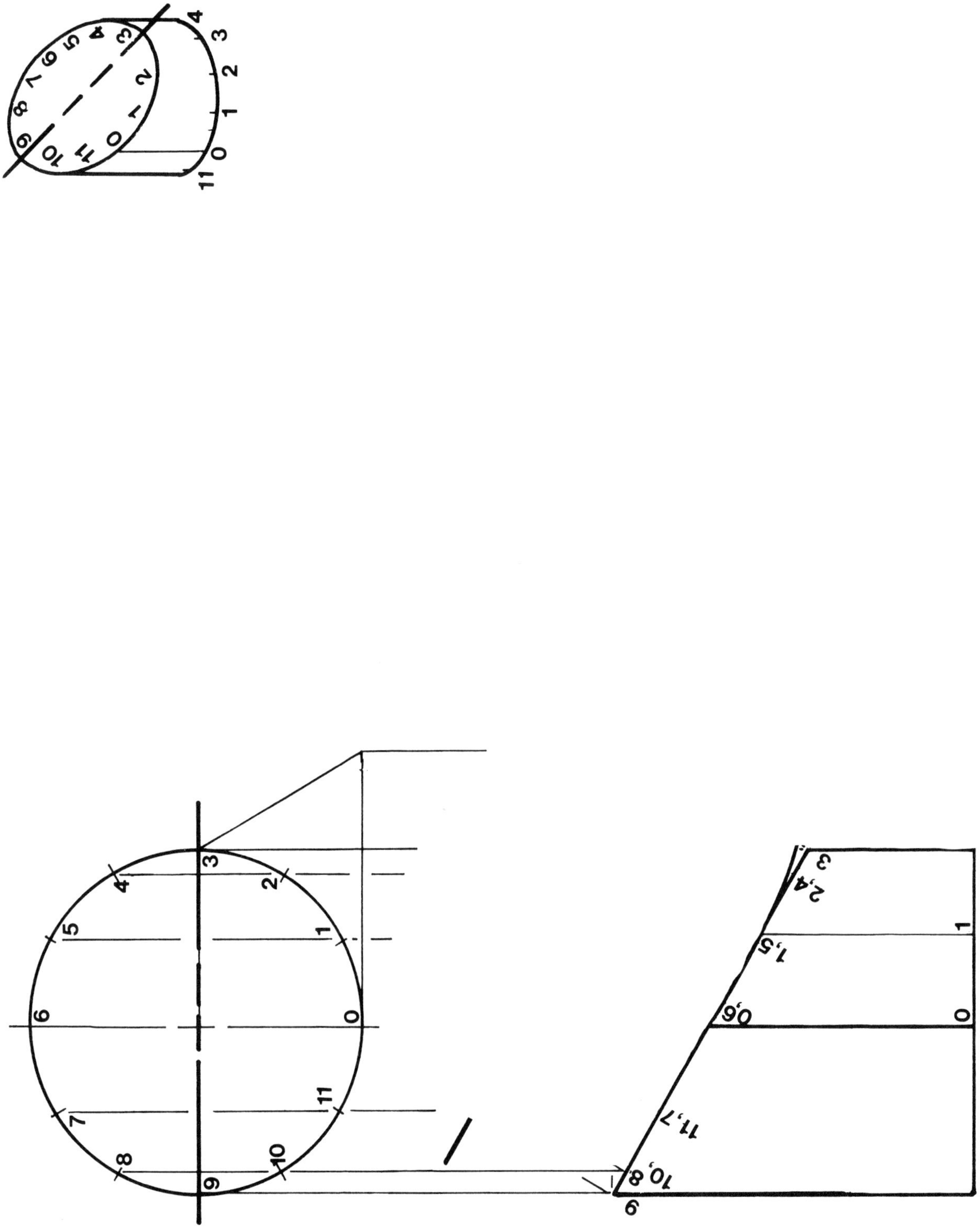

4-24 LAYOUT OF A CYLINDER WITH A SLANTED TOP. Study the drawing provided, then layout the cylinder with the slanted top. Be careful to include tabs for assembly. Cut out the pattern and assemble to check your work.

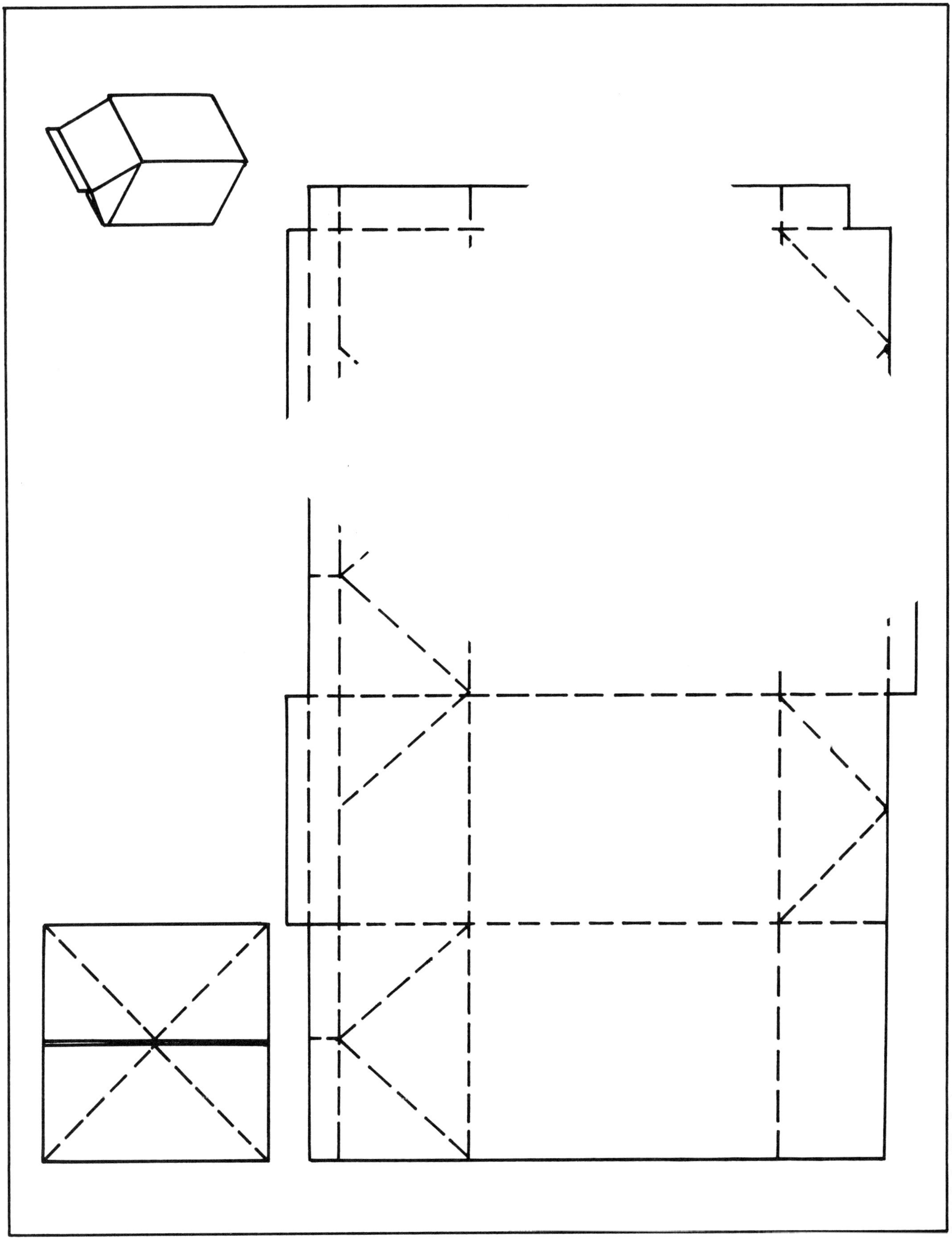

4-25 LAYOUT OF A LIQUID CONTAINER. Complete the pattern below. Label the surfaces. Cut out and assemble to check your accuracy in developing the pattern.

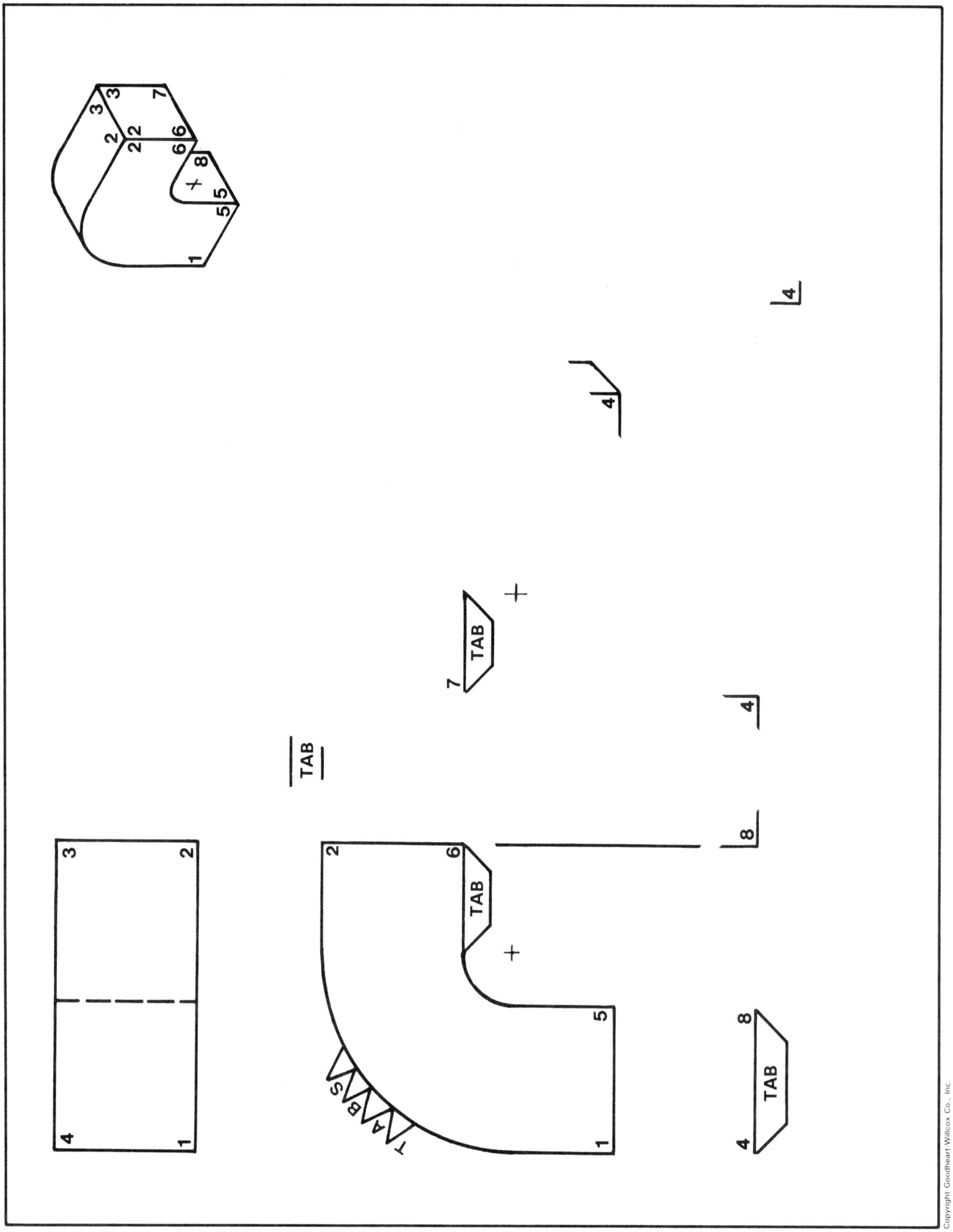

4-26 LAYOUT OF A 90 DEGREE RECTANGULAR DUCT. Study the drawing carefully. Complete the drawing for a pattern of a duct. Cut out the pattern and assemble to compare to the finished product shown in the drawing.

Chapter 5

DIMENSIONING

OBJECTIVES

After successfully completing this chapter on DIMENSIONING, you will be able to:

- ☐ *Draw sharp, crisp, and thin extension lines, dimension lines, and leaders.*
- ☐ *Accurately shape arrowheads on dimension lines and leaders.*
- ☐ *Make numerals and letters correctly and neatly.*
- ☐ *Place dimensions in appropriate locations to create a neat and uncluttered appearance.*
- ☐ *Dimension surfaces containing notches, steps, and angles.*
- ☐ *Dimension surfaces containing arcs and circles.*
- ☐ *Indicate unilateral, bilateral, limit dimensions, tolerances, and other notes.*
- ☐ *Apply basic terminology and concepts of Geometric Dimensioning and Tolerancing.*

Sketches and drawings are pictorial thoughts transferred to paper. As decisions are made about actually creating products from drawings and sketches, sizes and shapes must be identified and described.

As sketches evolve into products, several drawing phases occur. Examples of these phases include:

1. Design sketches are transformed into detailed drawings.
2. Detailed drawings are used to produce prototypes of original products.
3. Product changes require the whole process to repeat itself.

When one individual designs and builds an original product, dimensioning may be informal. However, when several people design and create a product, it becomes imperative to follow a series of drawing rules and dimensioning standards.

Dimensioning standards help eliminate mistakes and ensure a clear interpretation of sizes and shapes. Dimensioned drawings are used in manufacturing process from the initial sketches through the final inspection. This chapter discusses and illustrates the basic dimensioning practices for communicating sizes and shapes of parts and products.

FUNDAMENTALS

Dimensioning provides the necessary size and shape information for parts, mating parts, and products. The process of dimensioning includes:

- Overall size of an object.
- Size and location of details.
- Tolerances.
- Notes.

For a simple product like a small rectangular eraser, the length, width, and thickness completely describe its dimensions. Circular and cylindrical products, such as hockey pucks, are dimensioned by diameter and the thickness. These overall dimensions provide the size of products.

Often, parts are attached to mating parts or assembled with fasteners. Holes and slots for fasteners must be drilled the correct size and in the proper location to assure proper alignment. Remember the key words: size, location, and details.

Parts and products may have a certain amount of allowable error called **tolerance.** A chopping block may vary in size plus or minus 1/2 in. or more without affecting its appearance or function. Metal parts that fit together, such as in a bicycle brake, may require accuracy within plus or minus .001 in. or less to be acceptable.

It is helpful if the person doing the dimensioning knows how the part or product is to be used. Knowledge of the manufacturing processes also helps ensure that all necessary size and shape information is provided. Notes provide useful information on materials, assembly, etc. to those reading the print.

COMMON PRACTICES

There are many points to keep in mind while dimensioning. The following sequence of steps describes and illustrates the more common procedures for dimensioning basic shapes. Parts and products vary greatly, therefore, some of the steps are used repeatedly, while others are used only occasionally.

Dimensioning a Surface

When dimensioning a surface, drafters use lines and symbols that follow established standards. Be sure you draw and locate lines correctly and make symbols accurately. The following series of examples will provide the steps in dimensioning a simple rectanglar surface.

Selecting the Best View

Always dimension a rectangular object in a view which best describes its shape. Select the view which provides the most information.The L-shaped front view of Fig. 5-1 is more descriptive than the top view or the side view. The top or side views are necessary to show the depth of this object. Plan your work carefully by locating dimensions where they can be easily read and will not be misinterpreted.

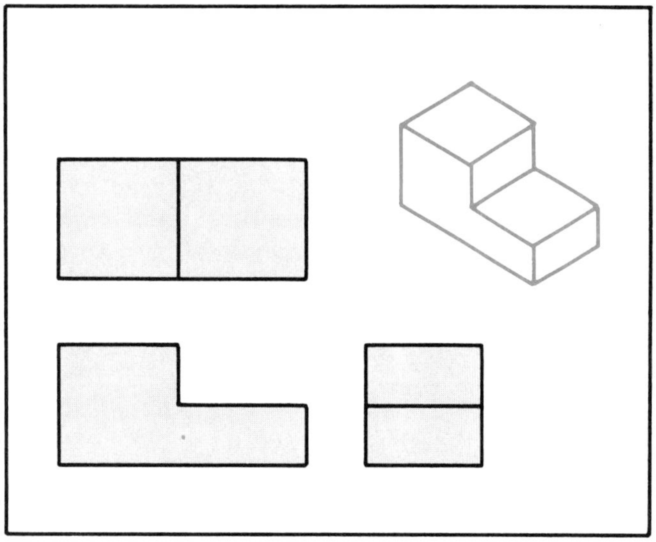

Fig. 5-1. Good dimensioning practice starts with selecting the view which best described an object.

Extension Lines

Extension lines move or "extend" the dimensions away from the object, Fig. 5-2. This avoids unnecessary clutter and improves clarity. Extension lines are sharp, black, and about half as wide as object lines.

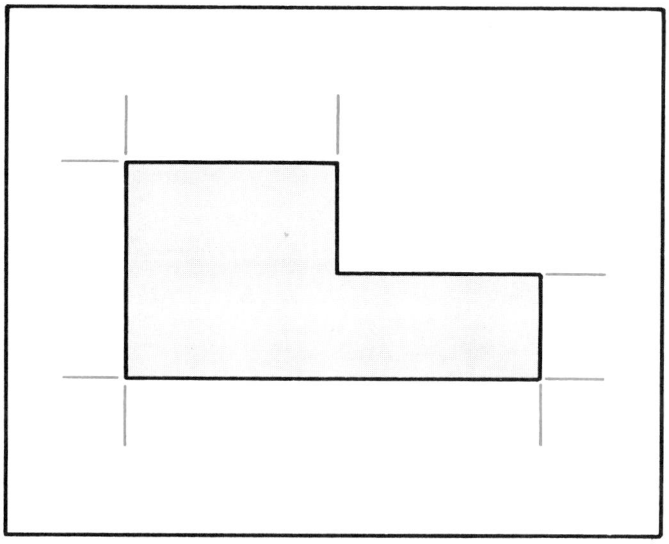

Fig. 5-2. Extension lines extend out from the object, but do not touch the object.

Use a 0.3 mm pencil or pen point to draw these lines. Extension lines start with a gap of .06 in., 1/16 in., or 1.6 mm from the object. They extend .12 in., 1/8 in. or 3.2 mm beyond the last dimension line. Refer to Fig. 5-2.

Dimension Lines

Dimension lines show the distance between the extension lines, Fig. 5-3. The first dimension line is commonly .40 in., 3/8 in., or 9.6 mm away from the object and parallel to the surface being dimensioned. Dimension lines are sharp, black, and made with a 0.3 mm pencil or pen point.

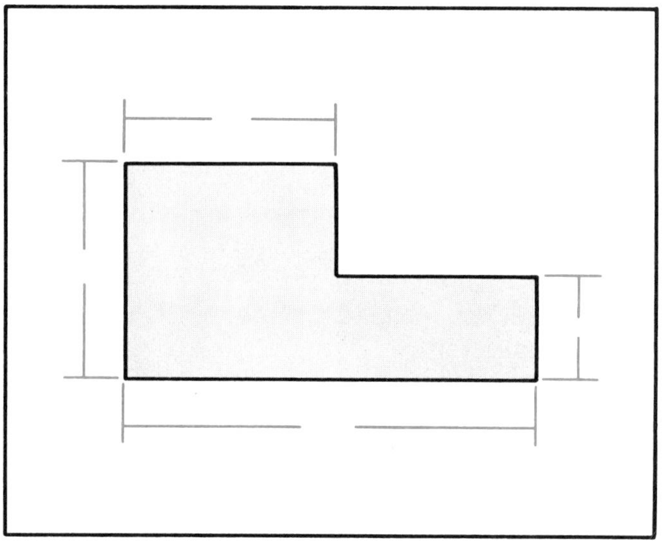

Fig. 5-3. When drawing dimension lines between extension lines, allow space for the dimension numbers.

Leave a space large enough for the numerals in the center of the dimension line to indicate the length of that surface. Numerals and arrowheads are added later.

Arrowheads

Arrowheads indicate the surfaces being dimensioned. They are placed on each end of a dimension line and point to the extension line, Fig. 5-4. Make arrowheads three times as long as they are wide. Your arrowheads should look neat and consistent. They are typically made as two slightly-curved lines left open on the tail end or filled in.

A common length is .12 in., 1/8 in., or 3.2 mm on small drawings.

Arrowheads are the last addition to the completed drawing. Place arrowheads on all dimension lines and leaders.

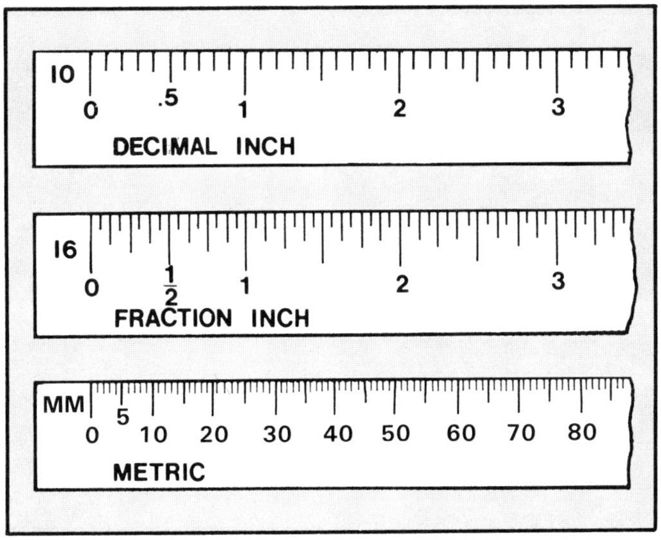

Fig. 5-5. Three common measuring systems used by the drafter.

Measuring Systems

Three common measuring systems used in dimensioning are the decimal-inch system, fraction-inch system, and the metric system, Fig. 5-5. The **decimal-inch system** utilizes inches and tenths of inches. The **fraction-inch system** utilizes inches and fractions of inches. The **metric system** utilizes millimeters and meters, Fig. 5-5.

The decimal-inch and metric systems are preferred in mechanical drawings. The fraction-inch system is used in architectural and structural drawings. The decimal-inch and metric systems are used for the remainder of the examples in this chapter.

Unidirectional and Aligned Dimensioning

Two approved systems of dimensioning drawings are unidirectional and aligned. In the **unidirectional system,** all letters and numerals are read from the bottom of the drawing, Fig. 5-6. In the **aligned system,** the letters and numerals are read from the right side or the bottom of the drawing and are positioned parallel to the surface being dimensioned, Fig. 5-7. They may also be inclined.

Unidirectional dimensioning is preferred because it is easier to letter and read. The unidirectional system is used for engineering or architectural drawings. The aligned system may be used for architectural drawings.

Space guidelines .12 in. or 1/8 in. apart for lettering notes and numerals. Neat, accurate, and con-

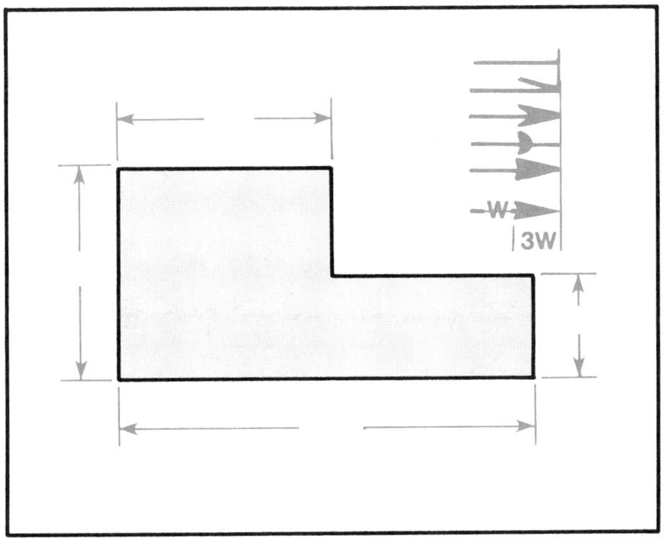

Fig. 5-4. Examples of arrowheads. The length of the arrowhead is three times its width.

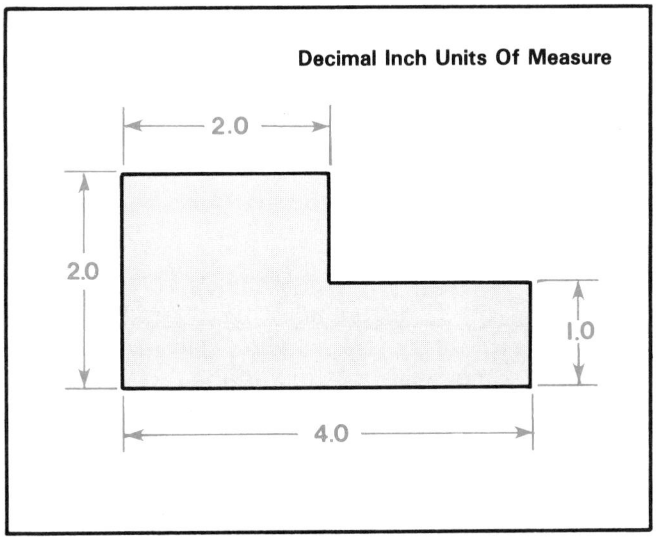

Fig. 5-6. Example of unidirectional dimensioning. The numbers are always on a horizontal plane.

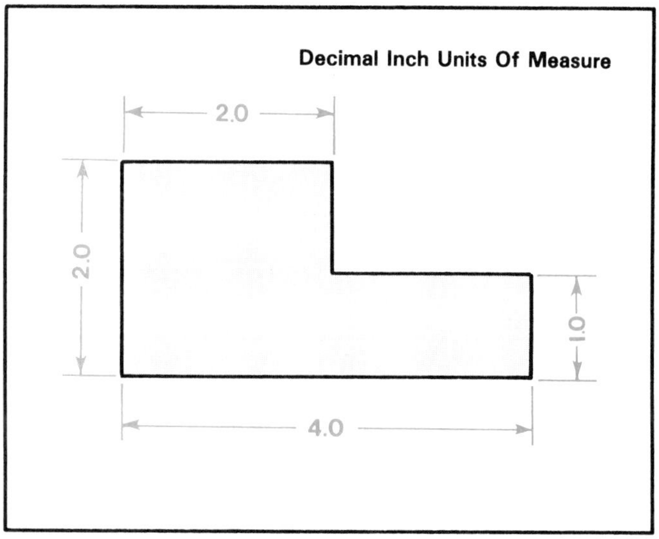

Fig. 5-7. Example of aligned dimensioning. Some numbers are on a horizontal plane while others are on a vertical plane.

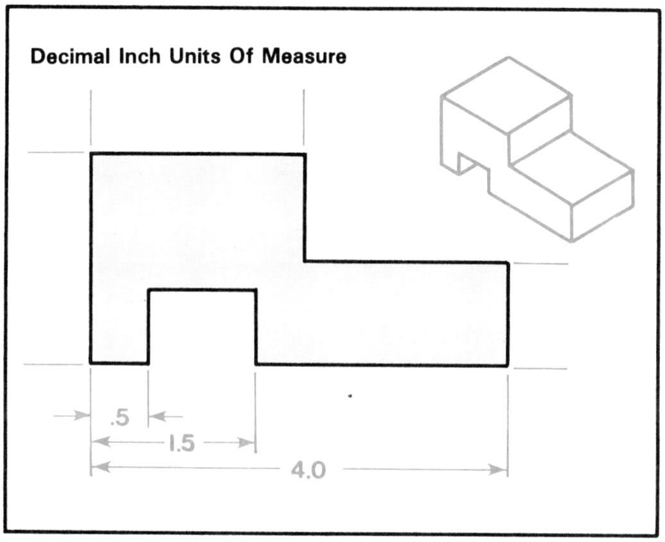

Fig. 5-8. When stacking dimensions, the shortest dimensions are located nearest the object.

sistent lettering make a drawing easy to read and look professional.

Review the Dimensional Drawing

Lettering is the last step in completing the drawing and provides a final touch to your work. As a final check of your drawing, analyze the dimensions to see if enough information has been supplied to make the part or product. There are various ways to dimension a surface and the best way is the one that looks the best and is easiest to understand.

DIMENSIONING COMPLEX SURFACES

Initially, extension and dimension lines are drawn lightly to keep drawings neat. This avoids the problem of erasing dark lines, if dimensions need to be relocated. Follow this layout sequence of using light lines until you have finished dimensioning. Finished lines are then either drawn in pencil or ink to attain maximum quality.

As objects become more complex, keep in mind the following concepts.

Stacking Dimensions

Consistent spacing and arrangement of dimension lines and extension lines add clarity and neatness. The first dimension line is .4 in., 3/8 in., 9.6 mm away from the object. Additional dimension lines stacked on the same extension lines are an additional .25 in., 1/4 in., 6.3 mm away from the object. The shortest distances are closest to the object. The largest distances are farthest away, Fig. 5-8.

This arrangement avoids confusion caused by crossing extension and dimension lines. Spacing may increase for larger drawings.

Chaining Dimensions

When several dimensions are **chained** (placed in a single line), it means the series of dimensions are related, Fig. 5-9. The least important dimension is usually omitted. This dimension may be found by the process of subtraction. By subtracting the chained dimensions from the overall size, the omitted dimension may be found. This indicates the area where an allowable error can exist. When chain dimensions are taken from one edge of the object, the chain dimensions relate to that common edge.

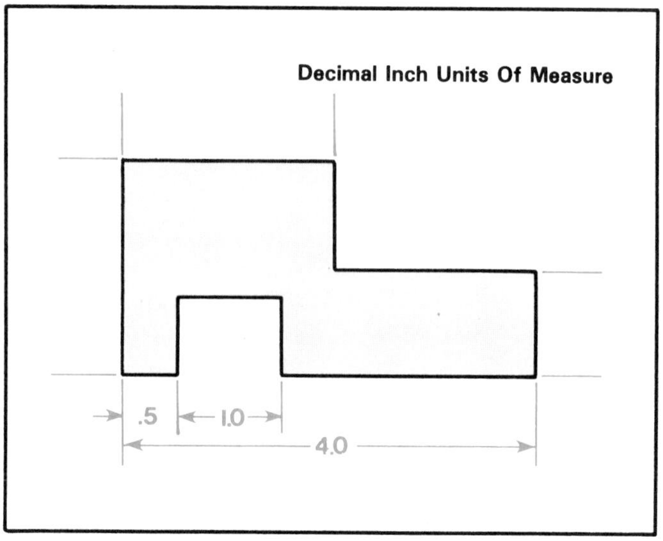

Fig. 5-9. Chaining dimensions indicates the dimensions are related. The missing dimensions may be found by either adding or subtracting from the chain dimensions.

Crossing Extension Lines

Avoid passing extension lines across the surface being dimensioned. Also, avoid extension lines that cross other extension lines. Both rules are sometimes violated, but only when necessary, Fig. 5-10.

When it is necessary for extension lines to cross, they do not touch the object at their origin. As they cross the object or other extension lines, they do so without a break in the lines.

Dimensioning an Angle

When dimensioning an angle, display the angle away from the object with the use of extension lines, Fig. 5-11. Draw an arc for the dimension line with an arrowhead at each end of the arc. A space is left near the center for the numerals and degree symbol. Horizontal and vertical distances are sometimes preferred to angular dimensioning, Fig. 5-11. This method is especially useful when distances are more critical than the angle itself.

DIMENSIONING CIRCULAR SHAPES

Many parts and products have circular shapes. The arcs and holes have specific sizes, locations, and, sometimes, thread specifications. Extension lines and dimension lines are usually used to dimension cylinders. Leaders are used to dimension holes. **Leaders** are dimension lines with an arrowhead and note. Leaders may locate circular shapes and give specific size information or other details.

Leaders

Leaders point toward or away from the center of the arc or circle they are describing, Fig. 5-12. An

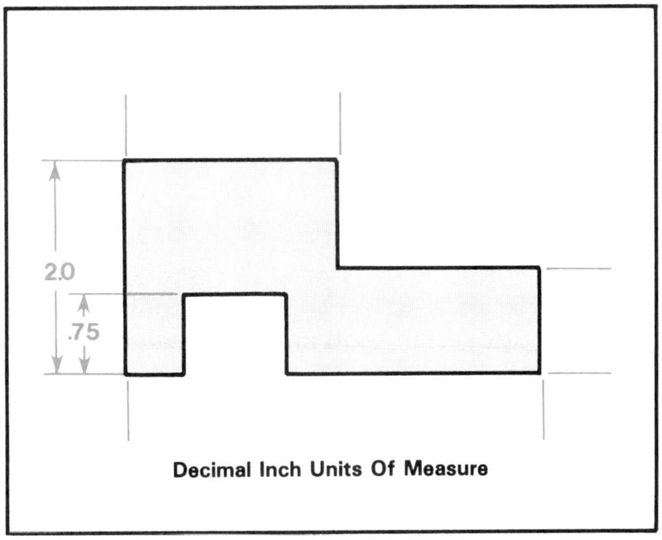

Fig. 5-10. For clarity, sometimes an extension line has to cross an object line. Sometimes, extension lines will have to cross one another.

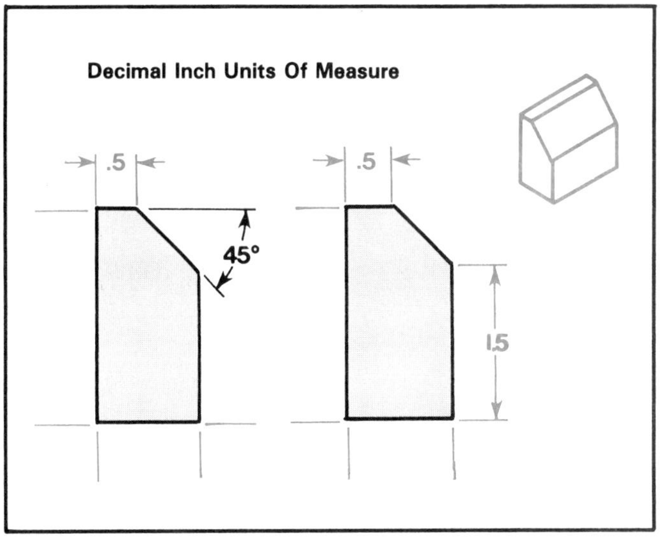

Fig. 5-11. Two methods used to dimension an object with an angle.

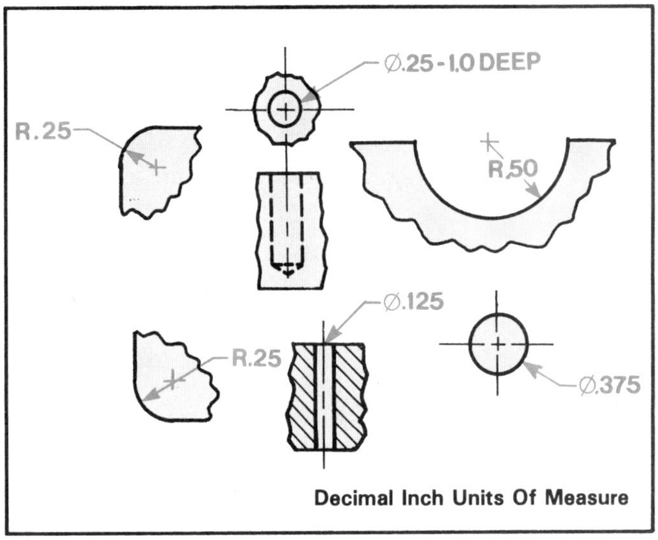

Fig. 5-12. Leaders used to dimension curved features of an object always aim at the center of the arc or circle.

arrowhead at the end of the leader touches the arc or circle. The horizontal tail of the leader is .25 in., 1/4 in., 6.3 mm long and is directed to the numerals or letters. It is midway between the guidelines for lettering the note.

Leaders are sharp and black with the same line width as extension and dimension lines. They are usually drawn at 30, 45, and 60 degree angles. Numerals are read from the bottom of the drawing.

Finishing Marks

A **finish mark** is a note and leader ending with a dot which may be used to describe a surface quality or condition, Fig. 5-13. An "∮" or "V" finish

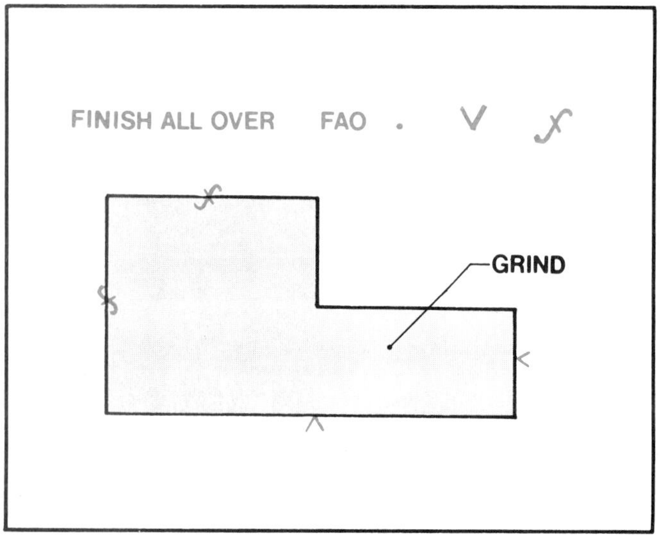

Fig. 5-13. Typical finish marks added to a drawing.

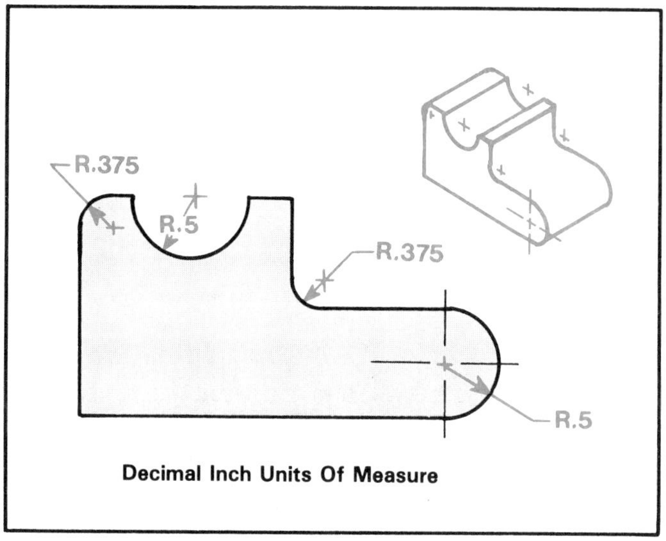

Fig. 5-14. Dimensioning arcs.

mark may be used on a line to designate a finished surface.

Surfaces may need to be filed, polished, sand blasted, or machined in a variety of ways to achieve the designated finish. The phrase "FINISH ALL OVER" or "FAO" is used on drawings for parts or products requiring that all surfaces be finished.

Dimensioning Arcs

Use a leader to dimension an arc as a radius, Fig. 5-14. Label the arc "R" followed by the size from the view where it appears as a curve on rectanglar-shaped objects. The arrowhead touches the arc and leader.

Notes may also appear in various locations on drawings. When the arcs are fillets and rounds, the note "ALL FILLETS AND ROUNDS 1/8 in." may be used instead of using leaders and notes for multiple features with repetitive dimensions.

Dimensioning Holes

Use a leader to dimension a hole as a diameter, Fig. 5-15. The leader always points to the center of the hole. Label the hole with θ (theta) followed by its size. A hole is dimensioned from the view where it appears as a circle. Refer to the isometric view in Fig. 5-15. It can also be dimensioned from the centerline where it appears as a pair of hidden lines.

When a series of holes are drilled symmetrically, one may be dimensioned with a leader followed by a note "DRILL 4 HOLES" or "X4" to save time.

Symbols are used to illustrate details such as depth, countersink, and counterbore, Fig. 5-16. Refer to the information in the illustration for propositions used to draw the symbols.

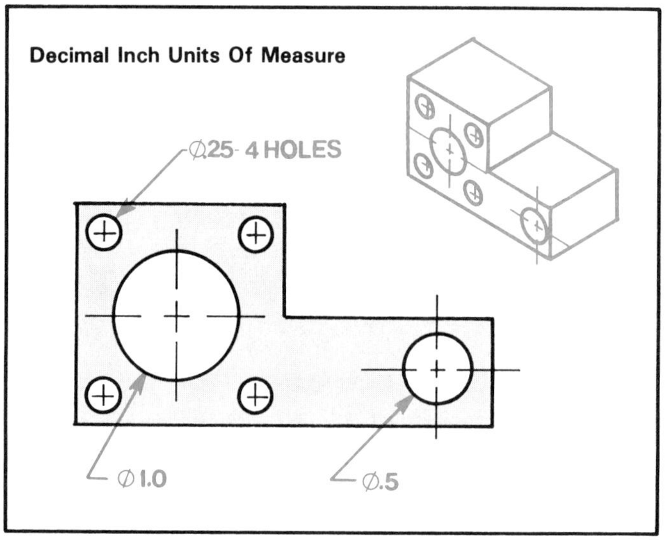

Fig. 5-15. Dimensioning holes using leaders and the ϕ symbol.

Locating Centers

Locate the center of holes and circular shapes by providing the distance from the centerline(s) to a reference point, Fig. 5-17. The edge of an object, finished surface, or another centerline are usually used as reference points.

When holes are drilled, the size specifications are provided on the tail of the leader. The location of the centerlines are shown with extension and dimension lines.

Dimensioning Cylinders

Dimension the overall size of cylindrical objects in the view where they appear as a rectangle, Fig.

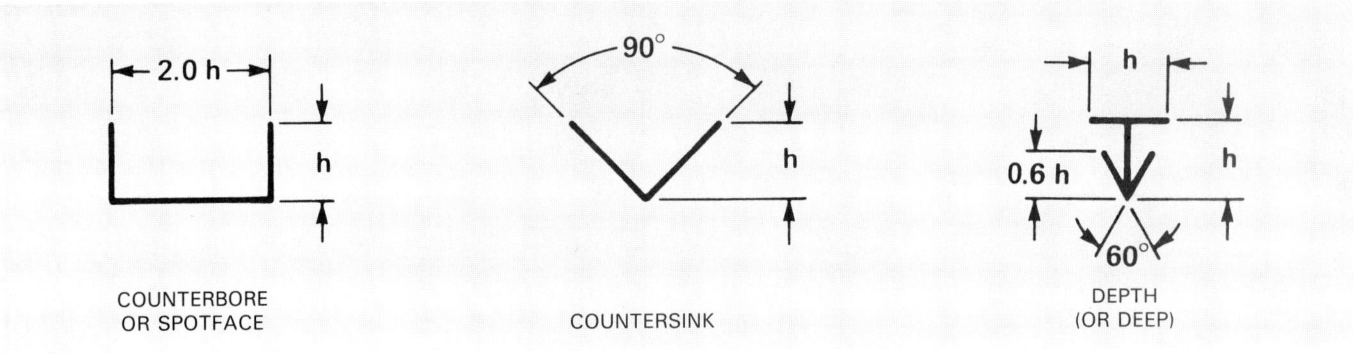

Fig. 5-16. Dimensioning symbols used for various features found on objects.

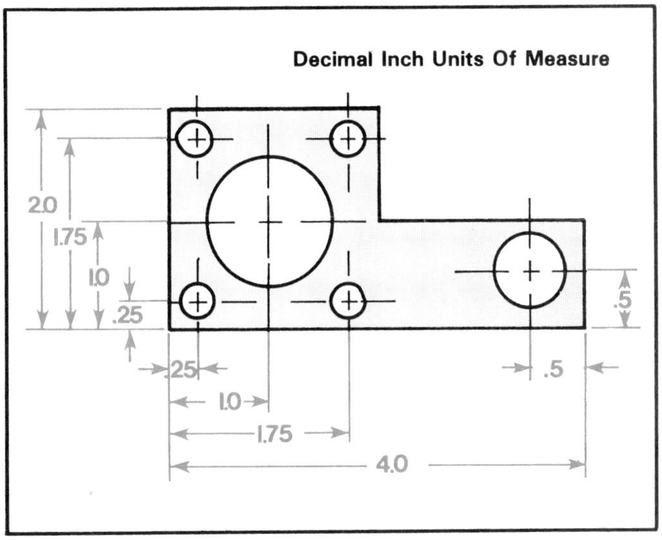

Fig. 5-17. Dimensioning used to locate the centers of holes and circular features.

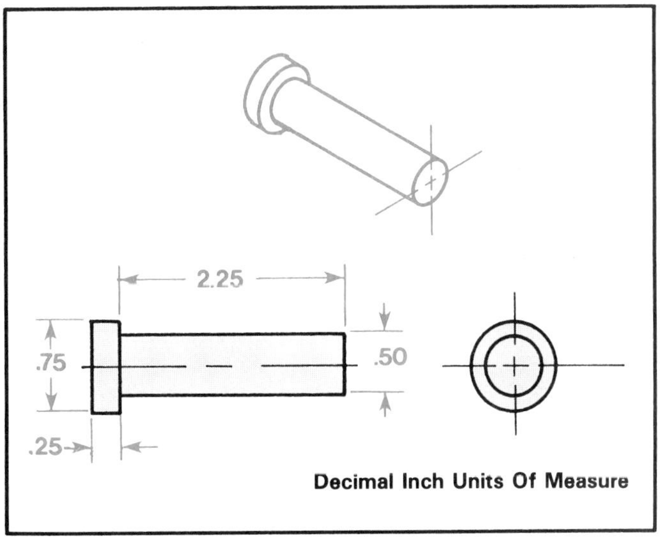

Fig. 5-18. Dimensioning cylindrical features.

5-18. It is easier to study one view which dimensions the length and diameter together. The pin in the illustration has two cylindrical shapes that are dimensioned in the rectangular view.

SPECIFYING TOLERANCES

Tolerance is the amount of deviation from the true size. This information should be specified on the drawing. Acceptable deviations allow the manufacturer or fabricator to use time and materials in the most efficient manner. The more accurate a product has to be, the more expensive it is to develop, machine, and produce.

Unilateral Tolerance

A tolerance provided on a drawing indicates the total amount of allowable error permitted. Tolerances are unilateral or bilateral.

If the designer, engineer, or builder allows error in only one direction, it is called **unilateral tolerance.** In the pin shown in Fig. 5-19, the pin length may be oversized as much as +.05 in. The pin diameter may be undersized as much as −.03 in. The pin length may not be undersize or less than 2.25 in. The pin diameter may not be larger than .50 in. Both of these are examples of unilateral tolerances.

Bilateral Tolerance

A **bilateral tolerance** is a size variation in a plus (+) or minus (−) direction, Fig. 5-20. The head of the pin may be any thickness between .35 and .19 in. The diameter of the pin head may be between .65 and .85 in. These are examples of bilateral tolerances. These size variations are common where parts do not mate and size variations are liberal. The smaller the tolerances for a part, the more expensive it is to manufacture, so the tolerances are often left as large as possible.

Limit Dimensions

When a pin is to pass unrestricted through a hole, use limit dimensions to describe the pin and hole

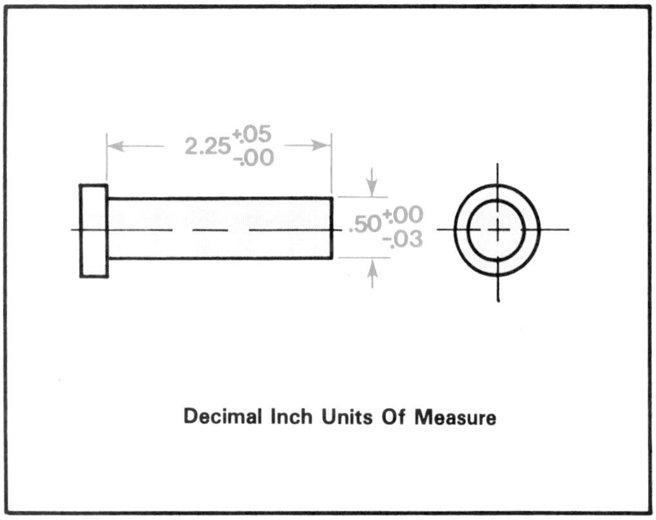

Fig. 5-19. Dimensioning of a unilateral tolerance permits variations in one direction only.

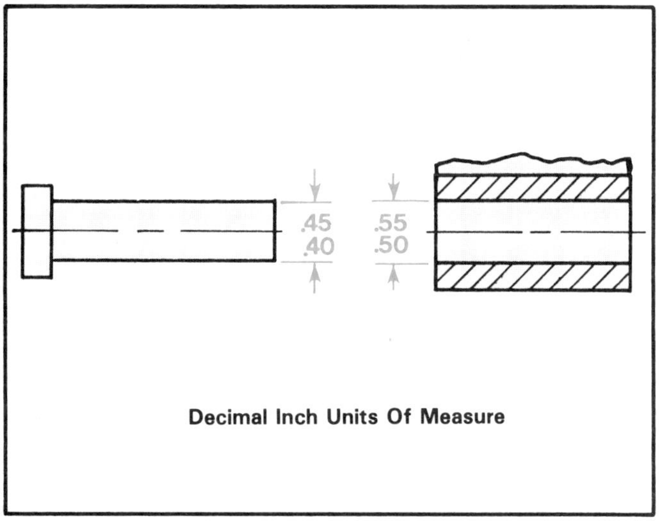

Fig. 5-21. Use of limit dimensions indicates the minimum and maximum sizes of various features.

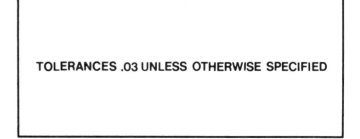

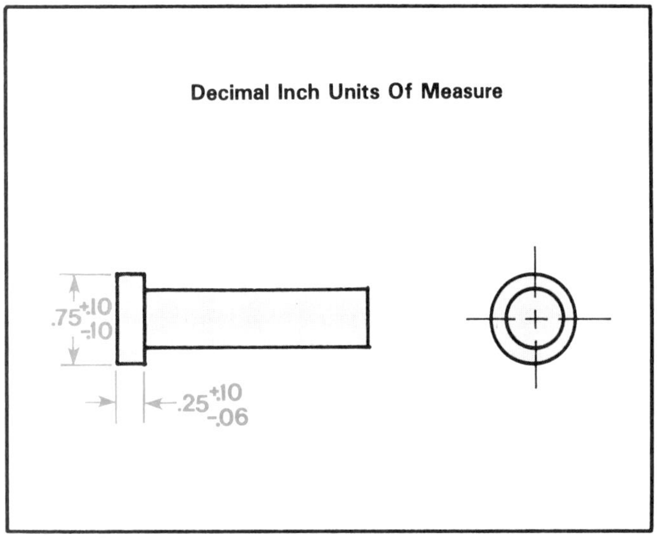

Fig. 5-20. Dimensioning a bilateral tolerance permits variations in two directions. This allows the object to be larger or smaller by the amount shown.

size variations, Fig. 5-21. The hole is to be drilled with a .50 in. twist drill and a plus +.05 in. tolerance is allowed for enlarging the hold diameter. The pin is turned in a lathe from a .75 in. diameter steel rod (to allow for the head) to a .45 in. diameter with a minus −.05 in. tolerance. Limit dimensions provide the machine operator with tolerance. The limit dimensions indicate the pin is to pass through the hole unrestrained due to the .05 in. difference between the two parts.

Tolerance Note

A single note may be used to describe all tolerances, Fig. 5-22. A company may also develop a standard tolerance statement in the title block. Thus, all components manufactured under this tolerance note contain the some degree of variation.

DIMENSIONING A MULTIVIEW DRAWING

You have learned the basic steps in conventional dimensioning. Review the examples of various procedures used in dimensioning. By combining these basic steps, dimensioning a multiview drawing of an object is now possible, Fig. 5-23.

Keep two objectives in mind. First, dimensions must provide a clear, easy-to-interpret description of the size of the object. Second, the finished drawing should look neat and uncluttered. Dimensioning an object requires practice to successfully satisfy both objectives.

Conventional dimensioning is used by a variety of people ranging from the hobbyist building a picnic table to the designers and engineers who are creating manufactured parts and products.

There are several choices available when locating and arranging dimensions on a drawing. You should

TOLERANCES .03 UNLESS OTHERWISE SPECIFIED

Fig. 5-22. Typical tolerance note added to drawings.

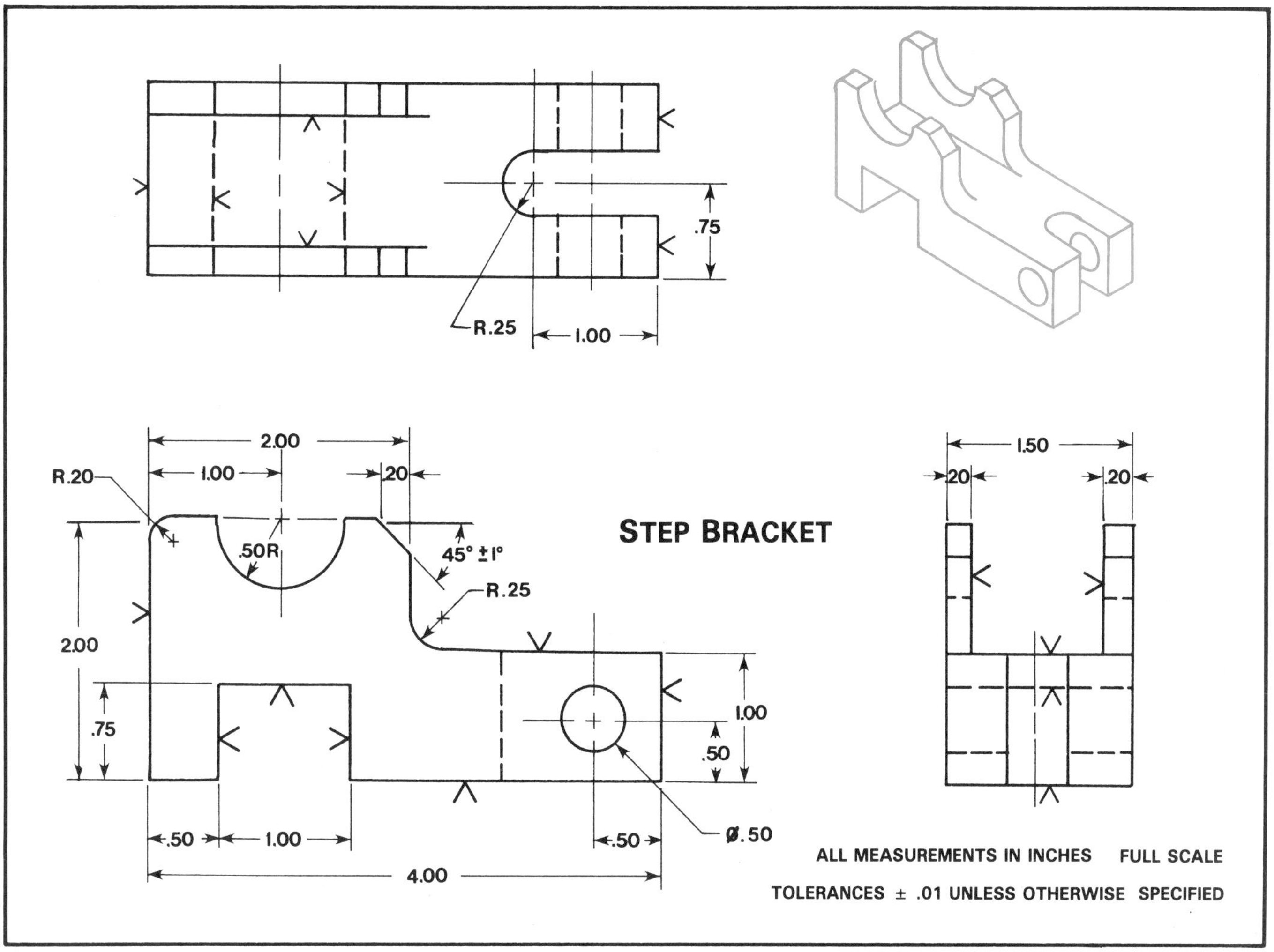

Fig. 5-23. Dimensioning a multiview drawing.

place the dimensions nearest the most descriptive shapes, and cluster the dimensions together in one area, whenever possible. Do not ''over dimension'' by duplicating unnecessary information.

INTRODUCING GEOMETRIC DIMENSIONING AND TOLERANCING

When many components or parts must fit closely together into a unit to perform a function, such as an engine or transmission, conventional dimensioning may not provide the necessary precision. Geometric dimensioning and tolerancing provides this precision. This type of dimensioning leads to a single interpretation of form, profile, orientation, and location. Form, profile, orientation, and location are new tolerance concepts you will learn about in this chapter. They relate to size, shape, and location of features in conventional dimensioning procedures. The units of measurement used in geometric dimensioning and tolerancing are the millimeter (mm) as established by ANSI (American National Standards Institute).

DATUMS

Datums are the reference surfaces or lines from which geometric characteristics and tolerances are measured. Letters are used to designate a specific datum. The datum is placed in a frame as shown in Fig. 5-24. In this illustration, the frames −A− locates the Datum A on the drawing which is the base of the object. Datum B is the right side of the object. Typically, the datums are read in order, with the primary datum being A, the secondary datum being B, and thirdly is C.

Basic Dimensions

A number inside a rectangle is a **basic** dimension which indicates the exact size or shape of a surface, Fig. 5-25. The basic dimension also locates features such as circles, arcs, notches, etc. Basic dimensions allow no room for error.

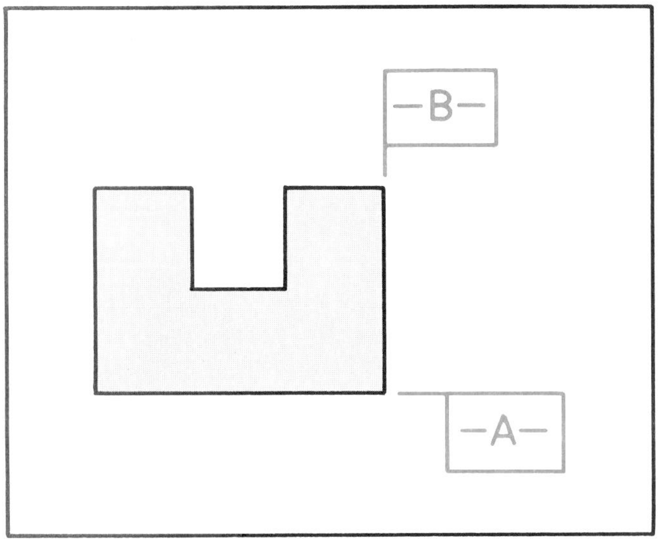

Fig. 5-24. Datums locate reference surfaces or lines.

CHARACTERISTICS SYMBOLS	
Form	
Flatness	⏥
Straightness	—
Circularity	○
Cylindricity	⌭
Profile	
Profile Of A Line	⌒
Profile Of A Surface	⌓
Orientation	
Angularity	∠
Perpendicularity	⊥
Parallelism	//
Location	
Position	⌖
Concentricity	◎

Fig. 5-26. Geometric characteristic symbols.

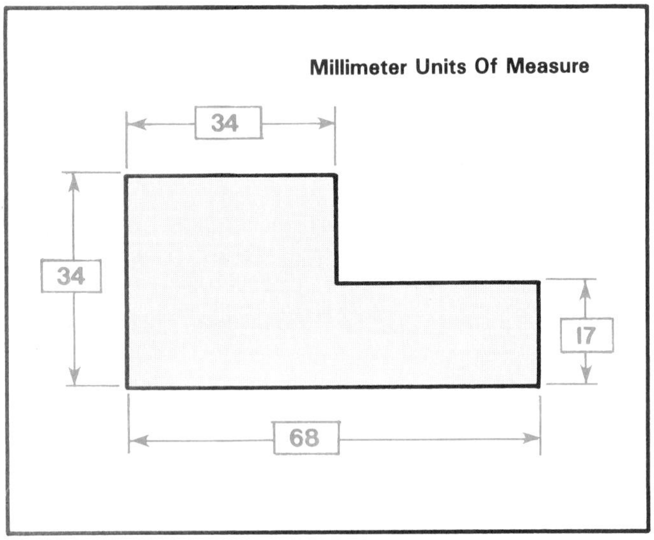

Fig. 5-25. Basic dimensions are placed inside boxes as shown. This basic dimension indicates there is no deviation allowed from the specific dimension.

The rectangular frame surrounding a basic dimension is a minimum of 8 mm high and 16 mm wide. The symbols and numerals inside each rectangle are 4 mm high.

Characteristics and Symbols

Conventional dimensioning practices used in Figs. 5-1 through 5-23 adequately describe the sizes and shapes of most objects.

The characteristics and symbols of geometric dimensioning, shown in Fig. 5-26, provide additional precisioin compared to conventional dimensioning. Study the form, profile, orientation, and location characteristics of the following illustrations. Relate them to the geometric symbols.

FORM TOLERANCE

Flatness, straightness, cylindricity, and circularity are the form tolerance characteristics you will be using. These form characteristics focus upon the shape of material to ensure proper fit of mating parts.

The step bracket shown in Fig. 5-23 and the pin shown in Fig. 5-18 will be used to introduce these concepts. The shaded areas on the figures represent the limit surfaces. Crosshatched areas represent an enlarged tolerance zone.

Flatness

Flatness is exactly what the term implies, Fig. 5-27. To be functional, the bottom of the step bracket must be flat when it rests on a smooth, level surface.

Perfect flatness causes the bottom of the step bracket to have total contact with the surface it rests upon. The tolerance zone shown as the crosshatch area in Fig. 5-27 indicates the acceptable deviation from perfect flatness.

Straightness

Straightness is the feature illustrated in Fig. 5-28 and is applied in many situations. A pin and bracket are used as examples of straightness, roundness, and cylindricity. The pin must fit freely through the two holes in the bracket. A straightness tolerance is needed for establishing an acceptable variation for the pin.

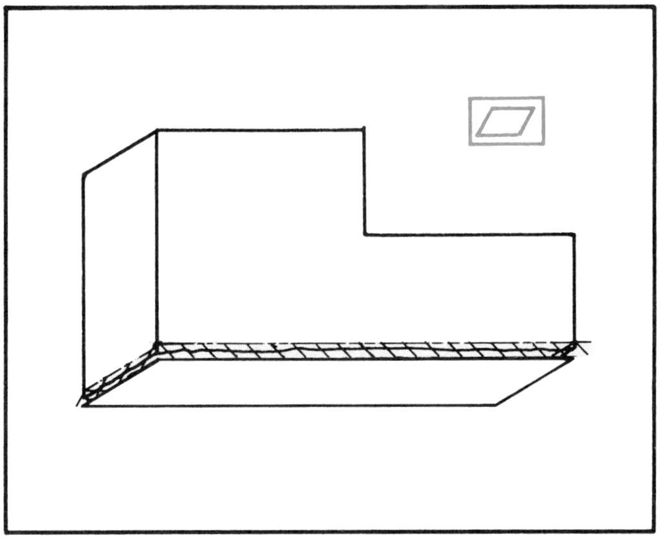

Fig. 5-27. Geometric flatness symbol applied to the bottom of the object.

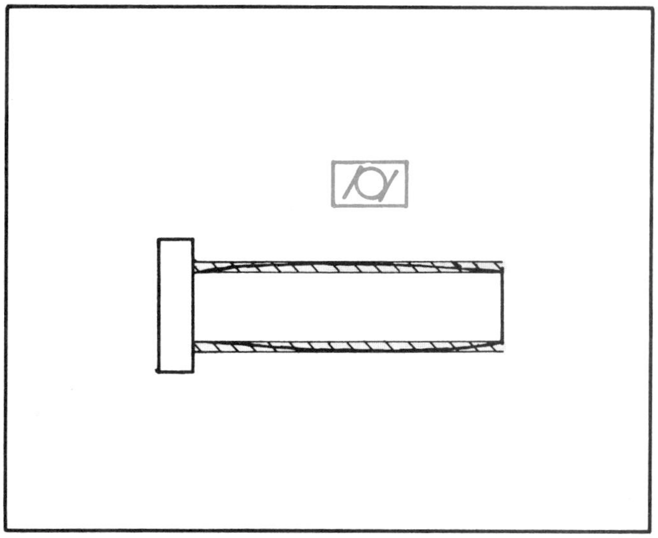

Fig. 5-29. Geometric cylindricity symbol applied to the shaft of a pin.

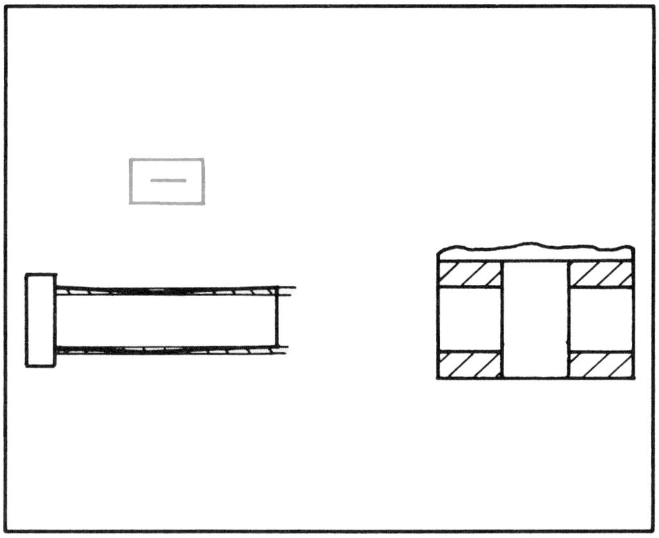

Fig. 5-28. Geometric straightness symbol applied to the shaft of a pin.

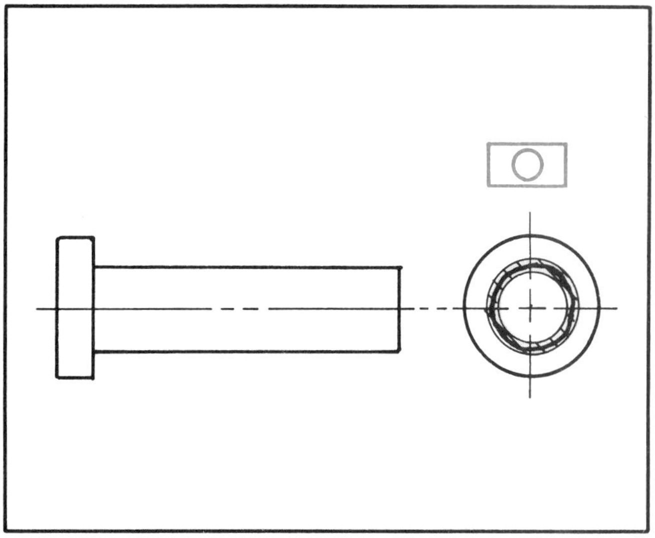

Fig. 5-30. Geometric circularity symbol applied to the shaft of a pin.

Cylindricity

The diameter of the cylinder is controlled throughout its entire length by **cylindricity,** Fig. 5-29. The amount of concave or convex variations are specified with a tolerance zone for cylindricity.

Circularity

The pin also needs to be perfectly round to fit through the drilled holes as indicated by the **circularity** feature, Fig. 5-30. The form characteristics of straightness, cylindricity, and circularity are specified with tolerances to control accuracy. The error zones indicate the amount of deviation in shape (crooked, bulged, or oblonged) the pin may have without being lodged in the hole of the bracket.

PROFILE TOLERANCE

Profile of a line and profile of a surface are two profile tolerance characteristics. The profile or shape of a curved line and the profile or shape of a curved surface may have tolerance zones established to control for their accuracy.

Profile of a Line

The curved line on the upper left corner of the object drawn in Fig. 5-31 is an important shape.

Therefore, a tolerance is supplied to specify the allowable error in its curved shape.

A free-form shape, such as is found down the center of an automobile hood is another example. An acceptable tolerance zone ensures smooth alignment of the chrome trim with the centerline of the hood.

Profile of a Surface

Behind the curved line of the object in Fig. 5-31, is a curved surface. It must be consistent from one side of the part to the other. An acceptable tolerance zone for the surface is produced by specifying a form tolerance, Fig. 5-32. For example, a profile of a surface tolerance may be used to control the shape of an extruded aluminum running board for a van. A close tolerance ensures the contour shape is consistent throughout its length.

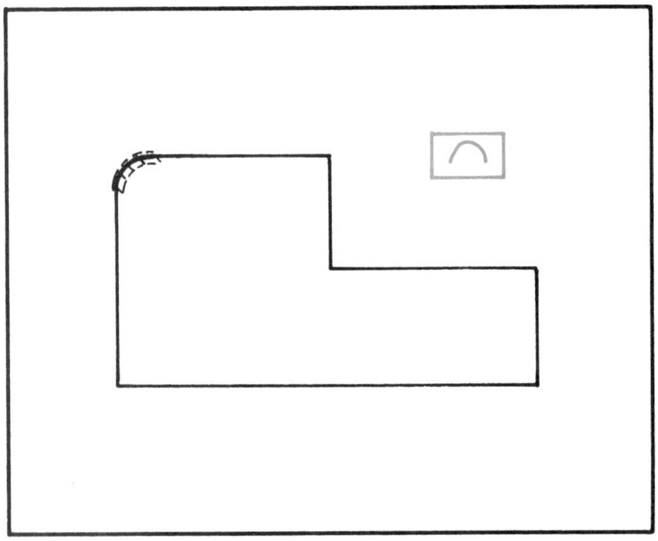

Fig. 5-31. Geometric profile of a line symbol applied to the curved shape.

ORIENTATION TOLERANCE

Perpendicularity, parallelism, and angularity are orientation tolerance characteristics you will be using. These characteristics could, for example, relate to the degree of squareness of a part, parallel relationship between its side, and accuracy of a given angle.

Perpendicularity

The back and bottom of the bracket are checked for squareness (perpendicular to each other). Designers and engineers identify perpendicular surfaces that must be consistent and precise. Refer to Fig. 5-33.

Tolerance zones establish the degree of flatness and/or perpendicularity necessary for a part or product to function properly.

Parallelism

The bottom surface of the step bracket should be parallel to the first step of the bracket, Fig. 5-34. The parallel relationship between these two surfaces needs a numerical tolerance value in order to control the amount of allowable parallelism.

Angularity

The 45 degree angle of the bracket must be cut accurately so it fits a mating part. An angularity tolerance determines the acceptable error zone, Fig. 5-35. As with parallelism and perpendicularity, the entire plane must be accurate.

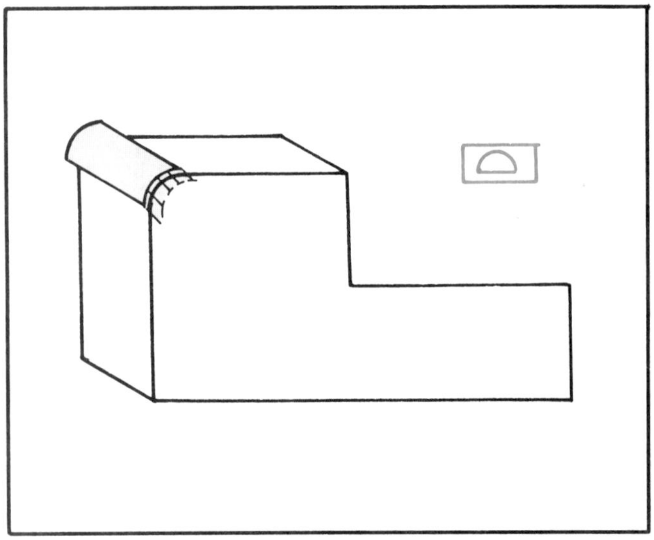

Fig. 5-32. Geometric profile of a surface symbol applied to an object.

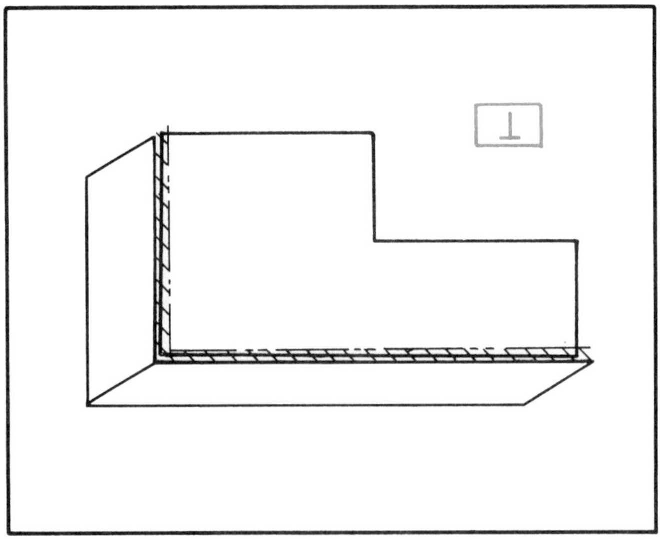

Fig. 5-33. Geometric perpendicularity symbol applied to two surfaces perpendicular to each other.

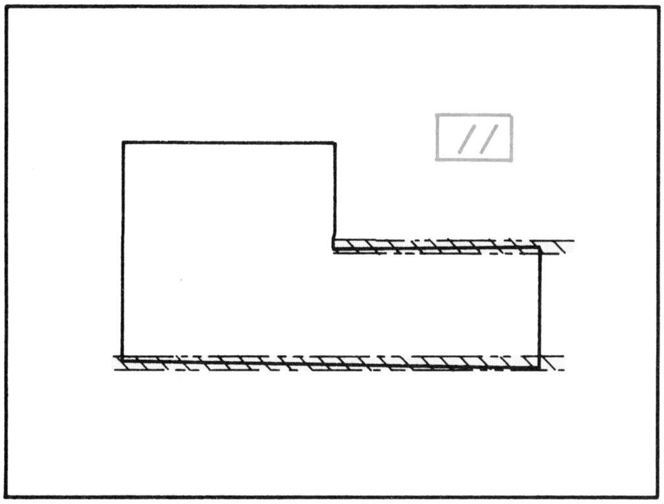

Fig. 5-34. Geometric parallel symbol applied to an object to indicate surfaces which are parallel to each other.

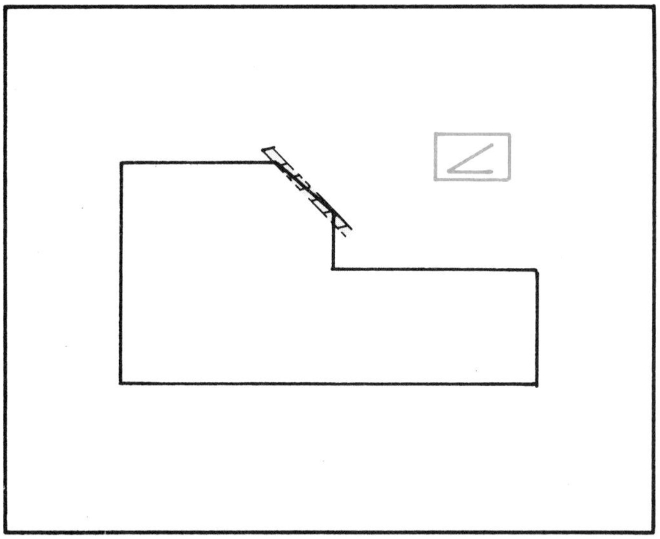

Fig. 5-35. Geometric angularity symbol applied to indicate an edge must be within the limits of a specific angle.

LOCATION TOLERANCES

Position and concentricity are location tolerance characteristics. As the name implies, **location** relates to the proper position of centerlines. When material is removed, such as in drilling or milling, and when circular shapes are arranged together, the location of their centerlines is important. A location tolerance specifies the degree of accuracy required.

Position

Sometimes position is referred to as "true position," which locates the center for features including holes and arcs. In Fig. 5-36, the true position for the center of the hole is 9 mm up from

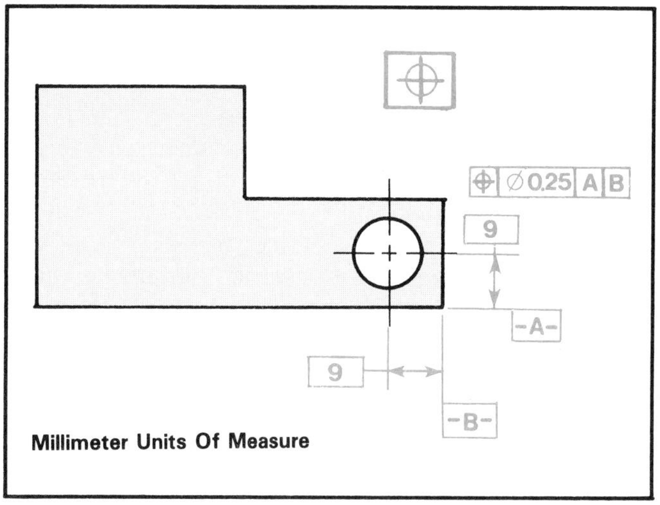

Fig. 5-36. Geometric position symbol applied to a hole. Note the sequence of the information presented on this drawing.

The chain of symbols explains the allowable true position with reference to Datums —A— and —B—. The chain of symbols illustrate the hole is to be drilled within a 0.25 mm tolerance zone from the basic dimension.

Concentricity

The relationship of the pin head to the pin shaft illustrates the concept of concentricity, Fig. 5-37. The closer the pin head is centered on the shaft, the smaller the concentricity tolerance zone. In this example, the concentricity of the pin with reference to Datum —A—, must be within a 0.10 mm tolerance zone.

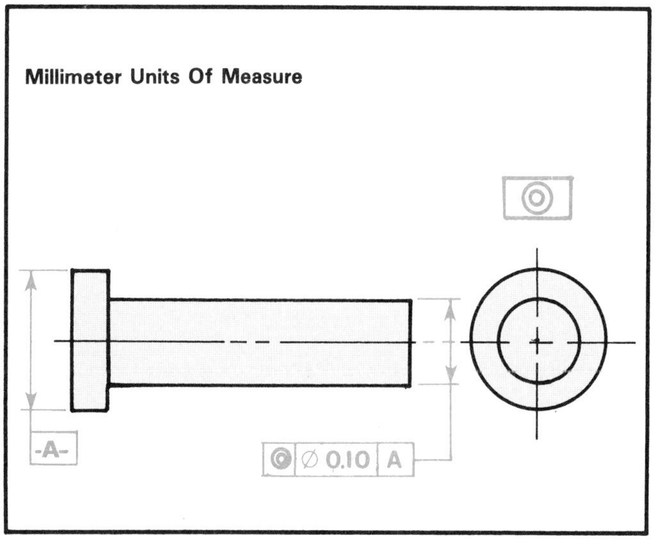

Fig. 5-37. Geometric concentricity symbol applied to a pin indicating the cylinder of the pin is concentric with the head of the pin.

ADDITIONAL GEOMETRIC DIMENSIONING AND TOLERANCING CONCEPTS

Sequence of Control Symbols

When using geometric dimensions and tolerancing on a drawing, to communicate clearly and according to convention, the symbols must be present in the proper order. Refer to the examples in Fig. 5-38 for typical geometric dimensioning and tolerancing symbols.

The sequence of control symbols is the geometric symbol, an assigned tolerance and a datum reference. In this example, the symbols for flatness, perpendicularity, and parallelism, are followed by a tolerance value in the chain of rectangular frames. This describes the precise relationship of these other surfaces to Datum A. The base of the object is within 0.03 mm of perfect flatness. The first step is within 0.1 mm of being parallel to the base. The left side is within 0.2 mm of perpendicular to the base, or Datum −A−.

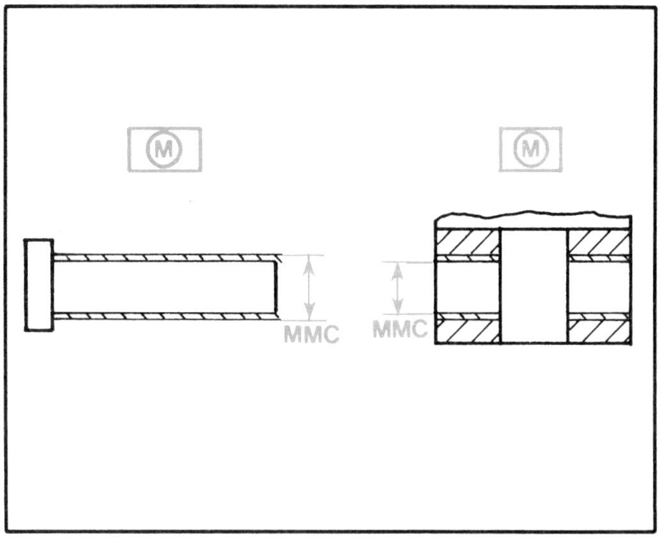

Fig. 5-39. Drawing indicating Maximum Material Condition (MMC) for the cylinder of the pin and the hole.

Maximum Material Condition

A common modifier used in geometric dimensioning and tolerancing is the phrase maximum material condition (MMC). It is especially useful when describing the tightness of fit between mating parts. **Maximum material condition** means that a certain feature of an object contains the maximum amount of material, Fig. 5-39. When a MMC is specified for a pin, reference is made to its largest diameter. When MMC is specified for a hole drilled in a part, it refers to its smallest diameter hole. Note the symbol M in a circle for MMC. A similar condition exists for **least material condition,** LMC, with the symbol L in a circle.

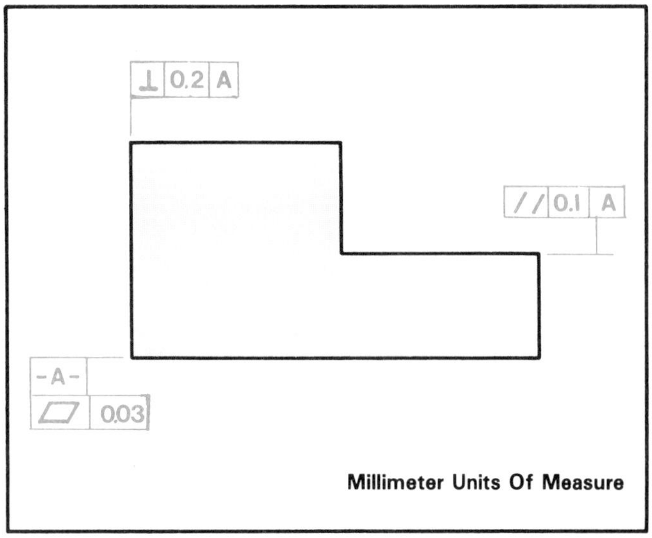

Fig. 5-38. Read these geometric symbols in the following sequence of information. Datum A, the base, is flat within a tolerance of 0.03.The side is perpendicular within a tolerance of 0.2 relative to the base or Datum A. The upper surface is parallel within a tolerance of 0.1 relative to the base or Datum.

PLACEMENT OF GEOMETRIC DIMENSIONING AND TOLERANCING

There is a similarity between conventional dimensioning shown in Fig. 5-23 and geometric dimensioning and tolerancing shown in Fig. 5-40. The main difference is the additional degree of precision specified by the characteristic symbols.

ADDITIONAL EXPLANATION

The step bracket and pin illustrated in Fig. 5-40 demonstrate where geometric symbols and values may be placed. The following discussion provides additional information about these items.

The bottom surface, Datum A, has a flatness tolerance of 0.02 mm. Its basic dimension is 100 mm in length. A notch is removed with limit dimensions of 28.6 to 29.0 mm. The left side, Datum B, has a perpendicularity tolerance of 0.13 mm with Datum A. The basic dimension is 50 mm in height. The basic dimension of 17 mm is the notch height.

The top of the step, Datum C, has four conventional dimensions describing its shape. These include: 4 mm radius or round; 15 mm radius or semi-circle; the 45 degree angle or chamfer, and 6 mm radius or fillet. The distance across Datum C is controlled by the 51.8 to 52.3 mm limit dimension. The basic dimensions of 27 mm and 7 mm locate the vertical centerline and depth of the chamfer. The accuracy of the angular surface is specified by the 0.10 mm angularity tolerance.

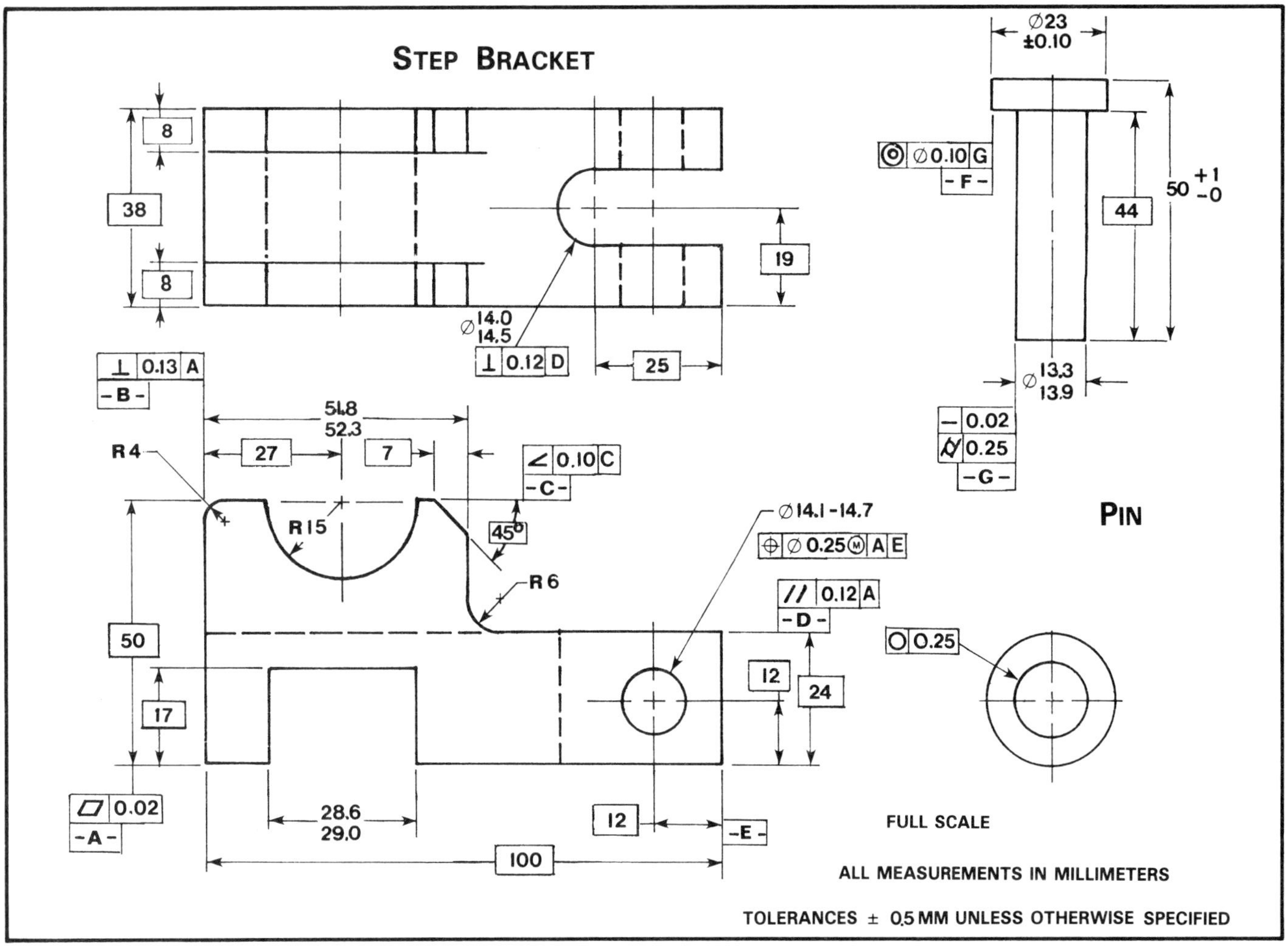

Fig. 5-40. Geometric tolerancing and dimensioning symbols placed on multiview drawing of step bracket and pin. This is typical of drawings used in industry.

The hole drilled on the right end of the step bracket has diameter limit dimensions of 14.1 to 14.7 mm. The location of the center point for drilling the hole is 12 mm from Datum A and E, the right side. A location tolerance of 0.25 mm at the maximum material condition is illustrated in the feature control frame.

The horizontal middle surface, Datum D, has a parallelism tolerance of 0.12 mm with Datum A.

On the left side of the top view, the basic dimensions indicate the thickness of the step bracket sides as 8 mm. The basic dimensions on the right side locate the center of the milled hole and slot. The hole and slot have a perpendicularity tolerance of 0.12 mm with Datum D.

The head of the pin has a diameter of 23 mm with a bilateral tolerance of + or − 0.10 mm. The shaft has limit dimensions of 13.3 to 13.9 mm. The length of the shaft is a basic dimension of 44 mm. The total length of the pin is 50 mm with a unilateral tolerance of + 1 mm. The head diameter, Datum F, has a concentricity tolerance of 0.10 mm with the shaft diameter, Datum G. The shaft diameter also has three other geometric tolerance features: straightness of 0.02 mm, cylindricity at 0.25 mm, and circularity of 0.25 mm.

SUMMARY

The examples given provided in this chapter are the building blocks used to dimension parts and products. Use these figures and descriptions as references when you practice your drafting skills. Also, practice dimensioning parts and products that you create and develop.

Conventional dimensioning is appropriate for initial designs and is adequate for most products that are developed. In comparison, geometric tolerancing and dimensioning may become necessary when a product requires a high degree of precision that cannot be assumed. This precision is evident in manufactured parts that are interchangeable. Examples include appliances, automobiles, aircraft, and thousands of other additional parts and products in industry.

As you dimension your drawings, use the criteria below to evaluate your work.

1. Consistent line width of object lines extension, dimension, and centerlines.
2. Use of guidelines, accurate lettering, and accurate arrowheads.
3. Appropriate placement of dimensions.
4. Overall neat appearance.
5. Provide the necessary information.

Chapter 5—DIMENSIONING

Review What You Have Learned

Write your answers on a separate sheet of paper. Do not write in this textbook.

Essay:

1. Explain in a short paragraph the fundamentals of dimensioning.
2. Write a step by step description of how to dimension a part of product. (You may want to include a numbered list of steps.)

Multiple Choice: Carefully read the statements below and write the letter of the best answer for each of the items on your answer sheet.

3. A common length for arrowheads on a small drawing would be:
   a. 1/16 in.
   b. 1/8 in.
   c. 3/16 in.
   d. 1/4 in.
   e. 5/16 in.
4. The final step in dimensioning a product is to add:
   a. Extension lines.
   b. Dimension lines.
   c. Leaders.
   d. Lettering.
   e. Guidelines.
5. Dimension lines for a angular feature are:
   a. Horizontal.
   b. Vertical.
   c. Angular.
   d. Circular.
   e. Parallel.
6. A line with an arrowhead on each end is called:
   a. Dimension line.
   b. Extension line.
   c. Leader.
   d. Guideline.
   e. Centerline.
7. Numerals used to dimension parts are usually how tall?
   a. 1/16 in.
   b. 1/8 in.
   c. 1/4 in.
   d. 3/8 in.
   e. 1/2 in.
8. Which of the following dimensions is consistent with the current ANSI standards?
   a. R2.
   b. Dia 1.
   c. 2R.
   d. D1.
   e. 1 Dia.
9. The limit dimensions for a 1 in. shaft with a bilateral tolerance of .01 are:
   a. 1.00 - 1.01.
   b. .99 - 1.09.
   c. .99 - 1.01.
   d. .09 - 1.00.
   e. .09 - 1.01.
10. The limit dimensions for a 1 in. hole with a unilateral tolerance of +.05 are:
    a. 1.00 - 1.10.
    b. 1.00 - 1.05.
    c. .95 - 1.05.
    d. .95 - 1.00.
    e. .90 - 1.00.
11. Tolerance may be specified as:
    a. Limit dimensions.
    b. Bilateral tolerances.
    c. Unilateral tolerances.
    d. Within a general tolerance.
    e. All of these.
12. The phrase "Maximum Material Condition" refers to the:
    a. Largest diameter size.
    b. Smallest hole size.
    c. M.
    d. A and b only.
    e. All of these.

True or False: Carefully read the statements below. Write a "T" on your answer sheet for the statements which are true. For the statements which are false, write an "F." Rewrite each false statement so it becomes true.

13. The language of industry utilizes a technical vocabulary in paragraph form to explain the sizes and shapes of products. True or False?
14. Tolerance is determined by the function of the product. True or False?
15. Extension lines touch object lines. True or False?
16. Extension lines have an arrowhead on each end. True or False?
17. Dimension lines are very light lines. True or False?
18. Dimension lines have a space left in their midsection for a numeral. True or False?
19. All numbers are read from the bottom of the page in aligned dimensioning. True or False?
20. Chained dimensioning occurs when several dimensions appear in a single line. True or False?

21. Extension and dimension lines are used to locate the center of a circle. True or False?
22. The larger the tolerance the more it costs to produce the product. True or False?
23. A tolerance note may read: "tolerances .05 in. unless otherwise specified." True or False?
24. A basic dimension indicates the exact size and shape of a surface. True or False?

Completion: After studying this chapter, read the incomplete sentences below. Write the missing word or words on your separate answer sheet.

25. An arrowhead is ________ times as long as it is wide.
26. Extension lines begin about ________ in. from object lines.
27. Extension lines extend ________ in. beyond the last dimension line.
28. The first dimension line is at least ________ in. away from the object.
29. The ________ measuring system is used for architectural and the structural drawings.
30. The ________ or ________ measuring system is used in mechanical and engineering drawings.
31. Dimensioning must supply enough ________ to make a part and make the drawing look ________.
32. When stacking dimensions, the ________ dimension is farthest away from the object.
33. A circular shape must have its ________ located and its ________ dimensioned.
34. When dimensioning a radius, the tail of the leader is at the ________ and the arrowhead touches the ________ of the arc.
35. When dimensioning a hole, the arrowhead of the leader touches the ________ of the circle and points toward the ________ of the circle.
36. When the tolerance of a part may be only oversized or only undersized it has a ________ tolerance.
37. When tolerance may be over or undersized, it has ________ tolerance.
38. ________ ________ and ________ is a dimensioning system that is more precise and detailed than conventional dimensioning.
39. When a box is drawn around a dimension, it is a ________ dimension.

Matching: In the three groups below, start with the numbered item in column A and list the appropriate response from column B. The three groups cover the topics of line widths, form tolerance, and orientation tolerance.

Match the line types in column A with the appropriate line widths in column B.

Column A	Column B
40. Extension lines.	a. 0.3 mm.
41. Dimension lines.	b. 0.5 mm.
42. Leaders.	c. 0.8 mm.
43. Object lines.	d. 1.0 mm.

Match the words that describe form tolerance in column A with the form tolerance symbols in column B.

Column A	Column B
44. Flatness.	a. —
45. Straightness.	b. ⌒
46. Roundness/Circularity.	c. ○
47. Cylindricity.	d. ⌭
	e. ▱

Match the words that describe orientation tolerance in column A with the orientation tolerance in column B.

Column A	Column B
48. Angularity.	a. ⌓
49. Parallelism.	b. ∠
50. Perpendicularity.	c. //
	d. ∟
	e. ⊥

Practice What You Have Learned: Pick up the drawings you completed in the section Practice What You Have Learned in Chapter 3 on Instrument Drawing or Chapter 4 on Projecting Images. Add dimensions to these drawings.

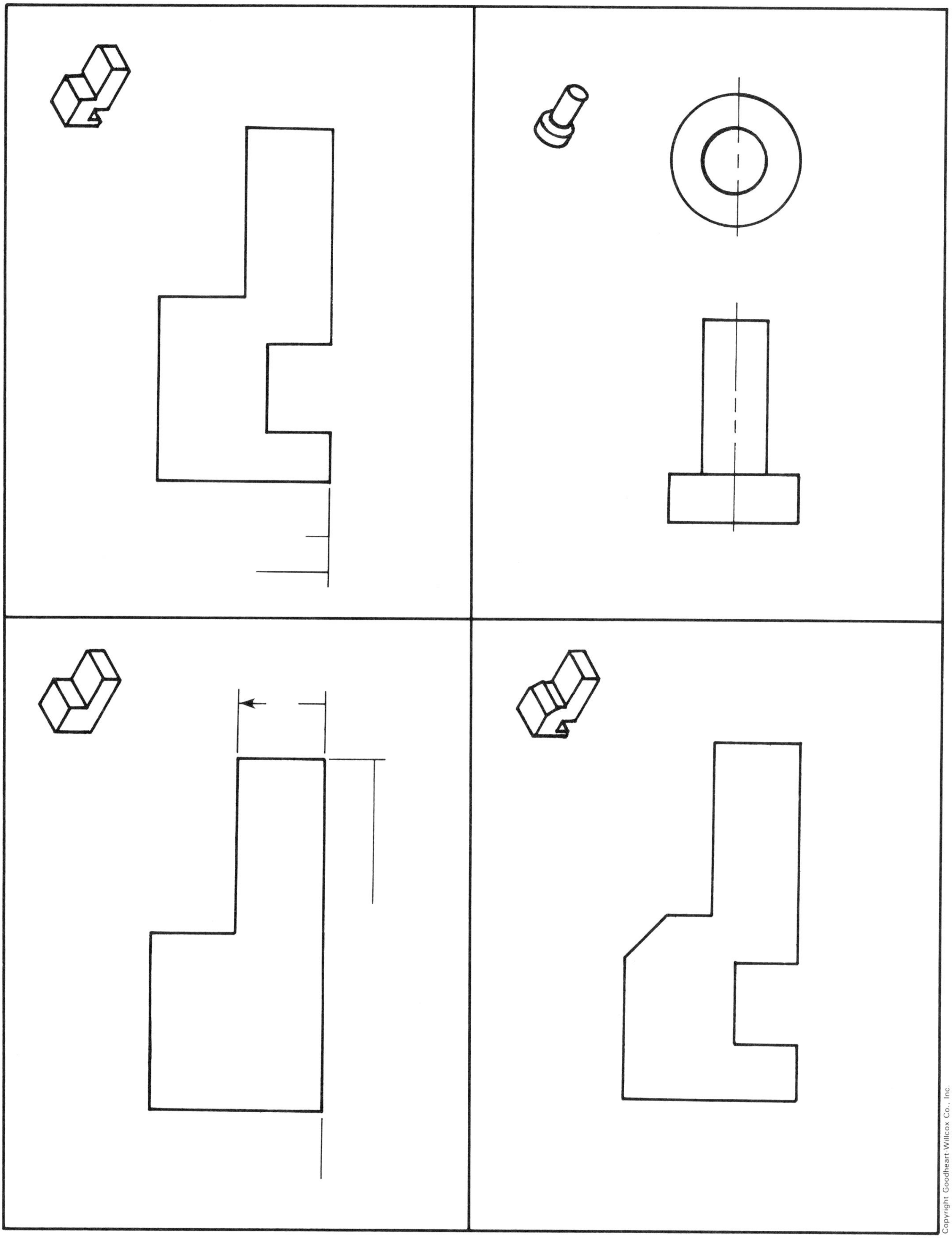

5-1 DIMENSIONING RECTANGLES AND CIRCLES. Draw all lthe extension lines, dimension lines, leaders, and arrowheads needed to completely dimension the objects.

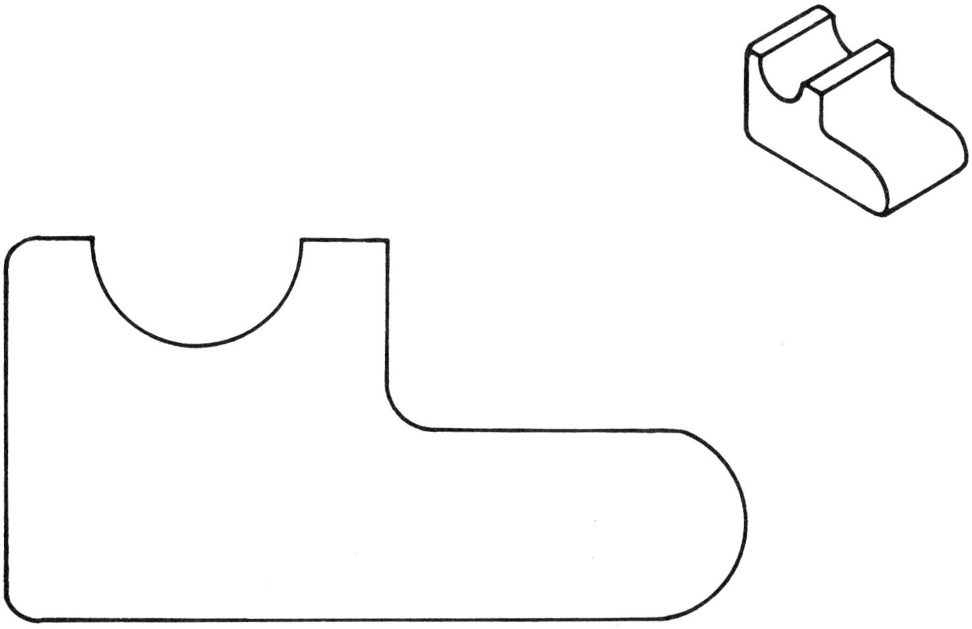

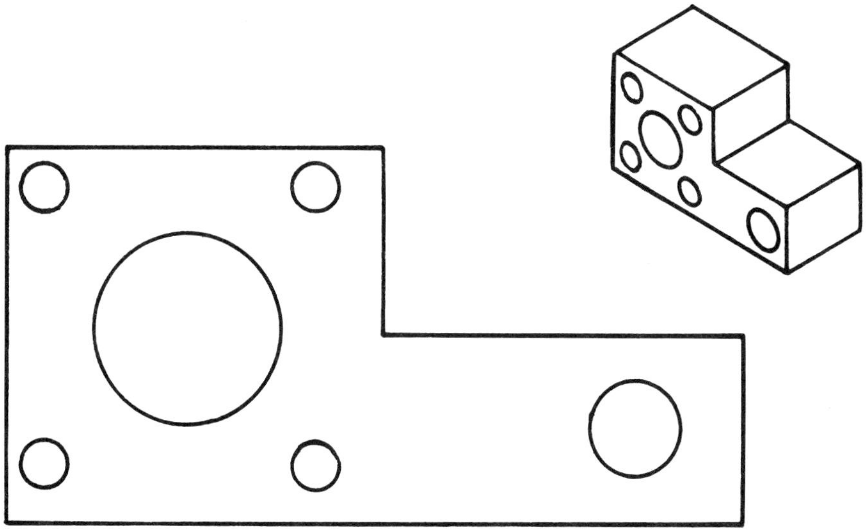

5-2 DIMENSIONING OBJECTS WITH ARCS AND CIRCLES. Draw all the extension lines, dimension lines, leaders, and arrowheads to completely dimension the objects shown.

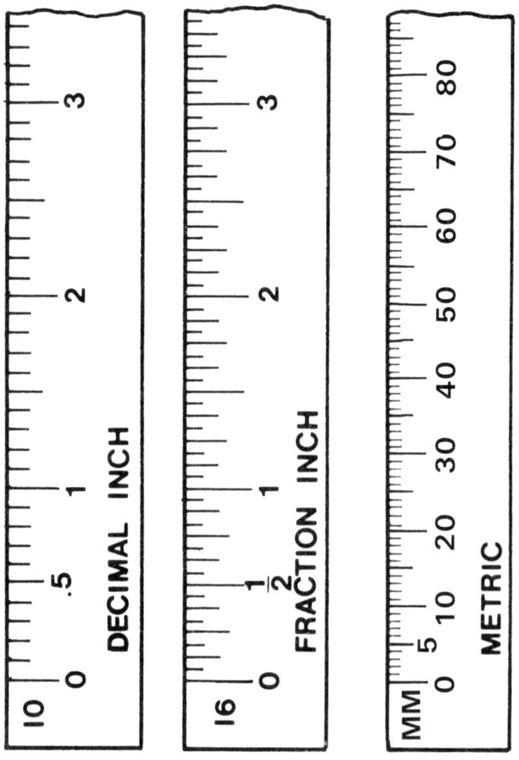

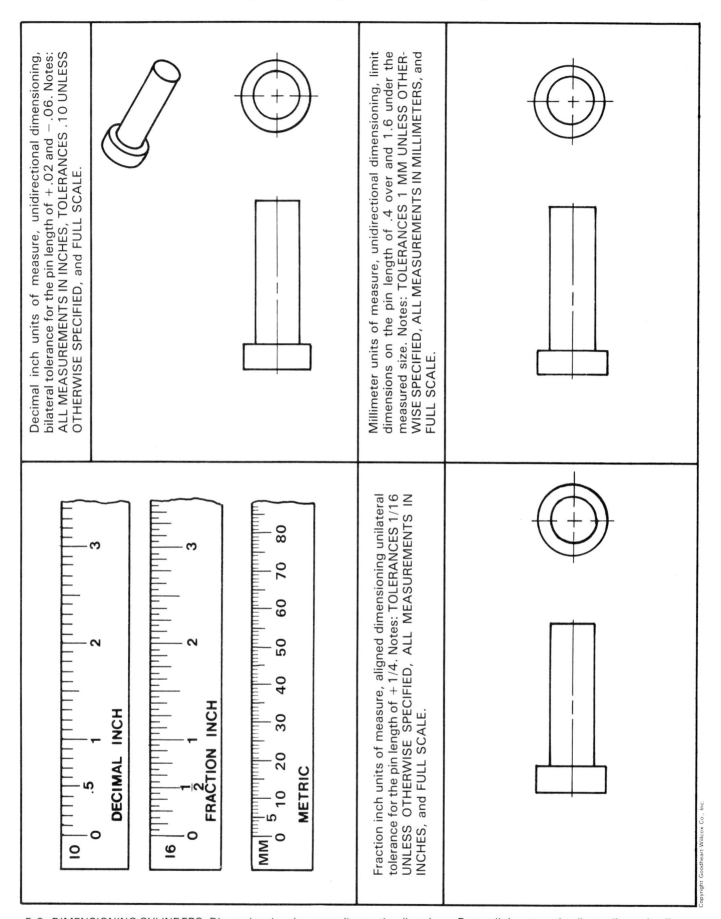

Decimal inch units of measure, unidirectional dimensioning, bilateral tolerance for the pin length of +.02 and −.06. Notes: ALL MEASUREMENTS IN INCHES, TOLERANCES .10 UNLESS OTHERWISE SPECIFIED, and FULL SCALE.

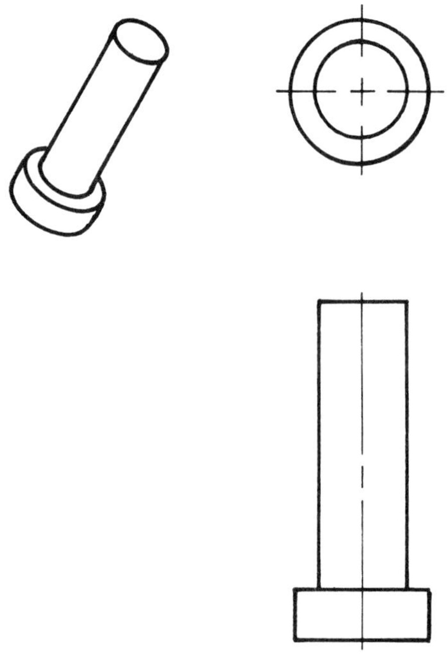

Fraction inch units of measure, aligned dimensioning unilateral tolerance for the pin length of +1/4. Notes: TOLERANCES 1/16 UNLESS OTHERWISE SPECIFIED, ALL MEASUREMENTS IN INCHES, and FULL SCALE.

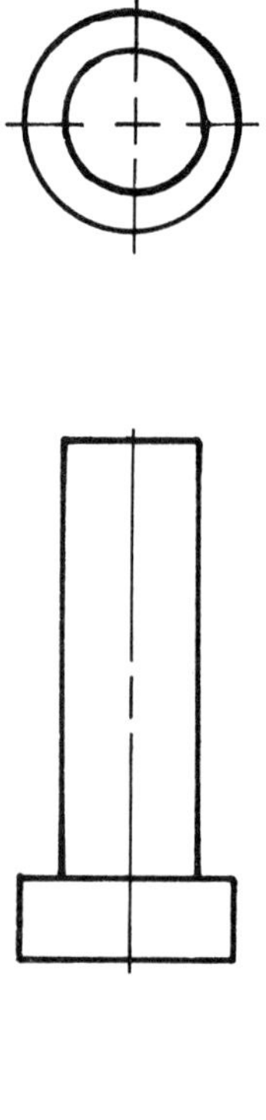

Millimeter units of measure, unidirectional dimensioning, limit dimensions on the pin length of .4 over and 1.6 under the measured size. Notes: TOLERANCES 1 MM UNLESS OTHERWISE SPECIFIED, ALL MEASUREMENTS IN MILLIMETERS, and FULL SCALE.

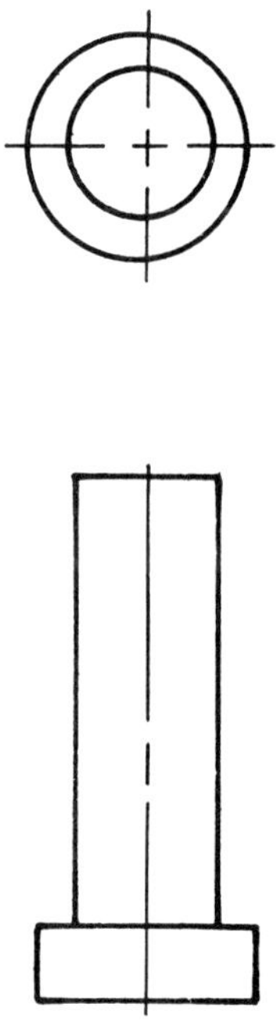

5-3 DIMENSIONING CYLINDERS. Dimension the pins according to the directions. Draw all the extension lines, dimension lines, leaders, and arrowheads to fully dimension the cylinders shown.

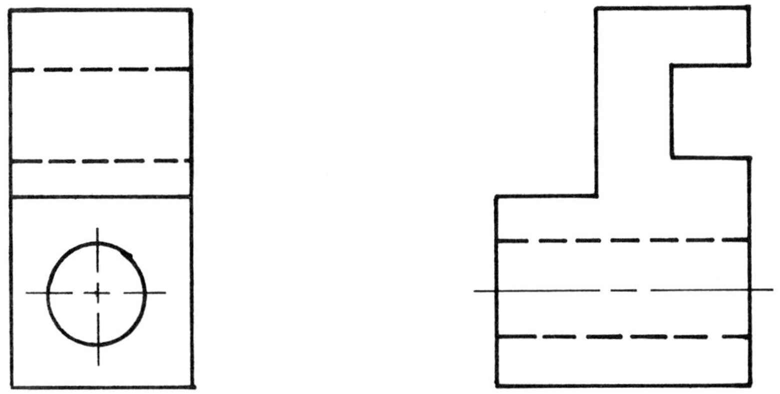

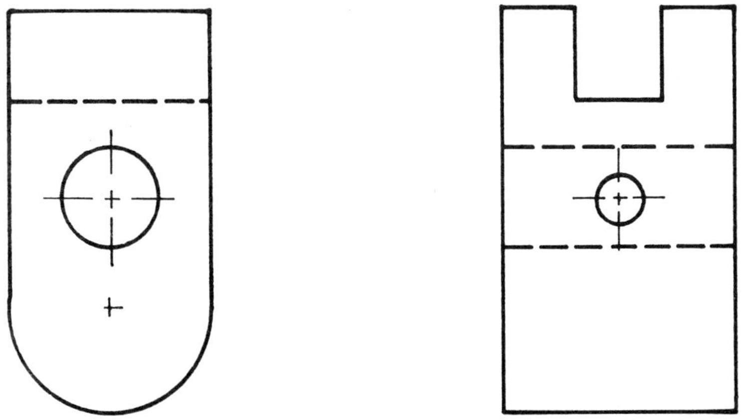

5-4 DIMENSIONING FIXTURES. Dimension each of the fixtures completely using the decimal unit units of measure, and unidirectional dimensioning. Add the notes: ALL MEASUREMENTS IN INCHES. TOLERANCES ±0.01 UNLESS OTHEWISE SPECIFIED. FULL SCALE.

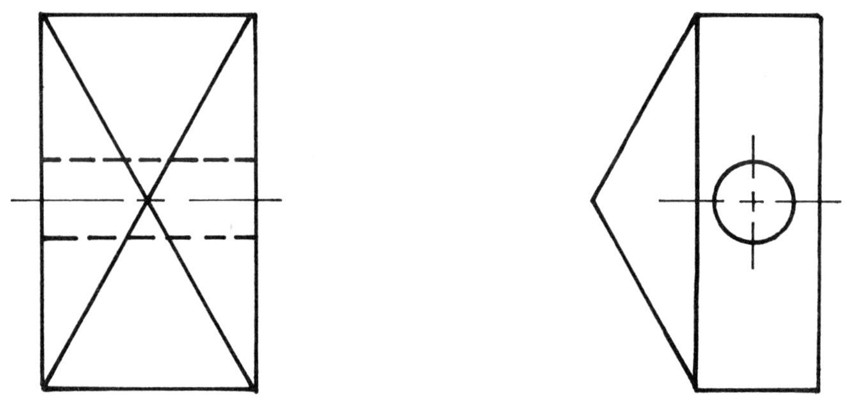

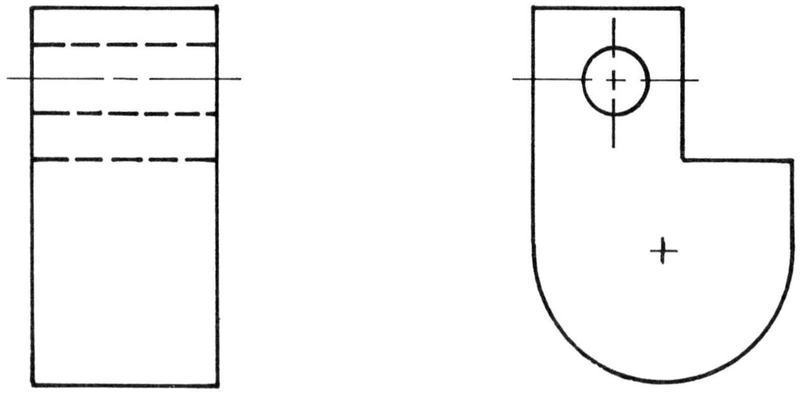

5-5 DIMENSIONING JIGS. Dimension each of the jigs completely using the millimeter units of measure along with unidirectional dimensioning. Add the notes: ALL MEASUREMENTS IN MILLIMETERS. TOLERANCES ±0.1 MM UNLESS OTHERWISE SPECIFIED. FULL SCALE.

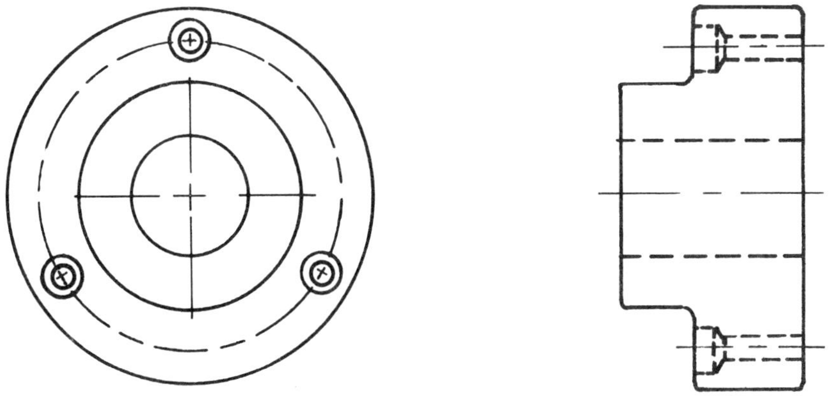

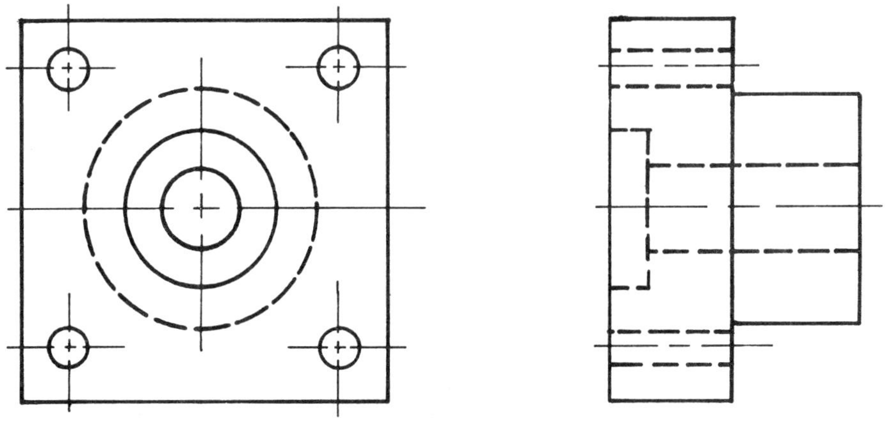

5-6 DIMENSIONING SPINDLES. Dimension each spindle completely using the millimeter units of measure, unidirectional dimensioning. Add the notes to each drawing: ALL MEASUREMENTS IN MILLIMETERS. TOLERANCES ±.01 MM UNLESS OTHERWISE SPECIFIED. The spindle on the top is drawn at 1:4 SCALE with ALL FILLETS AND ROUNDS AT R 1 MM. The spindle on the bottom is drawn at 1:2 SCALE.

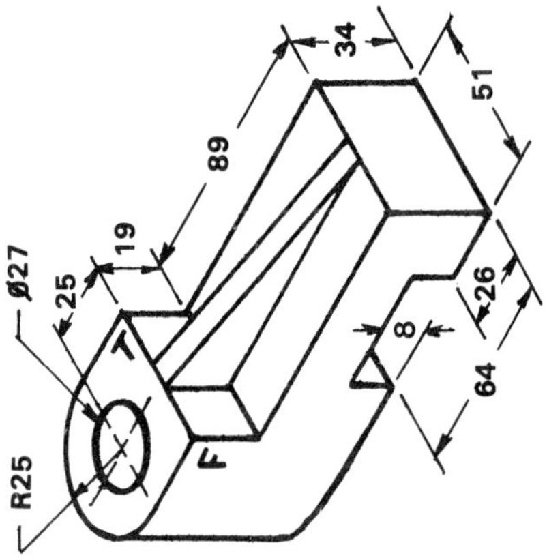

T

F

5-7 DRAWING AND DIMENSIONING A BRACKET. Draw the front and top views of the bracket. Dimension completely using millimeter units of measure, unidirectional dimensioning and the note: ALL MEASUREMENTS IN MM. TOLERANCES ±0.1 MM UNLESS OTHERWISE SPECIFIED. FULL SCALE.

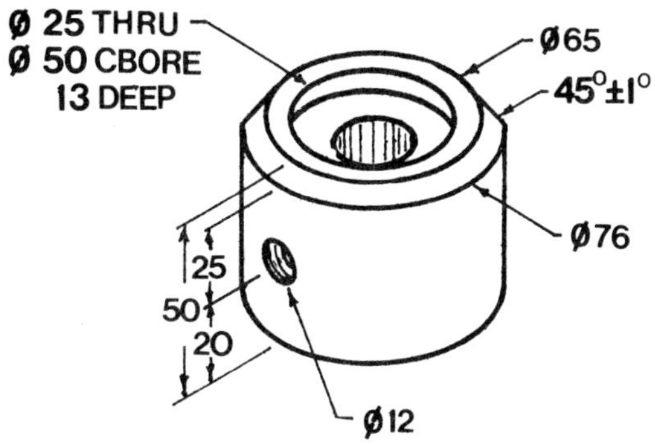

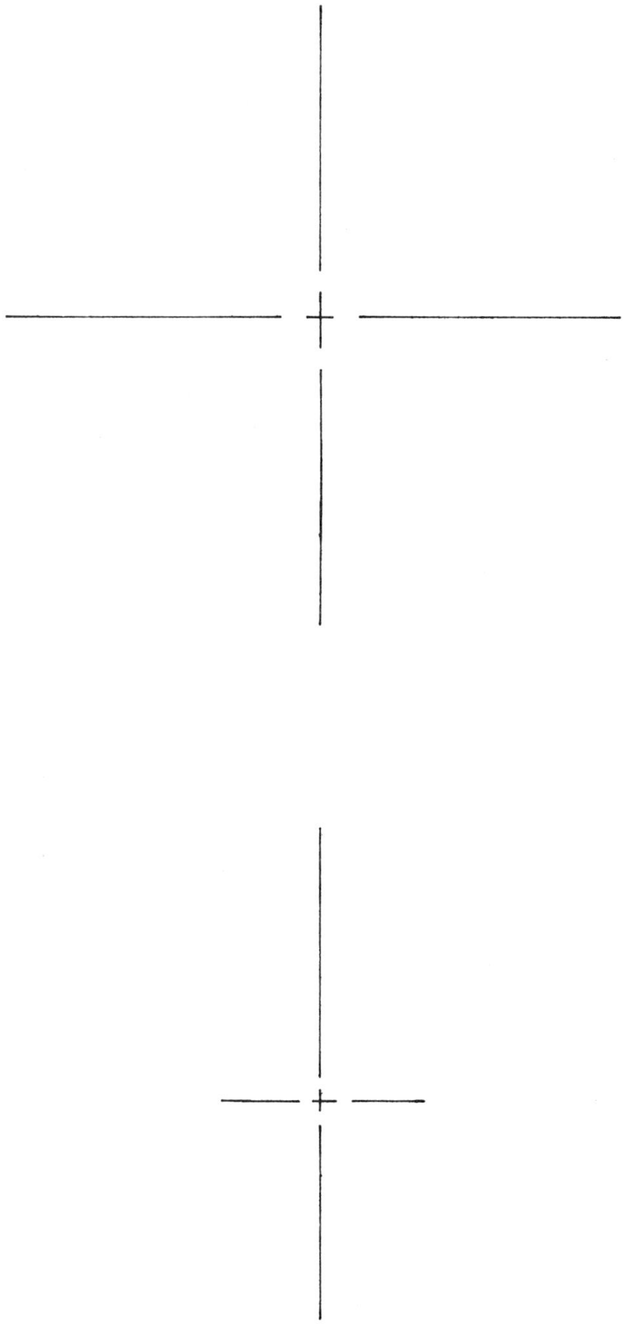

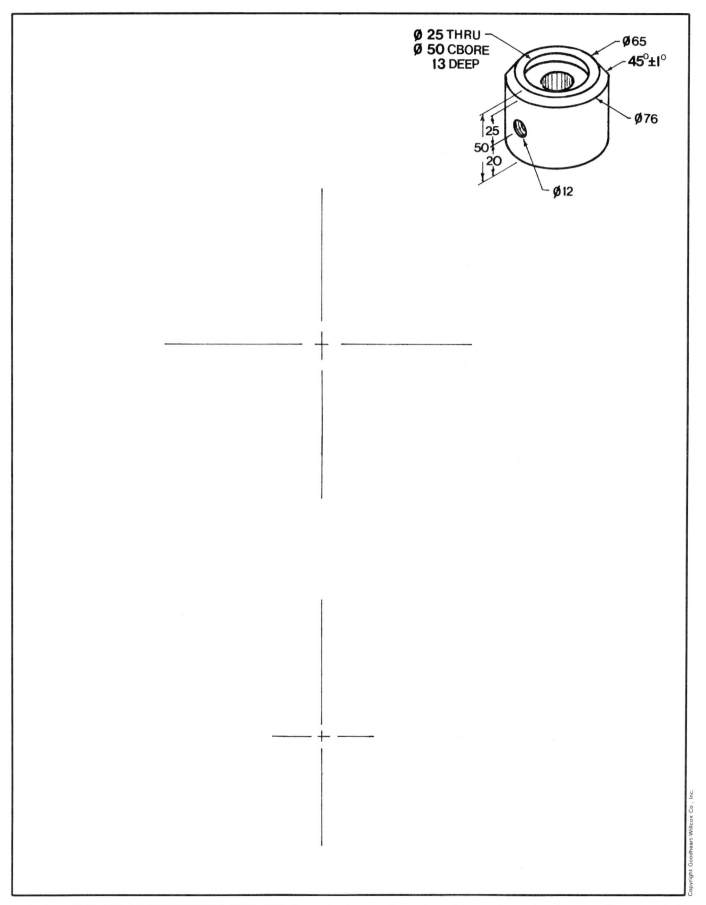

5-8 DRAWING AND DIMENSIONING A RETAINER. Draw the front and top view of the retainer using the centerlines provided. Dimension all the views completely. Include the notes: ALL MEASUREMENTS IN MILLIMETERS. TOLERANCES ±.01 MM UNLESS OTHERWISE SPECIFIED. FULL SCALE.

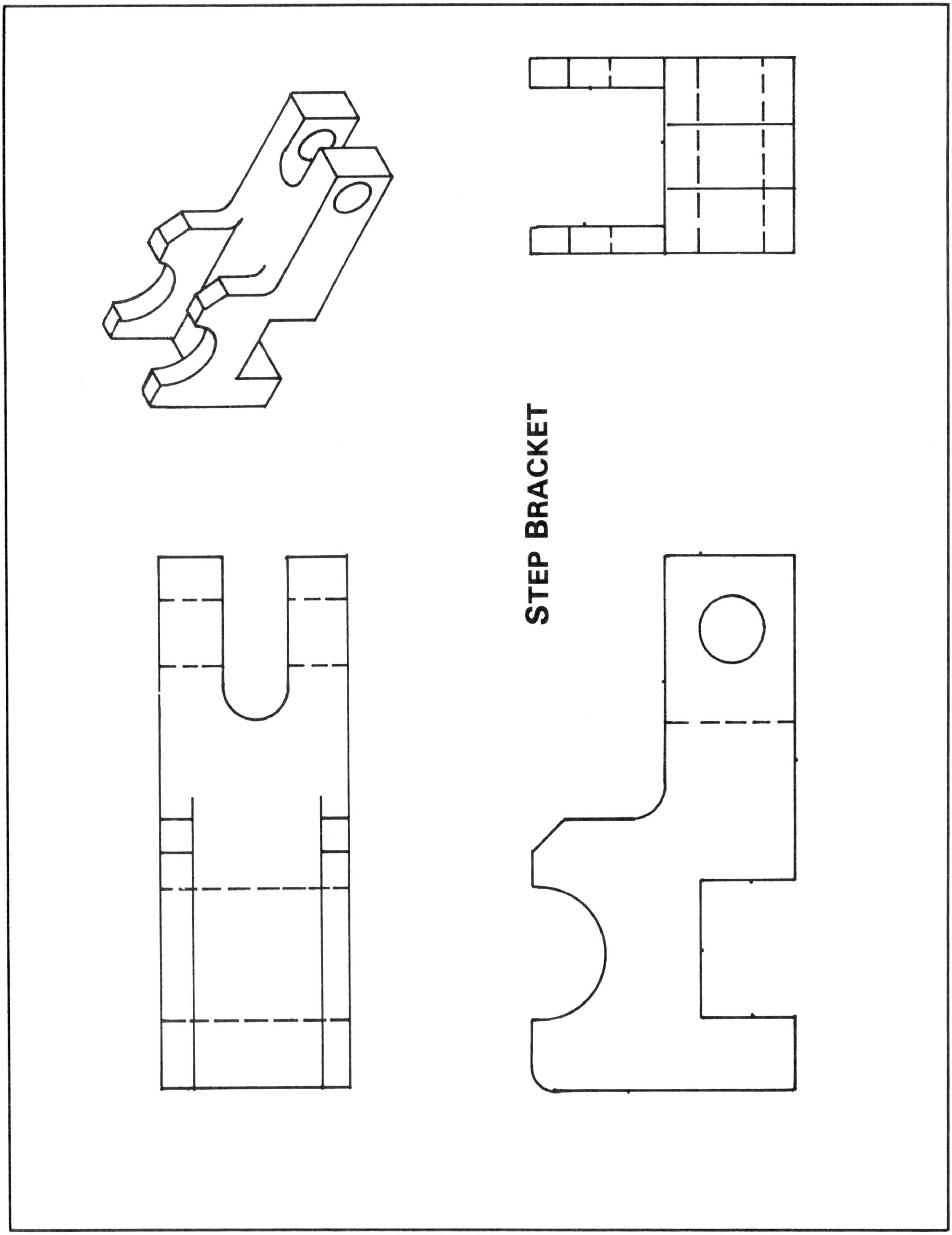

5-9 DIMENSIONING A STEP BRACKET. Dimension the step bracket shown using decimal inch units of measure, unidirectional dimensioning, finish marks on the dots in the sidse view, and the notes: ALL MEASUREMENTS IN INCHES. TOLERANCES ±0.01 UNLESS OTHERWISE SPECIFIED. FULL SCALE.

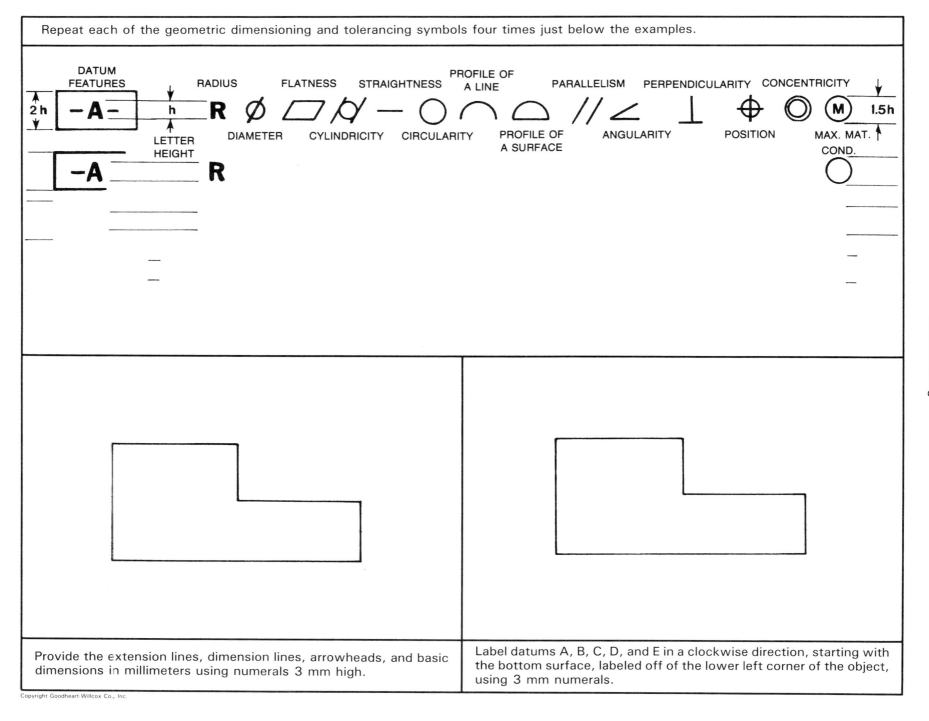

Repeat each of the geometric dimensioning and tolerancing symbols four times just below the examples.

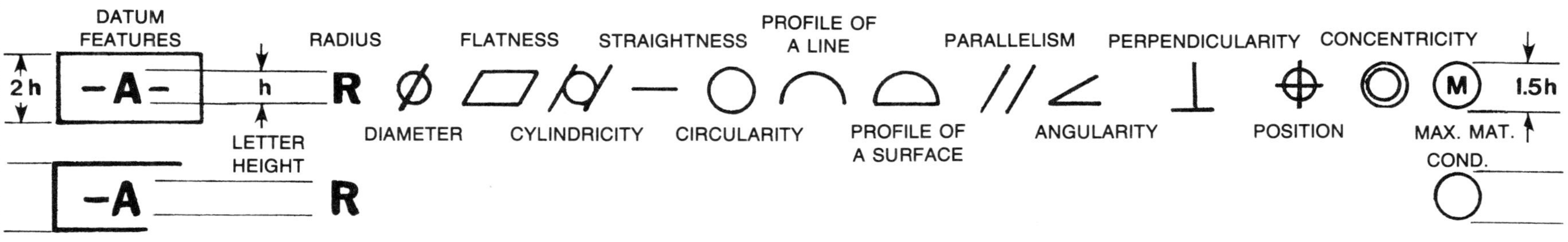

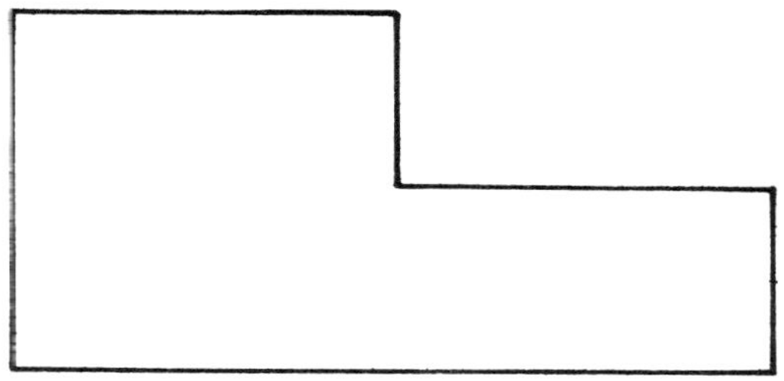

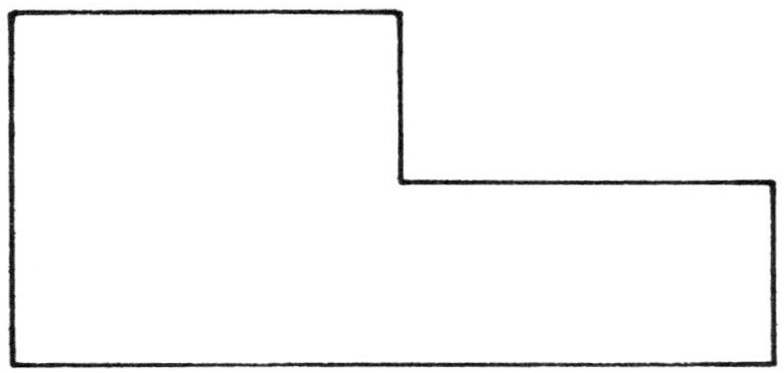

Provide the extension lines, dimension lines, arrowheads, and basic dimensions in millimeters using numerals 3 mm high.

Label datums A, B, C, D, and E in a clockwise direction, starting with the bottom surface, labeled off of the lower left corner of the object, using 3 mm numerals.

5-10 GEOMETRIC DIMENSIONING.

Dimension the pin using metric units of measure. The head diameter has a bilateral tolerance of ±0.10, the shaft diameter has a limit dimension of ±0.3 to +0.9 over the measured size, the total pin length has a unilateral toloerance of + 1 mm, and the shaft length is a basic dimension.

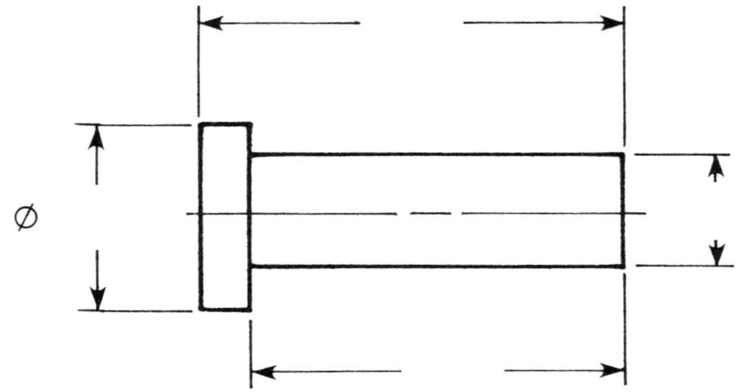

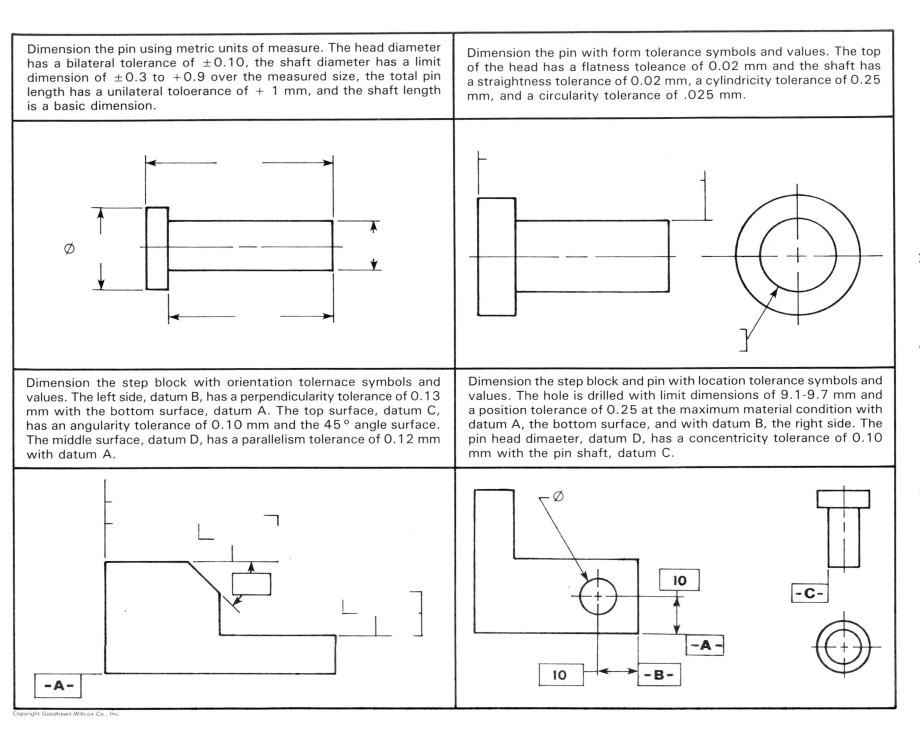

Dimension the pin with form tolerance symbols and values. The top of the head has a flatness toleance of 0.02 mm and the shaft has a straightness tolerance of 0.02 mm, a cylindricity tolerance of 0.25 mm, and a circularity tolerance of .025 mm.

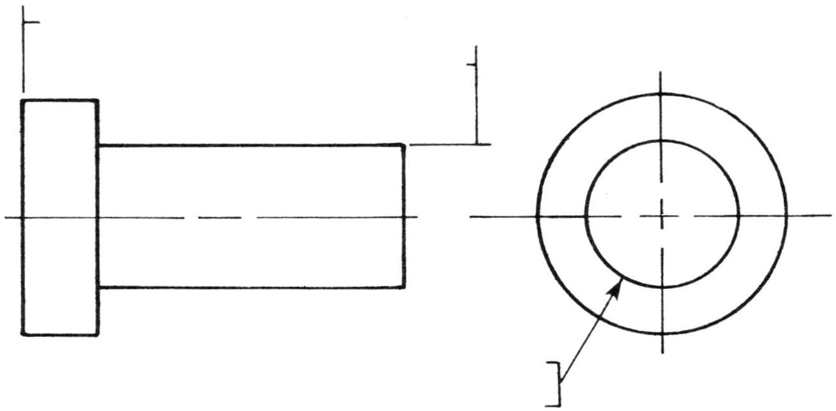

Dimension the step block with orientation tolernace symbols and values. The left side, datum B, has a perpendicularity tolerance of 0.13 mm with the bottom surface, datum A. The top surface, datum C, has an angularity tolerance of 0.10 mm and the 45° angle surface. The middle surface, datum D, has a parallelism tolerance of 0.12 mm with datum A.

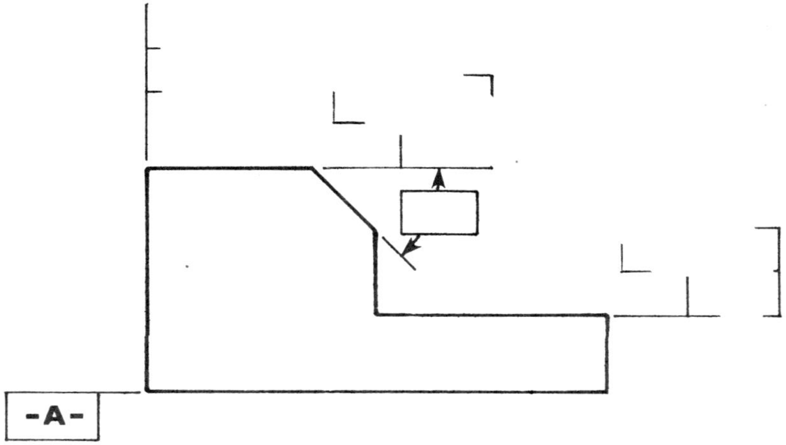

Dimension the step block and pin with location tolerance symbols and values. The hole is drilled with limit dimensions of 9.1-9.7 mm and a position tolerance of 0.25 at the maximum material condition with datum A, the bottom surface, and with datum B, the right side. The pin head dimaeter, datum D, has a concentricity tolerance of 0.10 mm with the pin shaft, datum C.

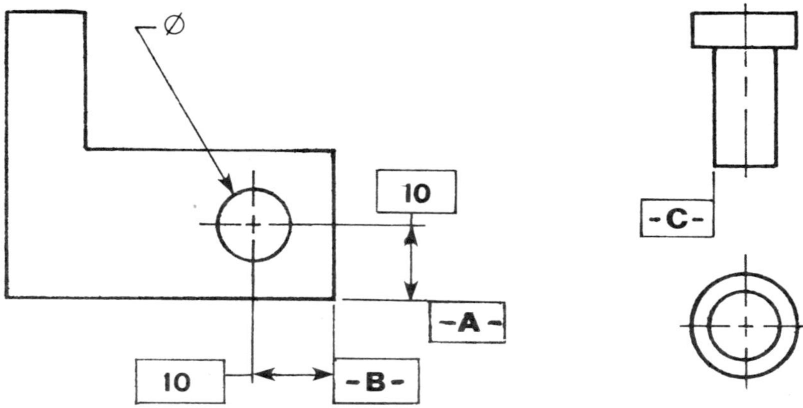

5-11 APPLYING GEOMETRIC DIMENSIONING AND TOLERANCING.

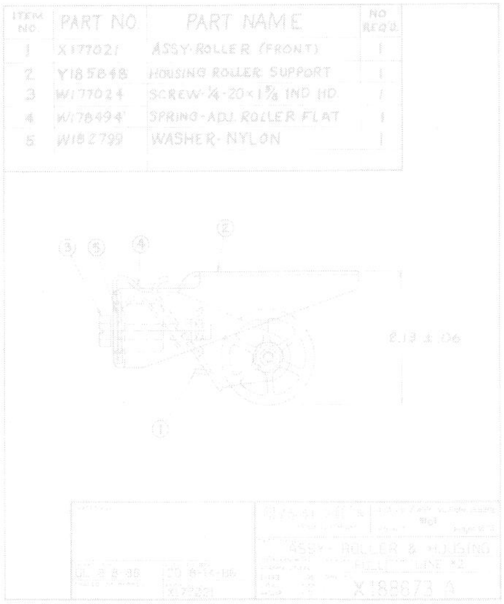

Chapter 6

WORKING DRAWINGS

OBJECTIVES

After completing this chapter on WORKING DRAWINGS, you will be able to:

- ☐ *Sketch multiview projections or isometric views in preparation for drawing.*
- ☐ *Lay out multiview projections.*
- ☐ *Lay out dimensions on the multiview projections.*
- ☐ *Select an appropriate scale for drawings.*
- ☐ *Draw the multiview projections with dimensions.*
- ☐ *Lay out isometric views.*
- ☐ *Draw additional views for clarity.*
- ☐ *Provide notes and details.*
- ☐ *Develop section views.*
- ☐ *Draw an isometric view.*
- ☐ *Develop exploded isometric views.*
- ☐ *Reproduce drawings using available printmaking equipment.*

The order in which the objectives are listed above is the exact same order in which the beginning drafter should proceed to develop a professional drawing. This list of objectives may be used as a checklist as you progress through the development of a drawing.

The most essential features of working drawings are their ability to communicate information clearly while avoiding any misinterpretations. A set of **working drawings** may include assembly drawings, detailed drawings, isometric views, exploded views, or whatever views are necessary to clearly communicate the product. Therefore, designers and drafters use working drawings to provide all the necessary details for the people who produce the parts and products.

Working drawings convey both the general ideas and the specific details for developing products. Working drawings may be sketched for simple products, especially when the sketcher is the person who constructs the product. In most industrial situations, sketches are initially made by designers. Then, working drawings are prepared by an engineering team. Duplicate drawings are printed and distributed to construct a prototype before production is started on the final product. The design and engineering team must remember that shop work can be completed only when drawings are correctly interpreted by the shop personnel.

Working drawings may vary in appearance and purpose. **Assembly drawings** identify and locate parts. A typical assembly drawing is illustrated in Fig. 6-1. It focuses upon an adjustable front roller and a lower door hinge. These two items will be used as examples throughout this chapter. Study this drawing carefully. Refer back to Fig. 6-1 as necessary.

Accurate communication of ideas relies upon use of a common graphic language by all industrial personnel. This language incorporates the basic concepts of multiview projection, isometric drawing, dimensioning, sectioning, and concise notes.

Drafting personnel utilize a great deal of creativity in preparing working drawings. This creativity involves using the best drafting techniques to illustrate the designer's idea.

When the need for a product becomes known, an idea is usually sketched in isometric to be visualized by others, Fig. 6-2. In the example used in this chapter, the designer has the responsibility of creating an adjustable front roller assembly for a refrigerator. Sketches are analyzed to determine how functional and efficient the idea may be. When the design and engineering team decide to follow through with a sketched idea, they visualize the best way to position the part for developing a series of working drawings.

Assembly drawings illustrate and label the parts. After careful study and analysis of the assembly drawings, the design and engineering team visualize the sub-parts. Detailed working drawings are then prepared.

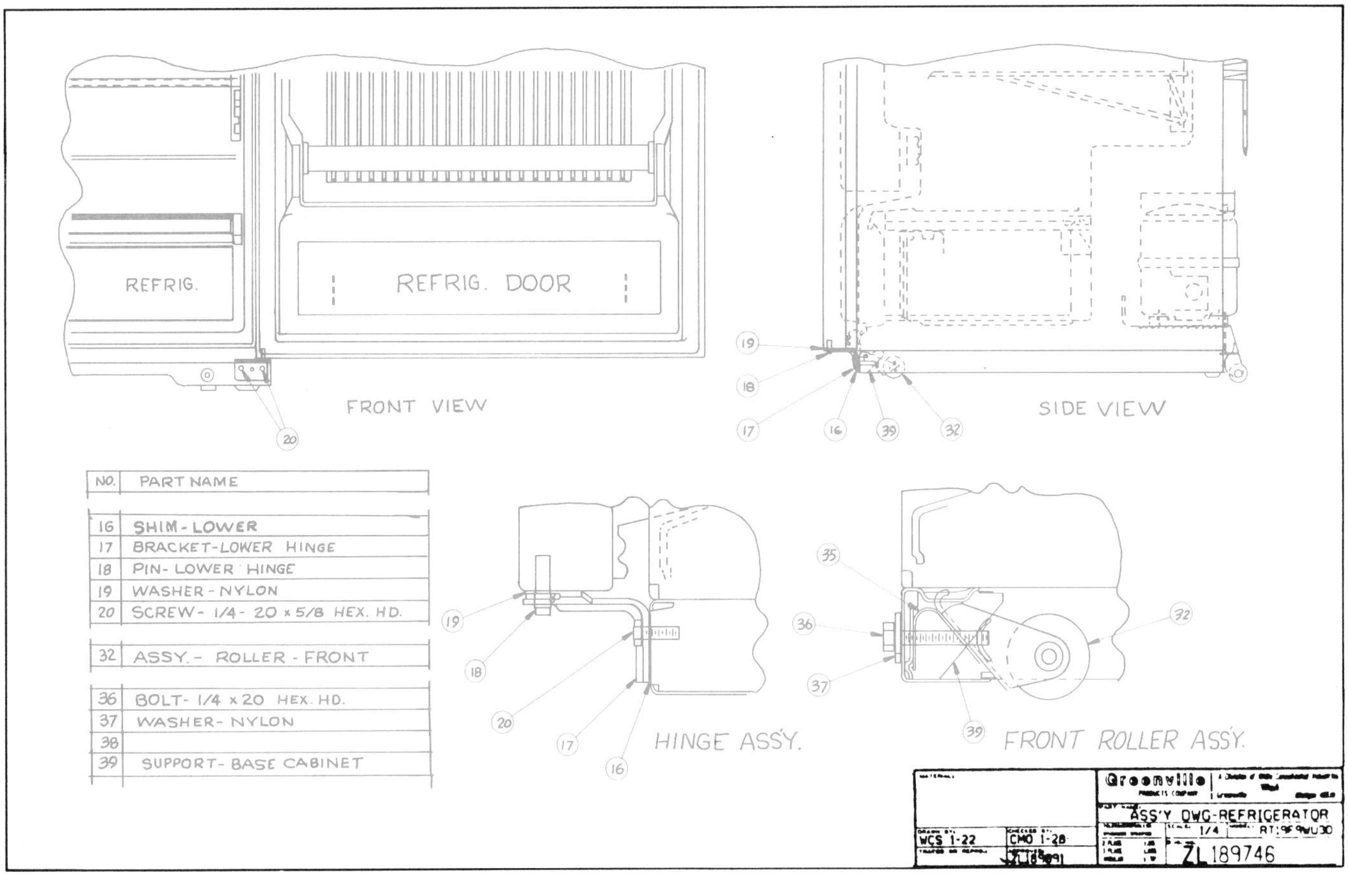

Fig. 6-1. A typical assembly drawing shows how and where parts fit into manufactured products. Review this drawing carefully as the items illustrated here will be used as examples throughout this chapter.

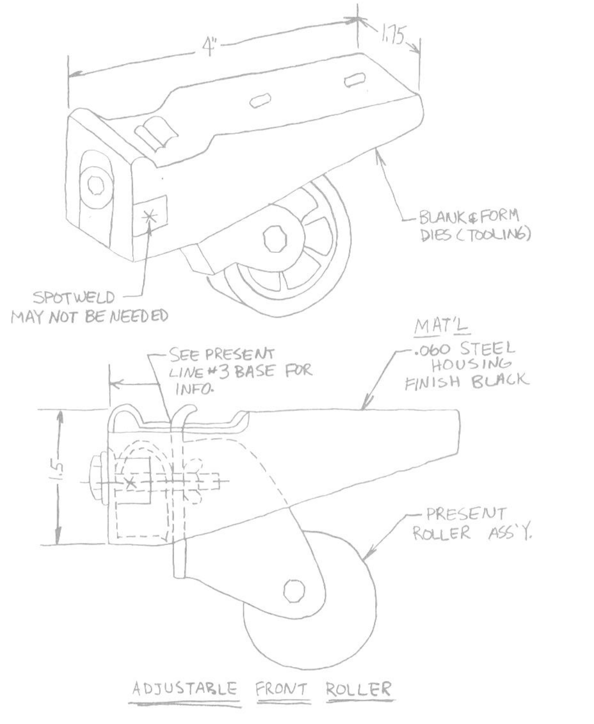

Fig. 6-2. Sketches prepared by a product engineer for the design of a new, adjustable front roller for a refrigerator. (Douglas Weaver)

Explicit details are usually provided in the multiview drawings. Be sure to notice the (ϕ) diameters, (R) radii, location dimensions, angular dimensions, stacked/chained size dimensions, and notes. Detailed working drawings provide enough specific information for construction of prototypes.

WORKING DRAWING FUNDAMENTALS

Before making a working drawing, sketch a three-dimensional isometric view of the object. This enables you to better understand the product. You will be able to study prominent or unusual features.

Analysis of the sketch may prompt the following questions: What surface is the front view? What additional views are needed? What dimensions are needed? Where will dimensions be located? Would a section view improve understanding? What information will be provided as notes? What scale is appropriate? When answering these questions, drafting personnel concentrate on providing adequate information in a clear and attractive manner.

The refrigerator lower door hinge assembly is drawn in Fig. 6-1 and illustrated in Fig. 6-3, and has three parts: the bracket, Fig. 6-4, the pin, Fig. 6-5, and the bearing, Fig. 6-6. Although these three

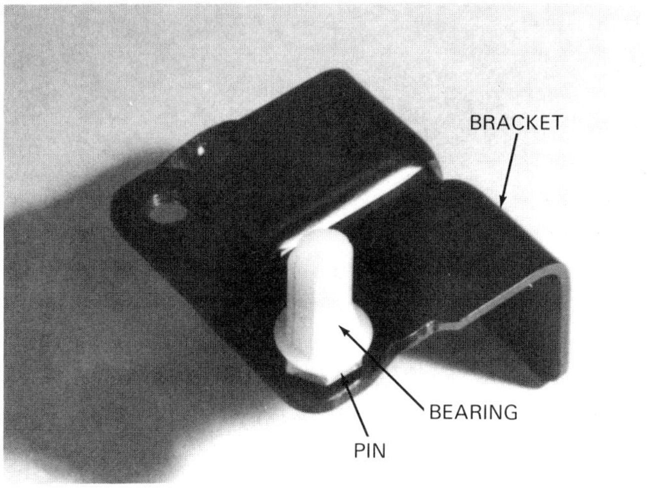

Fig. 6-3. Photograph of the assembled lower door hinge for a refrigerator.

Fig. 6-4. The bracket for the lower door hinge is designed for either a left- or right-hand opening door. By designing the bracket in this fashion, inventory was cut in half.

Fig. 6-5. The pin used in the hinge assembly screws into the threads of the bracket.

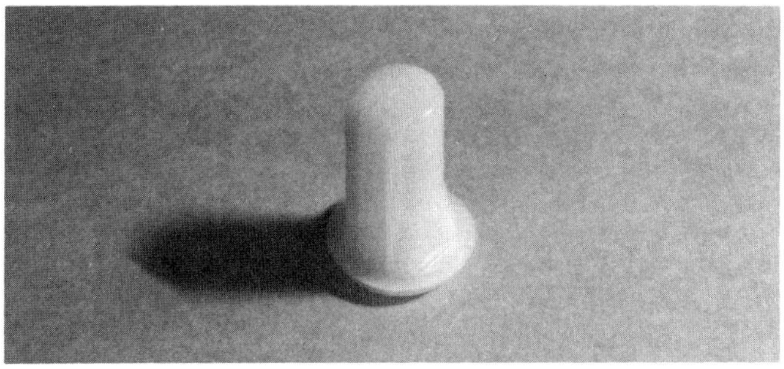

Fig. 6-6. The bearing of the hinge assembly slides down over the pin and allows the door to open with ease.

parts seem relatively simple, the detailed working drawings used to describe them are quite complex.

The detailed drawing for the bracket contains the top, front, and right side views with conventional dimensioning techniques, Fig. 6-7. Notice the diameters (ϕ), radius (R), limit diensions, size dimensions, location dimensions, angular dimensions, and notes.

In Fig. 6-8, the engineering team used a front, right side, and a left side view to describe the pin. There is also an additional drawing showing an alternative construction. Standard dimensioning techniques and notes are also used.

The bearing is the smallest part. It requires the most complex detailed drawing. Notice the front, top, and right side views drawn double size (2X) in the lower left corner of Fig. 6-9. Dimensions are provided in the multiview arrangement. View AA is enlarged four times (4X) to provide enough space for details. View AA is then cut in half to show section BB, also enlarged 4X. These drawings and three parts depicted are especially interesting. They are actual industrial drawings of a product being manufactured.

The previous chapters you have studied have provided the fundamentals for preparing working drawings. Additional concepts, such as section views, are illustrated and described in this chapter. Working drawings require the drafter to sketch, draw, resketch, and redraw until careful selection and placement of detailed information is achieved.

COMMON PRACTICES

The preparation of working drawings can be simplified when steps are followed in sequence. First, sketch an isometric view of the part or product. Analyze the sketch to determine which views are necessary to describe the product. Sketch these views in their proper multiview locations. Select the necessary dimensions and insert them in the appropriate locations. Complete this initial phase by adding notes,Fig. 6-2 shows a sketch of the adjustable front roller, created by a senior product engineer.

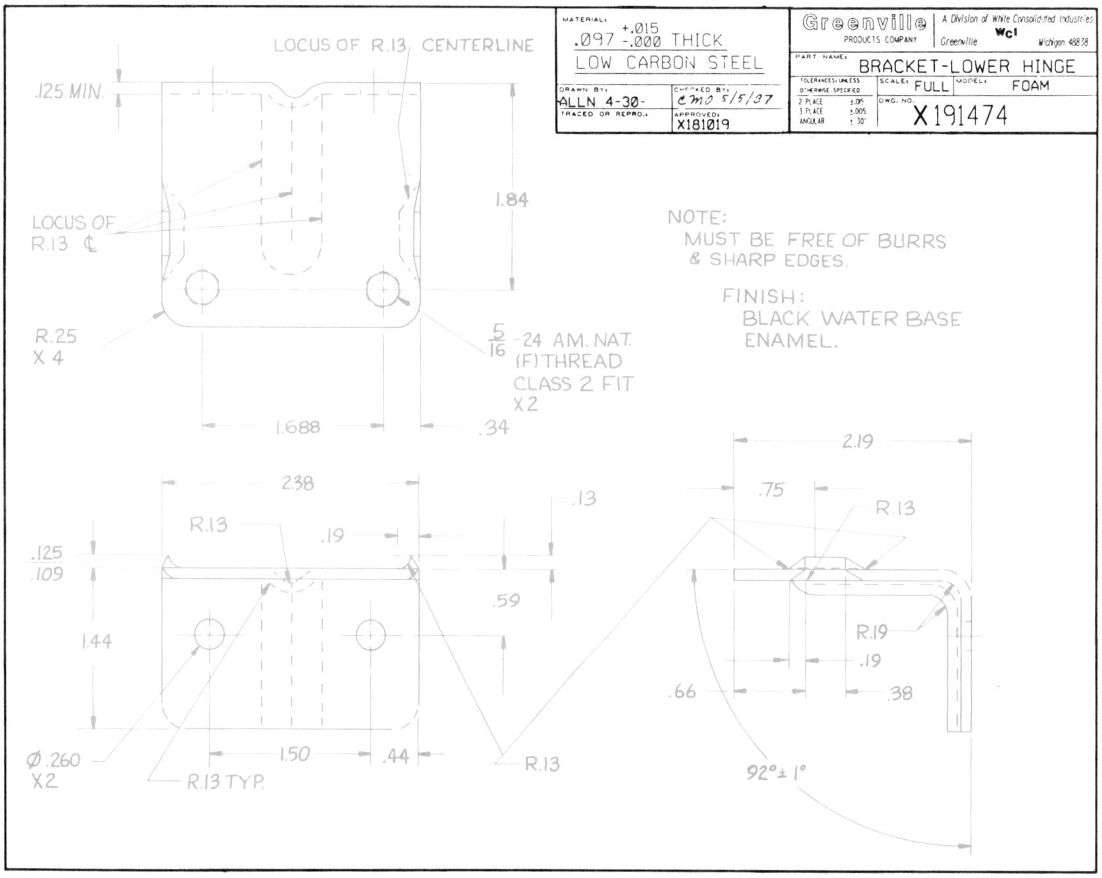

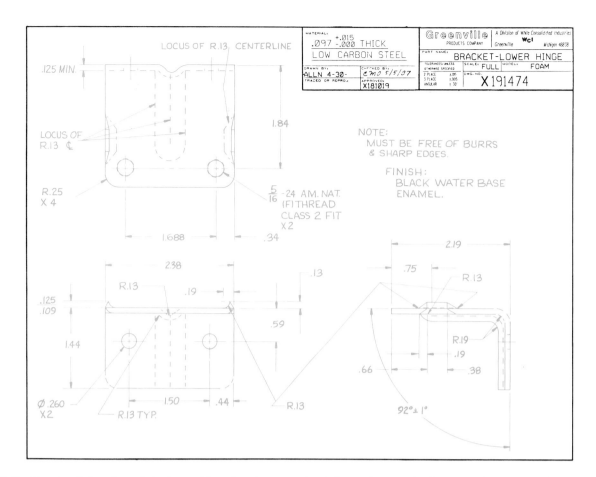

Fig. 6-7. The detail drawing of the lower hinge bracket contains information required to manufacture the part. Study the drawing and note: the name of the part, the drawing number, the tolerances, the material used, the scale, and special notes.

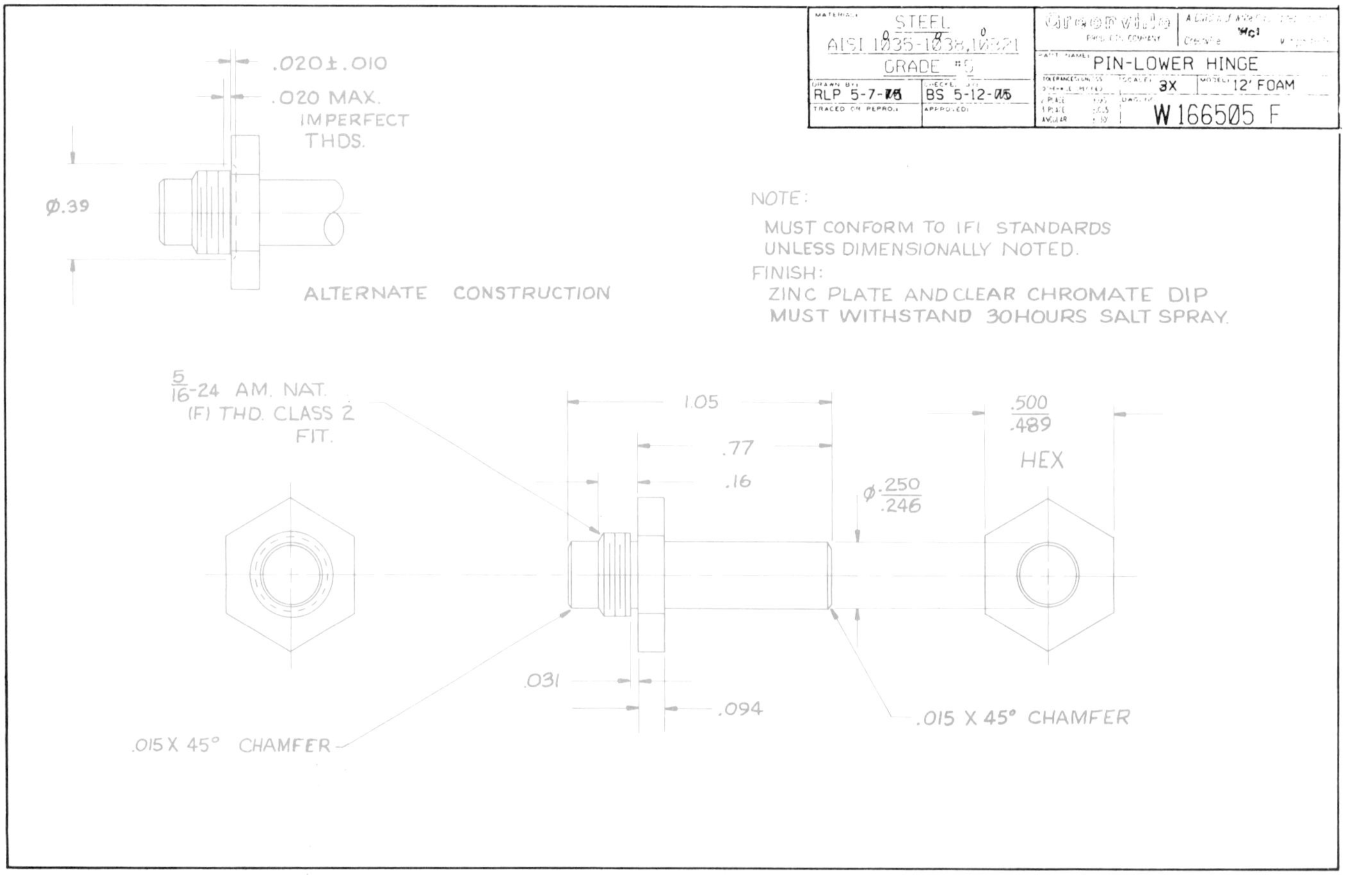

Fig. 6-8. The detail drawing of the pin used in the lower hinge assembly. Note the alternative construction.

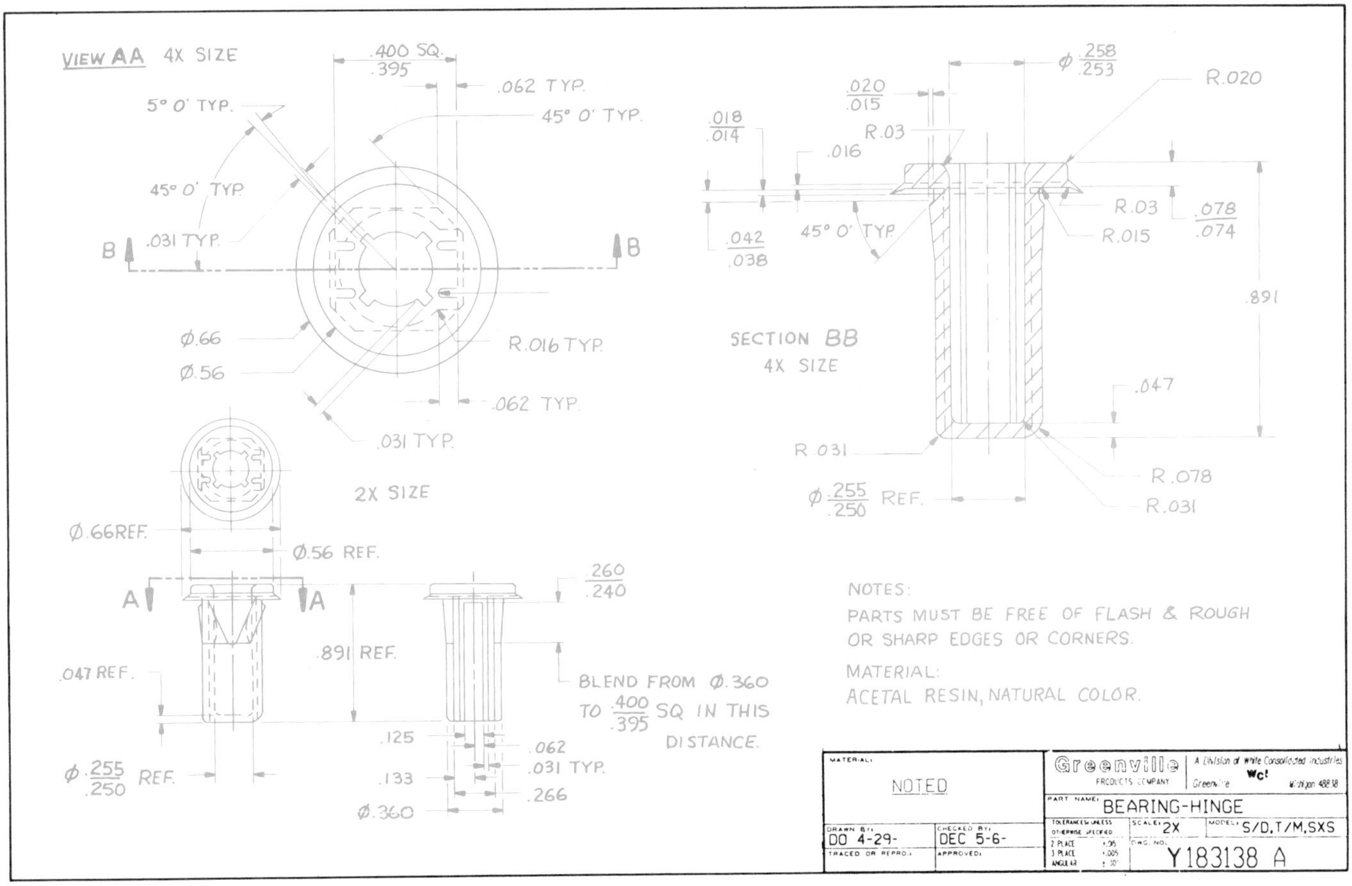

Fig. 6-9. The detail drawing of the bearing used in the lower hinge assembly for the refrigerator. Note the use of section views. Note the scale, some views are twice size, others are four times actual size.

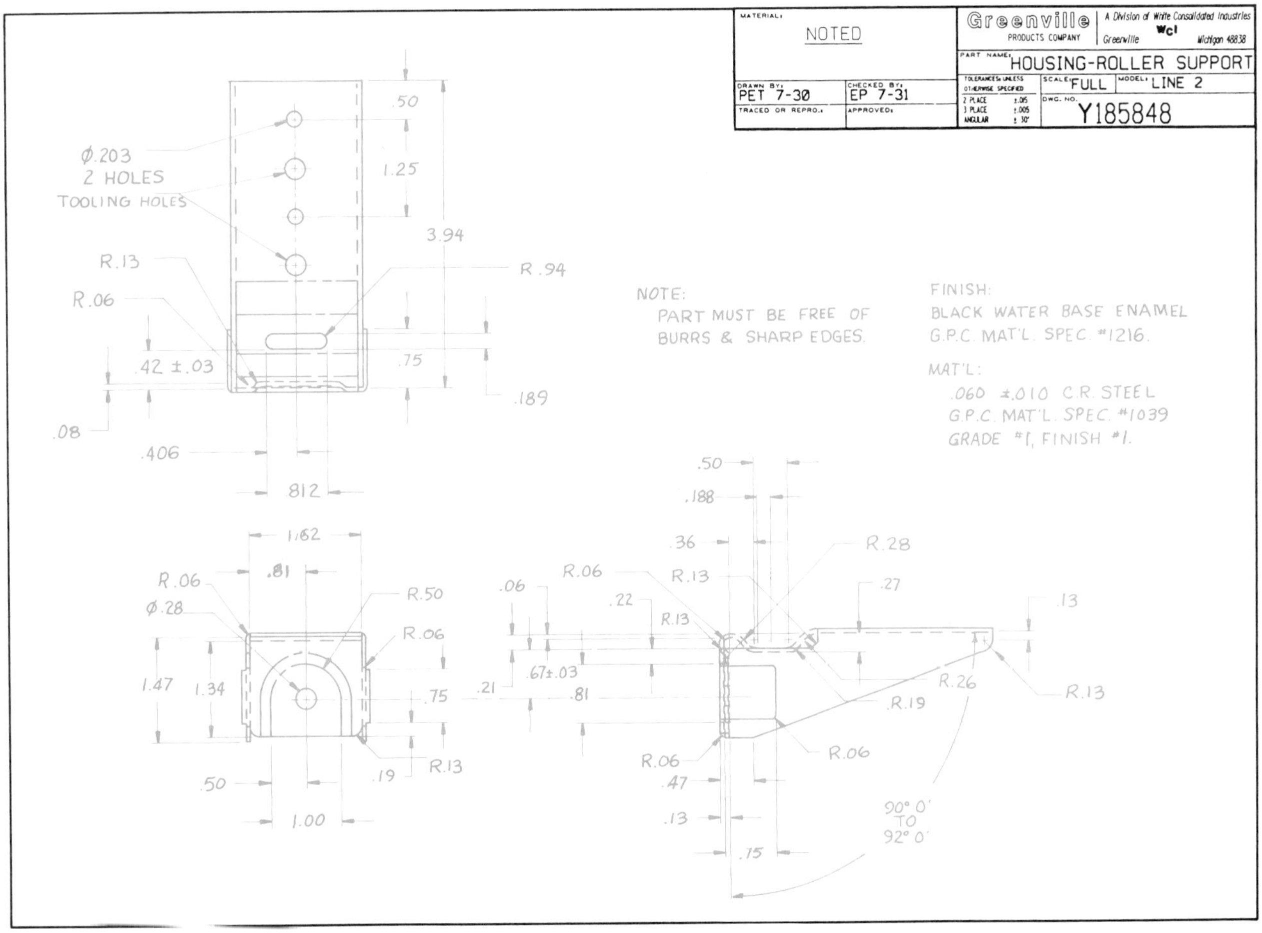

Fig. 6-10. Detail drawing for the roller support was made full size. The views are arranged to present the most information to the reader.

In the second step, the sketch is transformed into a layout drawing, Fig. 6-10. One important consideration on the layout drawing is scale. How large or how small should the views be to ensure clear interpretation? On what size paper will it be drawn? After answering these questions, the views are drawn to scale and dimensioned.

Many drawings are drawn full scale. However, notice that the part in Fig. 6-9 is very small so the multiview is drawn 2X or double size. The larger size is necessary to provide enough space for dimensioning and notes. View AA and Section BB are 4X or four times the actual size to allow space for dimensions and notes.

In architectural drawings, the product must be scaled down. A house plan may be drawn so 1/4 in. represents 1 foot.

The third step involves the need for additional information. Section views may be necessary to clarify details. Dimensions may need to be added, deleted, or rearranged. Rearrangement of the notes, or additional notes may improve clarity. After this check has been completed, a revised working drawing is begun. You will learn more about section views later in this chapter.

The fourth and last step is to redraw the revised working drawing. Pencils or technical pens are used on translucent material such as tracing paper, vellum, or mylar so prints can be made. Select the most appropriate tracing material and drawing instruments based on the final use of the drawing and the reproduction method.

PROTOTYPES

Prototypes serve as experimental models. Changes made to the prototype may improve the function and efficiency of the production part. As changes are made in design, they are noted on the original working drawings or they are redrawn, Figs. 6-11 and 6-12. Assembly and detail drawings communicate information necessary to manufacture the part. Section views and exploded isometric views ensure accuracy by providing additional detail. Figs. 6-13 to 6-16 show the development of a prototype.

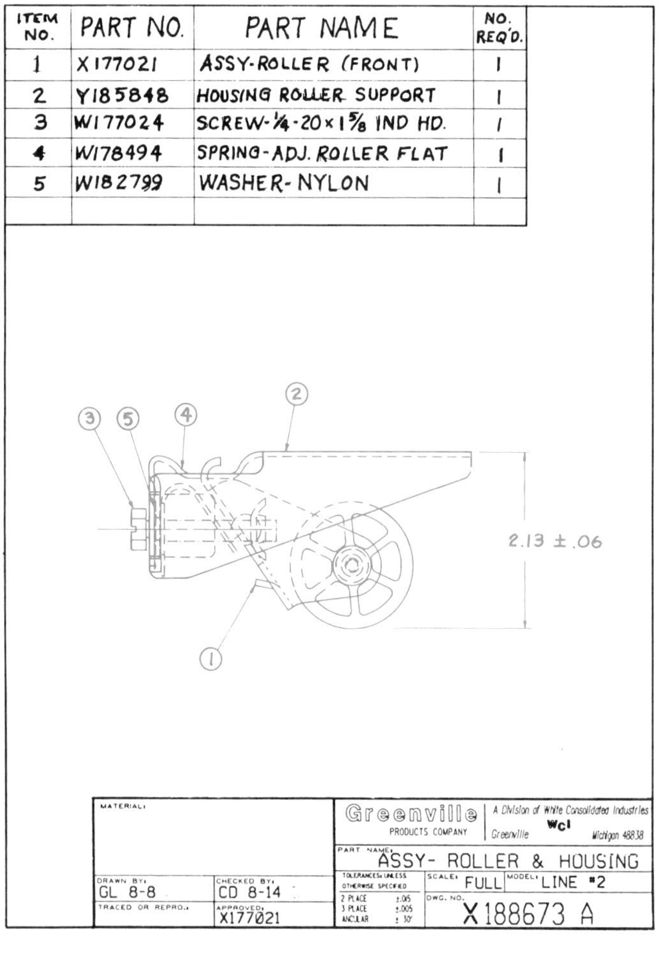

Fig. 6-11. Assembly drawing of the roller and the housing for the refrigerator. The assembly drawing shows how and where the parts fit together, as well as how the finished assembly will look.

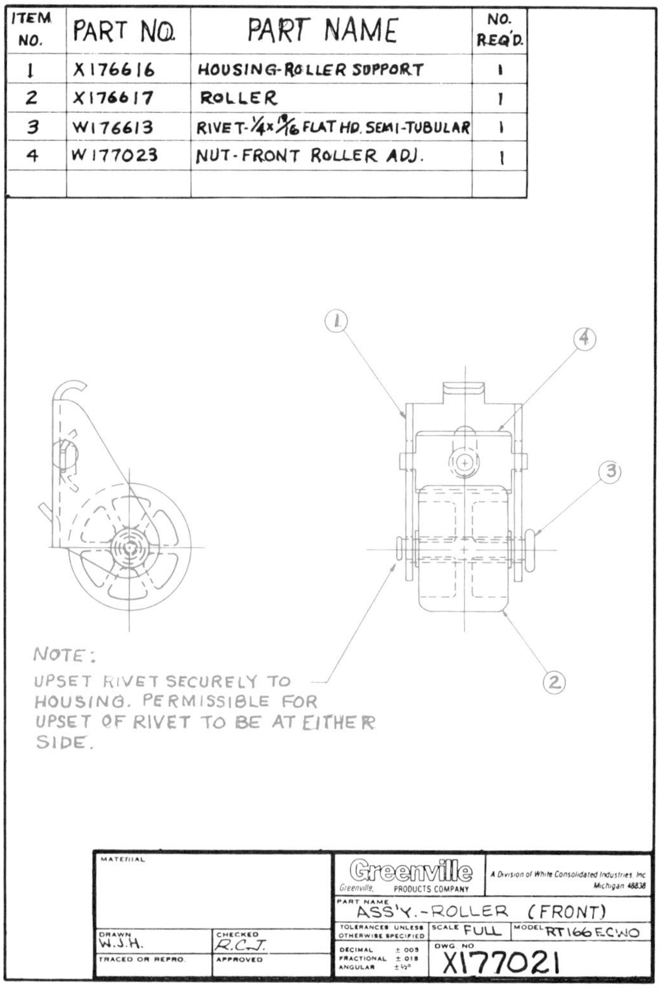

Fig. 6-12. Assembly drawing for the roller illustrated how to identify and locate subassembly parts or components.

Fig. 6-13. Photograph of the housing for the assembly example.

Fig. 6-16. Roller and housing assembled into the final product.

Fig. 6-14. Roller support.

Fig. 6-15. Roller and rivet fastened to the roller support as a subassembly.

DEVELOPING A SECTION VIEW

Section views show the cross-sectional area of a product. Imagine looking at the inside surface of an apple cut in half. The interior section is exposed for viewing. Engineering drawings use section views to clarify the internal structure of parts. Section views are also used in architectural drawings to show the cross section of building components.

Section Lining

Section lining symbolizes the type of material the builder is to use in making the object, Fig. 6-17. After the object has been visually cut apart, section lining is added to represent the material. General section lining is used when the type of material is not specified. Refer to the top left example in Fig. 6-17.

Section lining must have consistent line width, spacing, and connections to object lines. Use a 0.3 mm line for section lining. To ensure equal spacing, scratch a line parallel to the hypotenuse of your 45 x 45 x 90 degree triangle 1/8 in. from the edge, Fig. 6-18. Use this scratch as a reference by placing it over the previously drawn line to draw the next line. Extreme care must be taken to ensure precise starting and stopping points so they attach accurately to the object lines. Hidden lines are not used where section lining occurs. Fig. 6-19 is an example of properly spaced section lines.

Developing a Full Section View

A full section is developed by cutting the product through the middle to expose the interior structure. Study the bearing shown in Fig. 6-20. The location of the cut is illustrated by using a cutting plane line and labeled AA, Fig. 6-21. A cutting plane line is a thick line in a long-short-short sequence with large arrowheads on each end, Fig. 6-22. The ar-

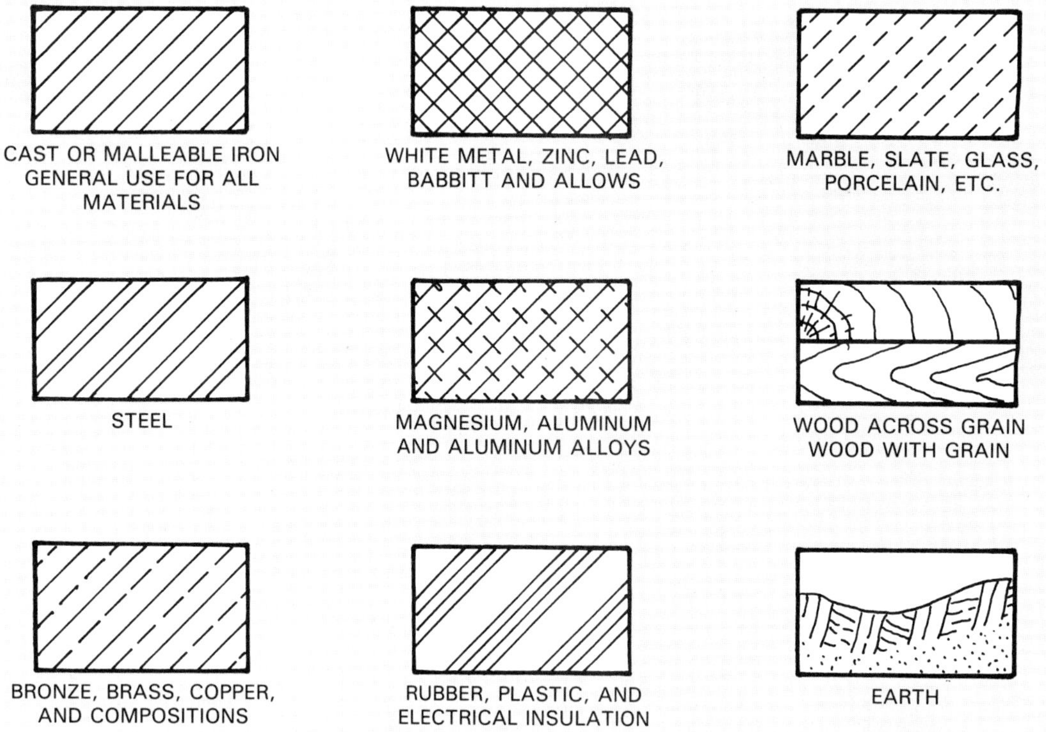

Fig. 6-17. Section lining used to represent specific industrial materials.

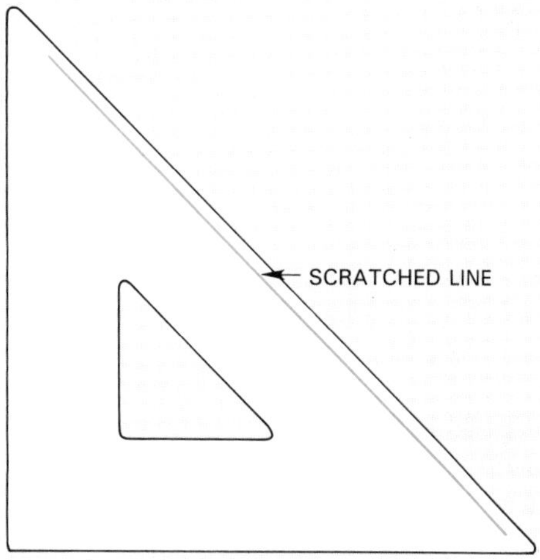

Fig. 6-18. Adding a scratch line parallel to the hypotenuse of your triangle will allow you to accurately draw section lines.

rowheads always point toward the part remaining after a portion has been removed.

The cutting plane line in the front view indicates the wheel has been cut through. The exposed area, seen from the adjacent view behind the arrowheads, displays the cross-sectional area. Section lining is

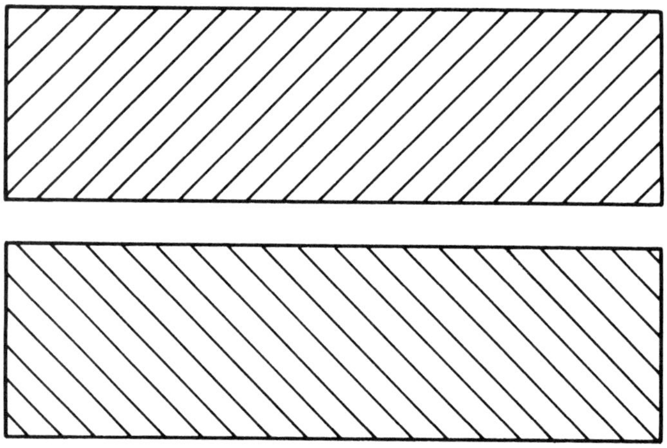

Fig. 6-19. Properly spaced section lines should not be drawn parallel to the sides of the objects.

then added to the portion cut to illustrate its interior shape, Fig. 6-23. The style of section lining specifies the type of material to be used. Section lining is added only to the areas that have made contact with the knife or saw when cut for viewing.

Developing a Half Section

Similar to a full section, a half-section view of a product has material removed to expose its interior

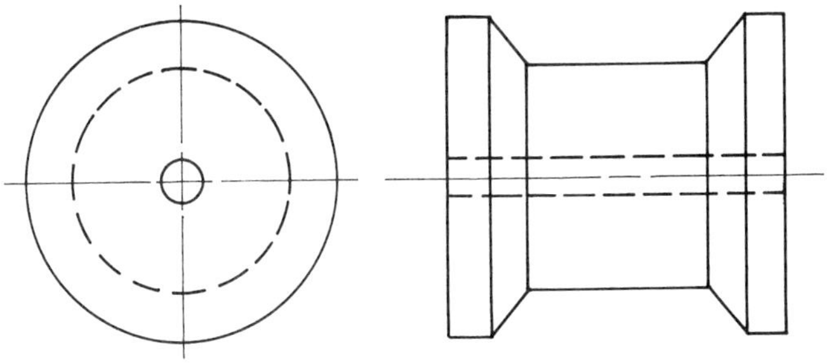

Fig. 6-20. Front and side view of a bearing that will be used as an example in creating a section view.

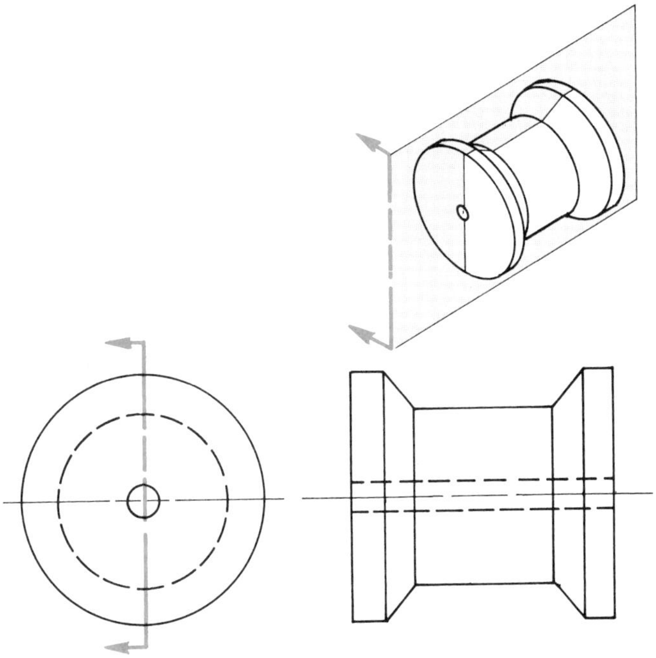

Fig. 6-21. The cutting plane A-A slices the bearing through the center.

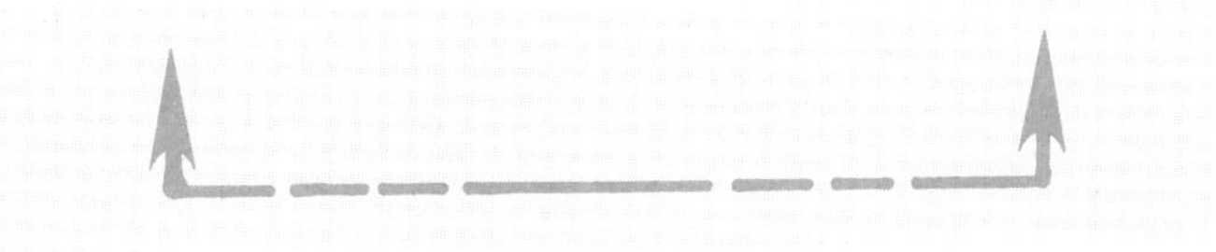

Fig. 6-22. Cutting plane line is a series of thick long-short-short sequences ending in arrowheads.

structure. Half sections may be used with symmetrical products such as a foam cup, Fig. 6-24. Both the internal (section-lined) and external can be viewed in a half section. The product is cut and the material removed exposes one-half its cross-sectional area. The cutting plane lines appear over the centerlines. Arrowheads point in the direction it is to be viewed. The section view appears behind the arrowhead in the adjacent view.

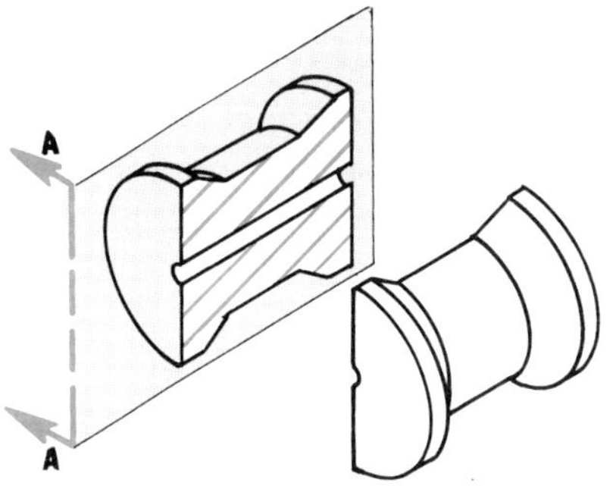

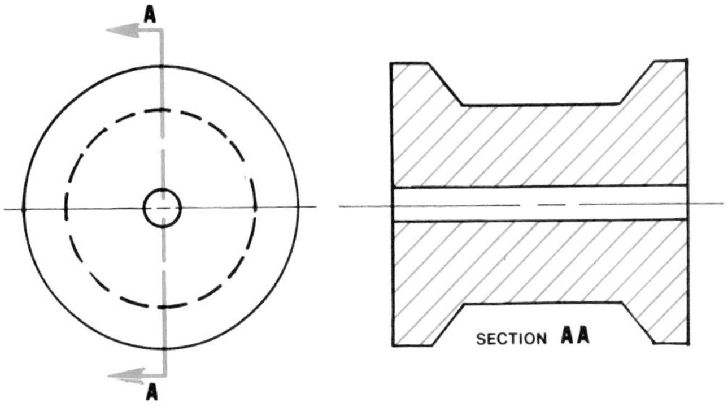

Fig. 6-23. A drawing of a full-section view of the bearing is a representation of the bearing cut through the centerline.

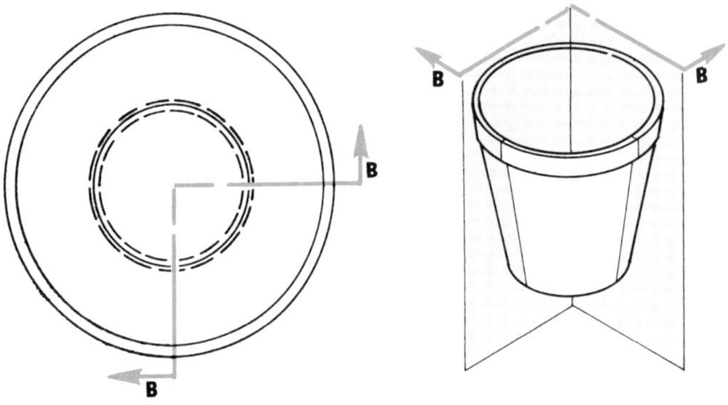

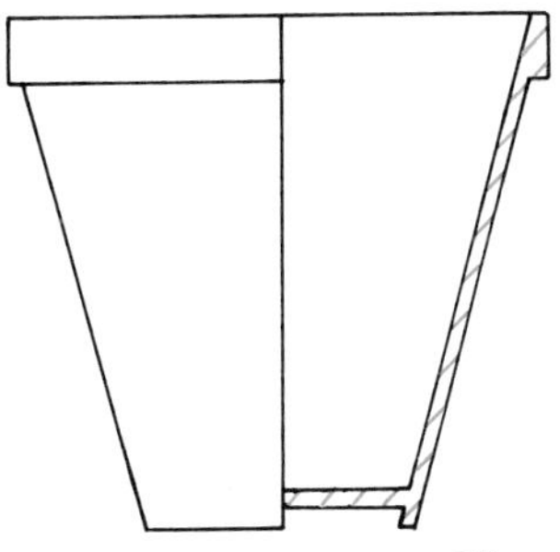

SECTION BB

Fig. 6-24. Example of a half-sectionview of a foam cup. Note the cutout portion and the section lining in the front view.

Developing Other Types of Section Views

Many variations of section views are used in industrial situations. These section views include offset sections, Fig. 6-25, revolved sections, Fig. 6-26, and removed sections. In each situation, the part is cut and the cross-sectional area exposed to add understanding.

DEVELOPING ISOMETRIC DRAWINGS

Isometric drawings provide a three-dimensional image of an object. Refer back to Chapter 4, PROJECTING IMAGES, to refresh your understanding of this topic. As with isometric sketching, there are three basic axes. The axes are: 1) vertical, 2) 30 degrees upward to the right, and 3) 30 degrees upward to the left.

In an isometric, front is on the left, the right side is on the right, and the top is on the top. Several problems occur when drawing an isometric view. These include: where to start, what scale to use, and how to draw arcs and circles.

Finding the Starting Point

Study Fig. 6-27 as you proceed to read this subject. First, locate the center of the rectangular drawing area. A simple way is to lightly draw diagonals across the rectangle from corner to opposite corner. Where the two diagonal lines intersect is the center point.

The starting point is 1/2 the height, 1/2 the length, and 1/2 the depth away from the center of the rectangle. If the desired starting point is at the low corner of the isometric view, move from the center of the rectangle down 1/2 the height. Next, move diagonally, down to the right 1/2 of the length. Then, move diagonally, down to the left, 1/2 to the depth. This is your starting point.

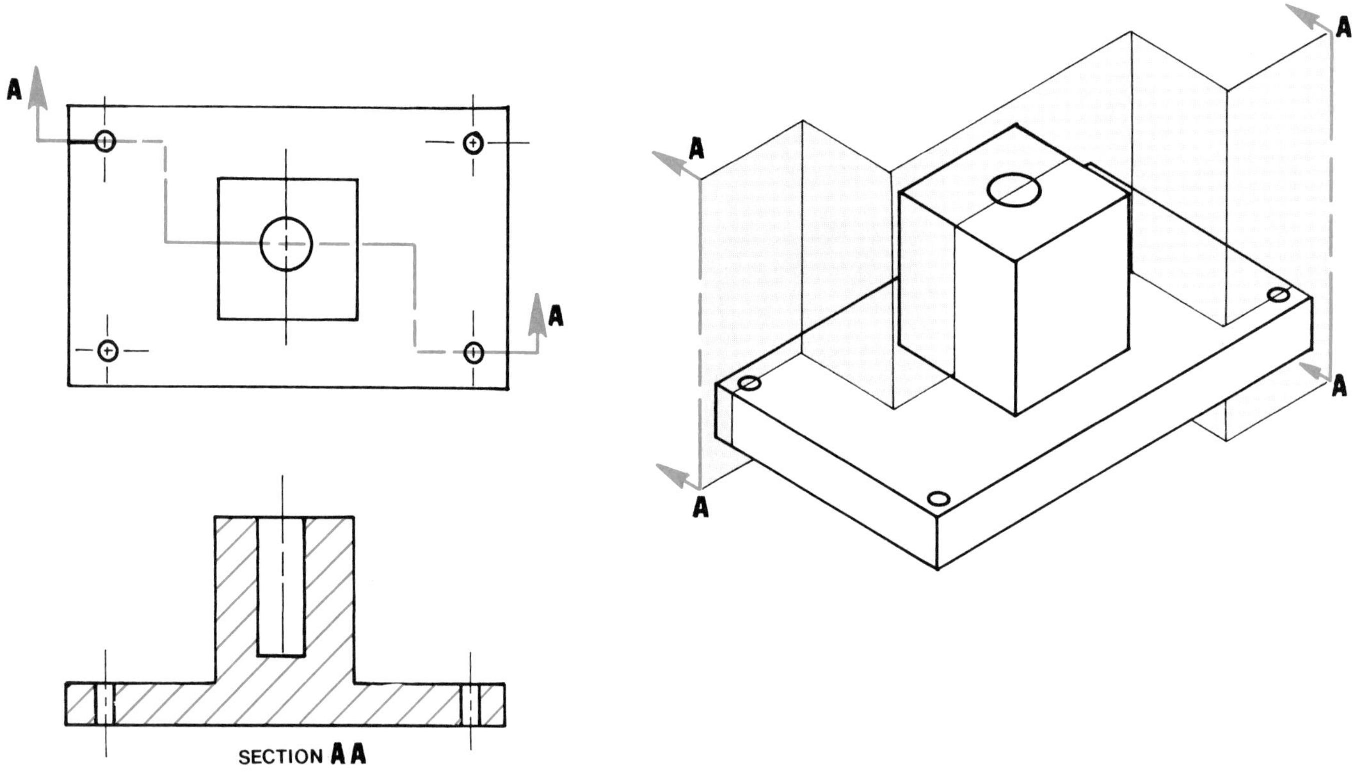

Fig. 6-25. Example of an offset section view showing how the cutting plane may zigzag across a part to produce the best view and understanding of the interior of the part.

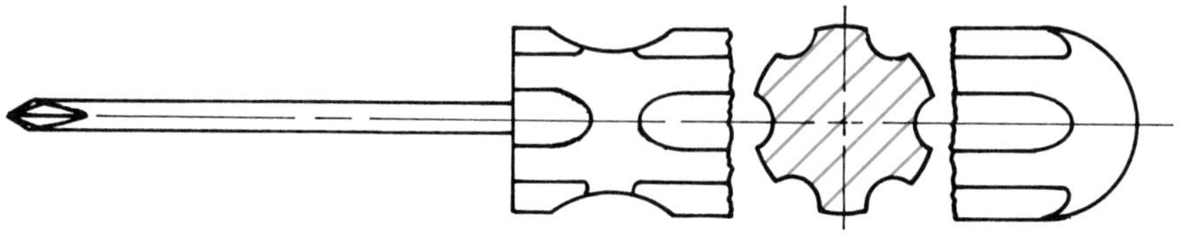

Fig. 6-26. Example of a revolved section view of a screwdriver handle. This turned or rotated section presents an accurate visualization of the part.

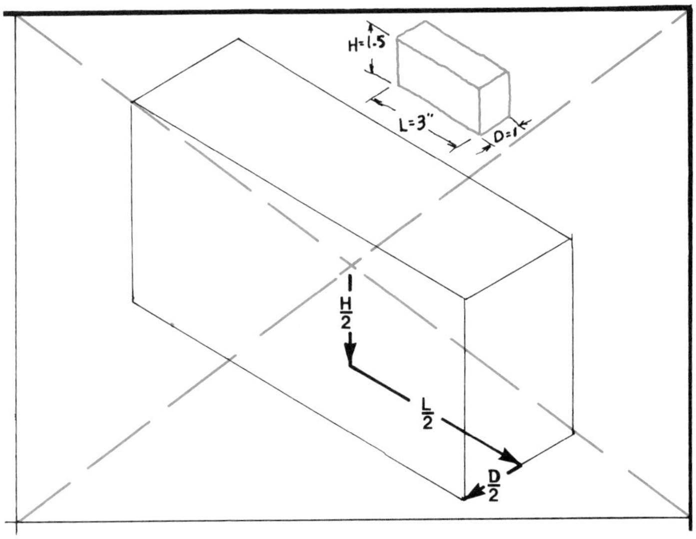

Fig. 6-27. How to locate the starting point for an isometric drawing. The light diagonal lines locate the center of the space.

Selecting the Scale

The scale for the isometric view does not have to be the same as the scale for the multiview drawing. Therefore, if the isometric drawing is too large or too small for the space available, select a more appropriate scale. Locate a new starting point and redraw the isometric.

Drawing Arcs and Circles

Drawing arcs and circles on an isometric drawing is completed by using an isometric template or the four-center method. Review the four-center method in INSTRUMENT DRAWING, Chapter 3, if necessary. As in sketching, first locate the center point of the circular shape and then draw the center lines. Use the isometric ellipse template or the four-center method to draw the circular shapes.

DEVELOPING EXPLODED ISOMETRICS

Exploded isometric drawings and sketches are useful when several parts are assembled, such as the refrigerator roller or door hinge, Fig. 6-28. These drawings, also called assembly drawings, are seen in owners manuals for products such as lawnmowers, barbecue grills, children's toys, etc., that consumers unpack and assemble.

The exploded views have advantages and disadvantages over multiview drawings. People readily understand them without drafting knowledge or experience. Their disadvantage is the amount of time and experience required to lay out and draw the exploded parts.

The first step in laying out an exploded view is to mentally explode each part of the drawing. The direction of the explosion of parts is vertical, 2 o'clock-8 o'clock, and 10 o'clock-4 o'clock directions. Then, sketch the parts in the sequence of their assembly.

Layout of the exploded views requires a considerable amount of trial and error to arrange all the parts in a logical sequence within a given space. You may use nonreproducible lead (blue lead) in the layout process. Confusion can be avoided if parts

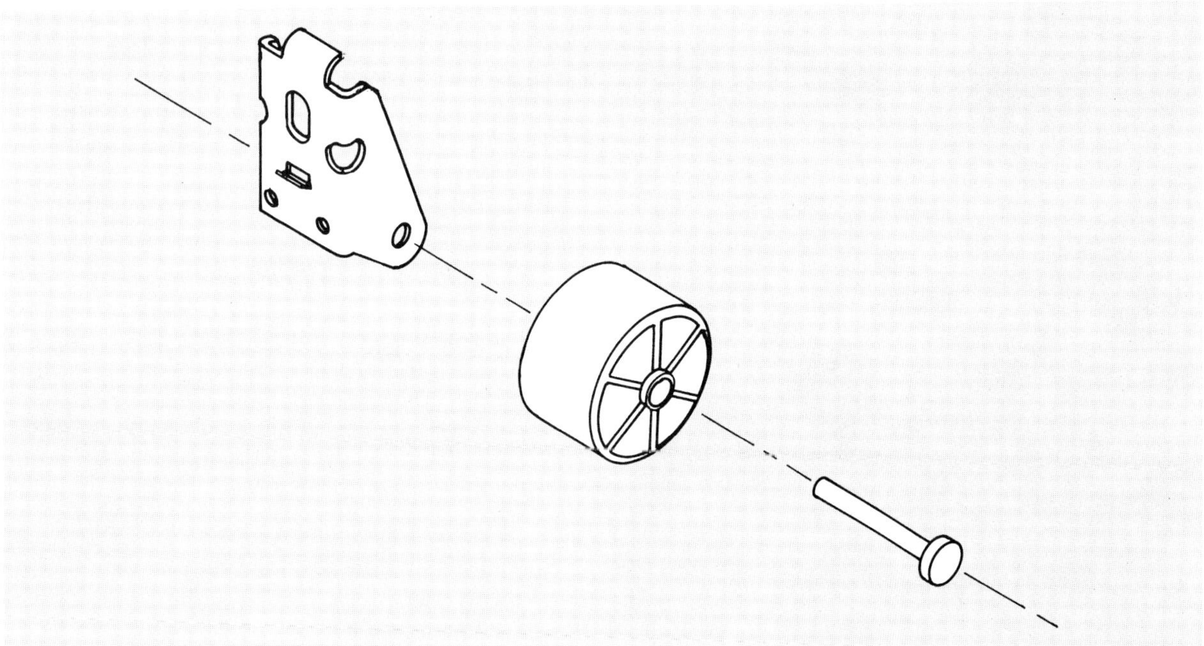

Fig. 6-28. Exploded isometric of the refrigerator components studied earlier in this chapter. Such views improve the understanding of how all of the components fit together.

do not overlap or touch each other. Centerlines, dashed lines, or thin, solid lines connect exploded parts to their assembled locations.

When layout has been completed, the exploded view is drawn professionally on tracing paper. It is then duplicated in a print machine.

PREPARING A DRAWING FOR REPRODUCTION

The drafter will derive satisfaction from accumulating all the information from the initial sketches and basic layout drawings and bring it together by creating working drawings. A working drawing includes all the revisions and improvements that drafting personnel make to clarify drawings for a part or product. Pencils or technical pens are used for preparing working drawings. Pencils are commonly used with tracing paper or vellum. Plastic lead works well with mylar.

Technical pens use a very black ink. They are easy to use and highly recommended. They provide the most professional looking and permanent drawings on tracing paper, vellum, or mylar. Many professionals use three different technical pen sizes for producing drawings, Fig. 6-29. A 3x0/.25 mm pen is used for thin line dimensioning and sectioning. A 1/.50 mm pen is used for thick object lines. A 3/.80 mm pen is used for cutting plane lines or other extra thick lines.

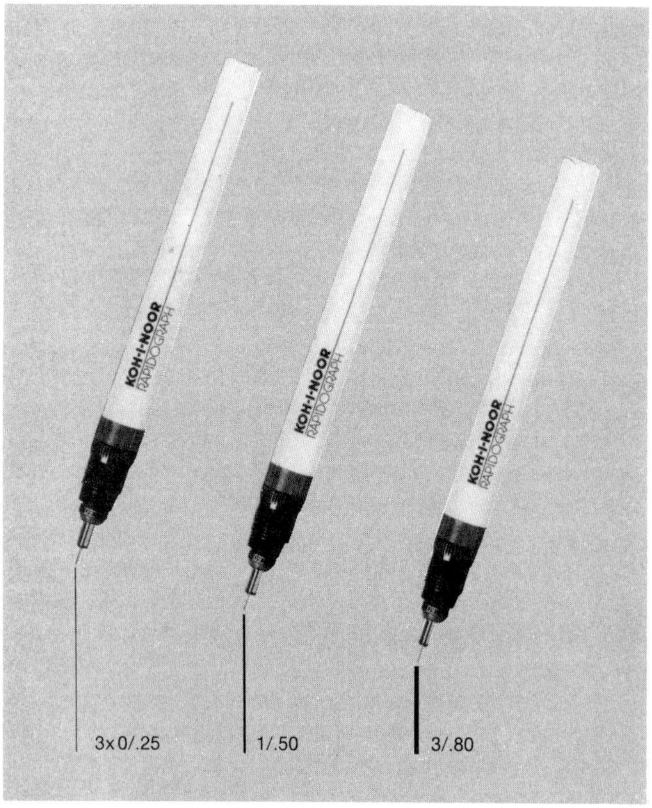

Fig. 6-29. Technical pens typically used for producing drawing which will reproduce well.

The advantage of using technical pens is they produce consistent, accurate lines with a single stroke. Drawings are developed efficiently when the following steps are drawn in sequence. First, draw circles and arcs. Next, draw slanted lines. Finally, draw vertical and horizontal lines. Pause for a few seconds after each line and wait for the ink to dry. This avoids smearing. Erase minor mistakes with the aid of an erasing shield. Fasten a new sheet over the original when major changes are needed and then retrace the lines.

SUMMARY

This chapter consolidates the knowledge and skills you acquired in lettering, sketching, instrument drawing, projecting, and dimensioning. Refer to previous chapters when necessary. You will use these concepts and your creativity to illustrate ideas and products.

Drawings that look professional combine an appropriate arrangement of views, dimensions, and notes. Details include consistent line width, line connections, precise dimensioning, section lining, accurate lettering, and notes. Overall neatness in appearance is a must.

The following checklist represents criteria that may apply to your drawings:

1. Select approprite views.
2. Arrange views correctly.
3. Select proper scale and paper size.
4. Demonstrate neatness in layout.
5. Use consistent line width.
6. Provide accurate line connections.
7. Use precision in dimensioning.
8. Provide consistent section lining.
9. Be accurate in lettering and notes.
10. Concentrate on overall neatness in appearance.

Keep this checklist handy by your board. As you develop a drawing, constantly refer to this list in order to product professional quality results.

Chapter 6—WORKING DRAWINGS
Review What You Have Learned

Write your answers on a separate sheet of paper. Do not write in this textbook.

Essay:

1. Write a brief statement describing the processes involved in developing a working drawing. Be sure to include specific detailed examples.
2. Write an explanation of how working drawings are used by a hobbyist and by an industrial team. One paragraph should compare the

similarities between the two uses. Another paragraph should contrast the differences between the two uses. You may use a hobby or personal examples in your explanation.

Multiple Choice: Carefully read the statements below and write the letter of the best answer for each of the items on your answer sheet.

3. Working drawings often include:
   a. Multiview projections.
   b. Dimensions.
   c. Section views.
   d. Notes.
   e. All of these.
4. When laying out a working drawing, it is recommended that you use a pencil and ________.
   a. Drawing paper.
   b. Tracing paper.
   c. Vellum.
   d. Mylar.
   e. Any of these.
5. When preparing a set of working drawings, the drafter may:
   a. Sketch.
   b. Draw.
   c. Resketch.
   d. Redraw.
   e. All of these.
6. Section-lining lines must be consistent:
   a. Width.
   b. Direction.
   c. Spacing.
   d. Starting/stopping points.
   e. All of these.
7. When a cutting plane line passes through the center of a circular object so the adjacent view is totally exposed, it is called a:
   a. Half section.
   b. Full section.
   c. Revolved section.
   d. Offset section.
   e. None of these.

True or False: Carefully read the statements below. Write a "T" on your answer sheet for the statements which are true. For the statements which are false, write an "F." Rewrite each false statement so it becomes true.

8. Preparing working drawings requires knowledge, skill, and creativity. True or False?
9. Final working drawings are usually drawn on light green or cream colored paper. True or False?
10. Working drawings may be changed in layout many times before they become finalized. True or False?
11. A working drawing with a top and front view only could not provide enough information. True or False?
12. Drafting personnel must focus on providing adequate information in a clear and attractive manner. True or False?
13. Whether a part is drawn for size, expanded, or reduced in scale, the dimensions are always actual size. True or False?
14. The spacing of section lining may be controlled by using a 45 x 45 x 90 triangle with a line scratched parallel to the hypotenuse. True or False?
15. Drawing circles or arcs on an isometric drawing may be completed by using an isometric template or the two-center method. True or False?

Matching: Read the numbered items in Column A and match the names of the materials with the symbols from Column B that represent the materials. Place your answers on the separate sheet you have been using for the other review questions.

Column A

16. Steel.
17. Aluminum.
18. Cast iron.
19. Brass/bronze/copper.
20. Unidentified material.

Column B

a. 

b. 

c. 

d. 

e. 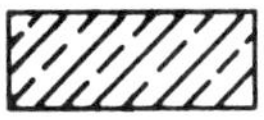

Match the names of lines in column A with their symbols from column B.

Column A

21. Cutting plane.
22. Object.
23. Hidden.
24. Center.
25. Dimension.

Column B

Practice What You Have Learned: On a fresh sheet of drawing paper, neatly prepare a set of working drawings for the items you sketched in Chapter 2 on Sketching for the section Practice What You Have Learned. Demonstrate all of the techniques which you have learned thus far in your studies.

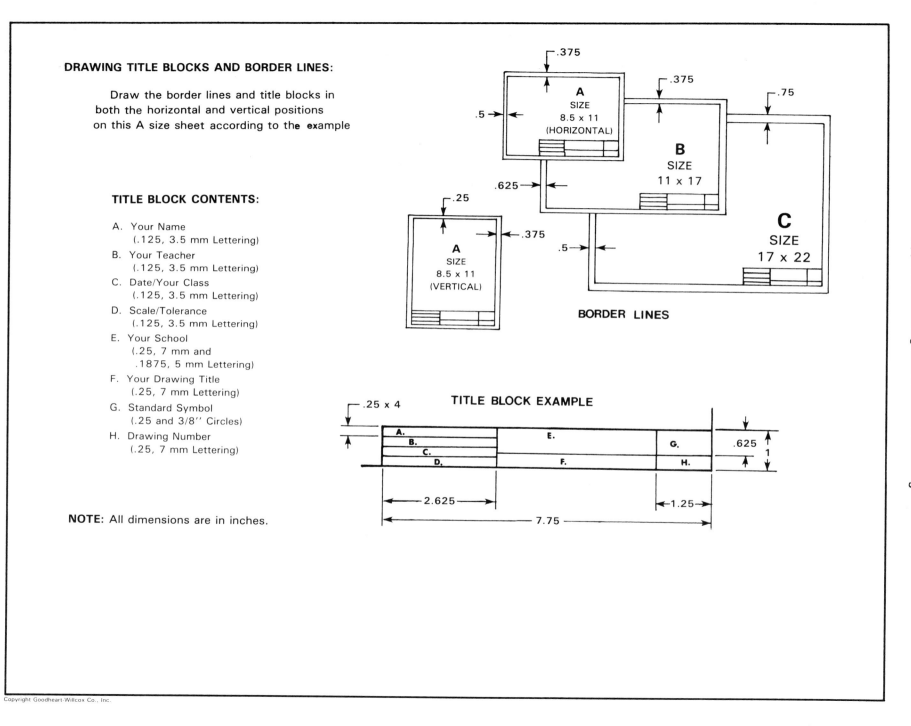

DRAWING TITLE BLOCKS AND BORDER LINES:

Draw the border lines and title blocks in both the horizontal and vertical positions on this A size sheet according to the example

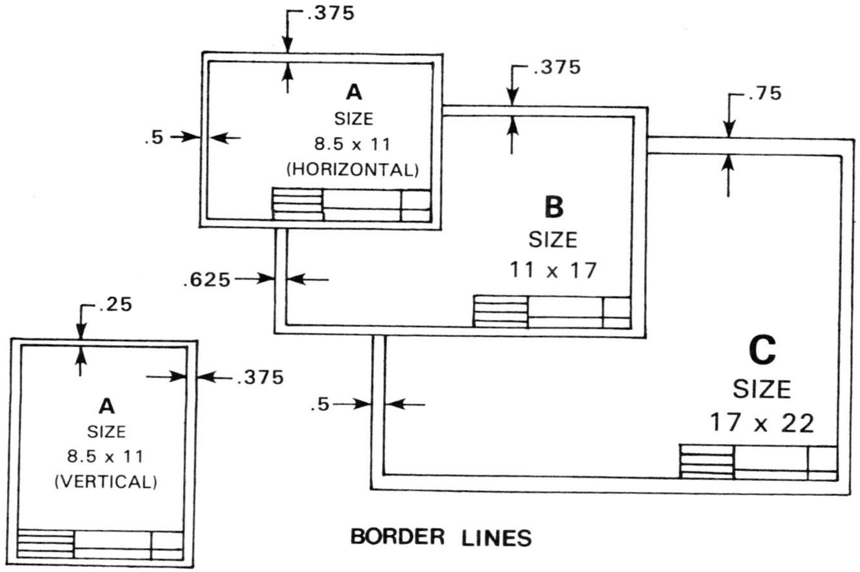

BORDER LINES

TITLE BLOCK CONTENTS:

A. Your Name
(.125, 3.5 mm Lettering)
B. Your Teacher
(.125, 3.5 mm Lettering)
C. Date/Your Class
(.125, 3.5 mm Lettering)
D. Scale/Tolerance
(.125, 3.5 mm Lettering)
E. Your School
(.25, 7 mm and
.1875, 5 mm Lettering)
F. Your Drawing Title
(.25, 7 mm Lettering)
G. Standard Symbol
(.25 and 3/8'' Circles)
H. Drawing Number
(.25, 7 mm Lettering)

TITLE BLOCK EXAMPLE

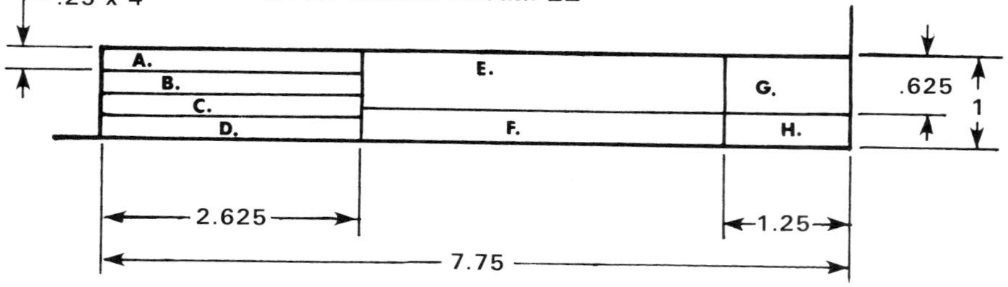

NOTE: All dimensions are in inches.

6-1 DRAWING TITLE BLOCKS AND BORDER LINES. On a separate sheet of paper, carefully draw the various title blocks.

NOTE: Rounds 1/8 radius.
All dimensions in inches.

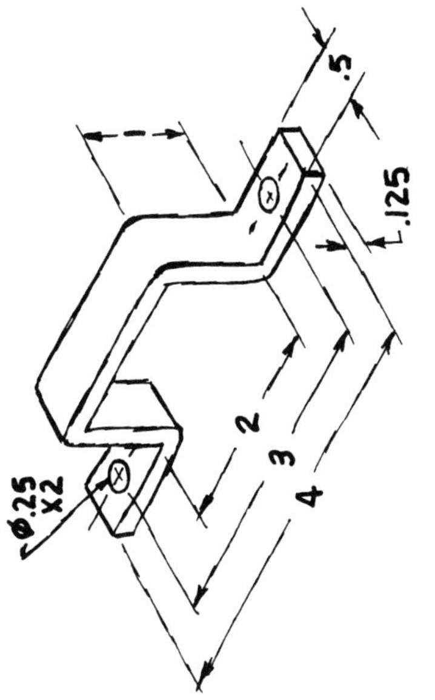

6-2 WORKING DRAWING OF LATCH. Using the sketch of the latch, lay out the title block, draw a multiview, and dimension to full scale. Provide the necessary information for the latch to be produced.

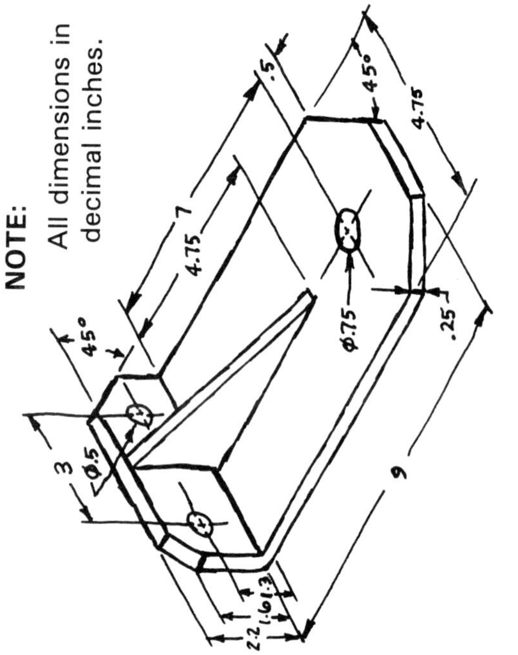

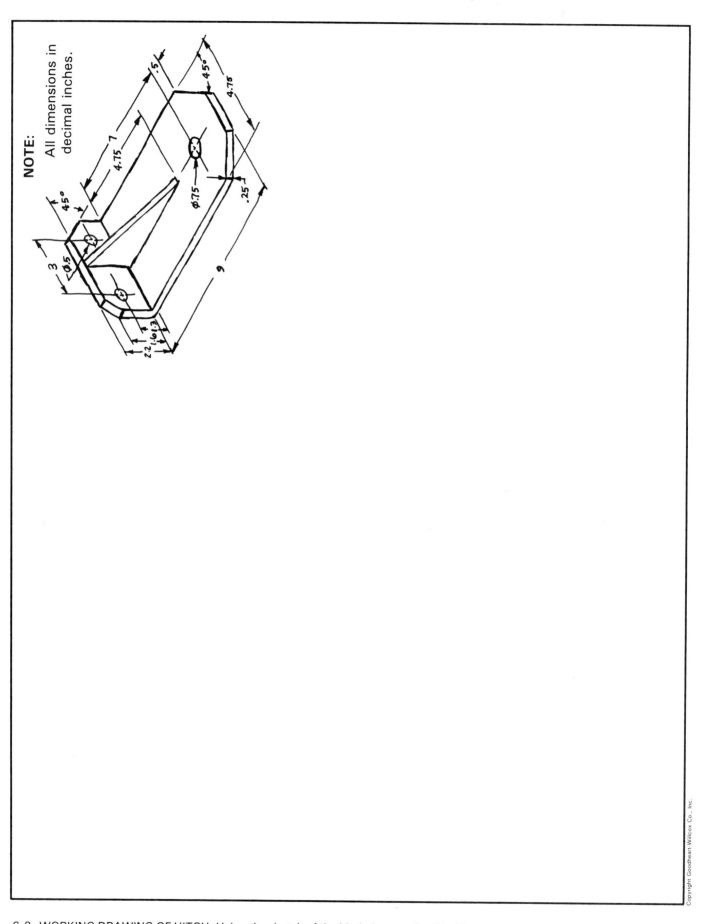

6-3 WORKING DRAWING OF HITCH. Using the sketch of the hitch, lay out the title block, draw the multiviews, and dimension to 1/2 scale by using the 20 scale engineer's scale.

NOTE:
All dimensions in millimeters.

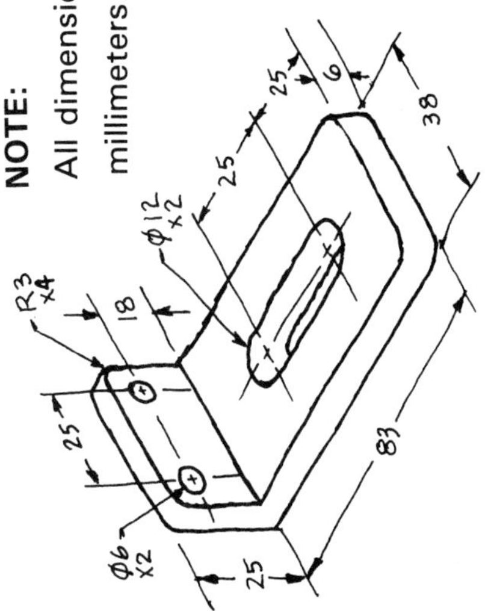

6-4 WORKING DRAWING OF BRACKET. Using the sketch of the bracket, lay out the title block, draw the multiviews, and dimension in full scale. Provide all the necessary information for the bracket to be produced.

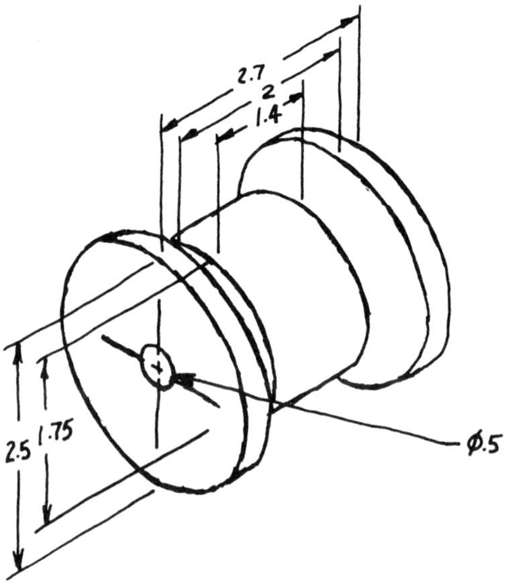

6-5 WORKING DRAWING OF SPOOL. Use the sketch of the spool to draw the working drawing which includes a full section view. Draw 1'' = 1' scale. Add a title block. Use the general cast iron symbol for section lines.

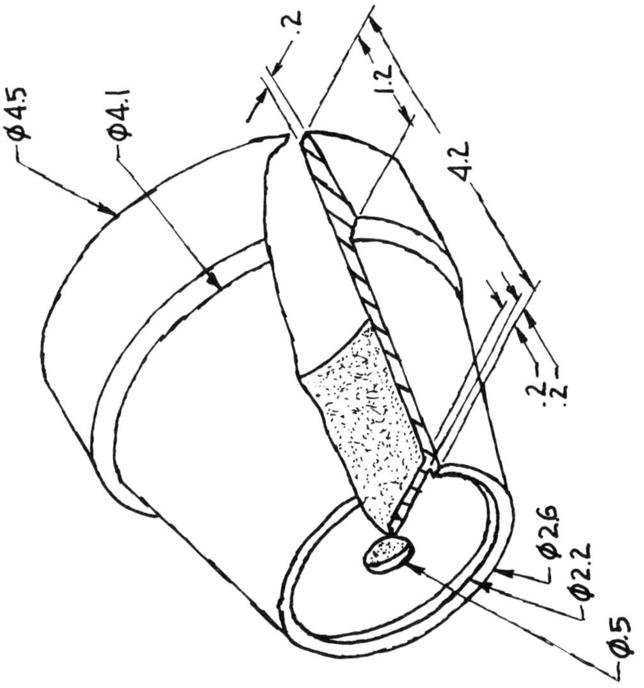

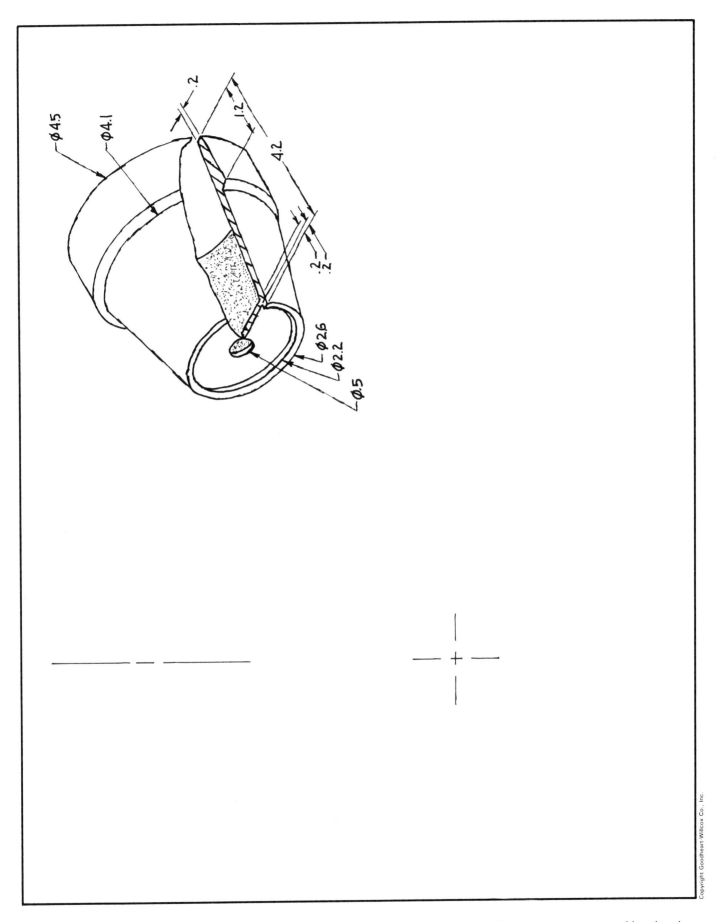

6-6 WORKING DRAWING OF FLOWER POT. Lay out a title block. Use the sketch of the flower pot to create working drawing which includes a half section view. Sectioin the material with the glass or white metal symbol. Draw to the 20 scale and dimension.

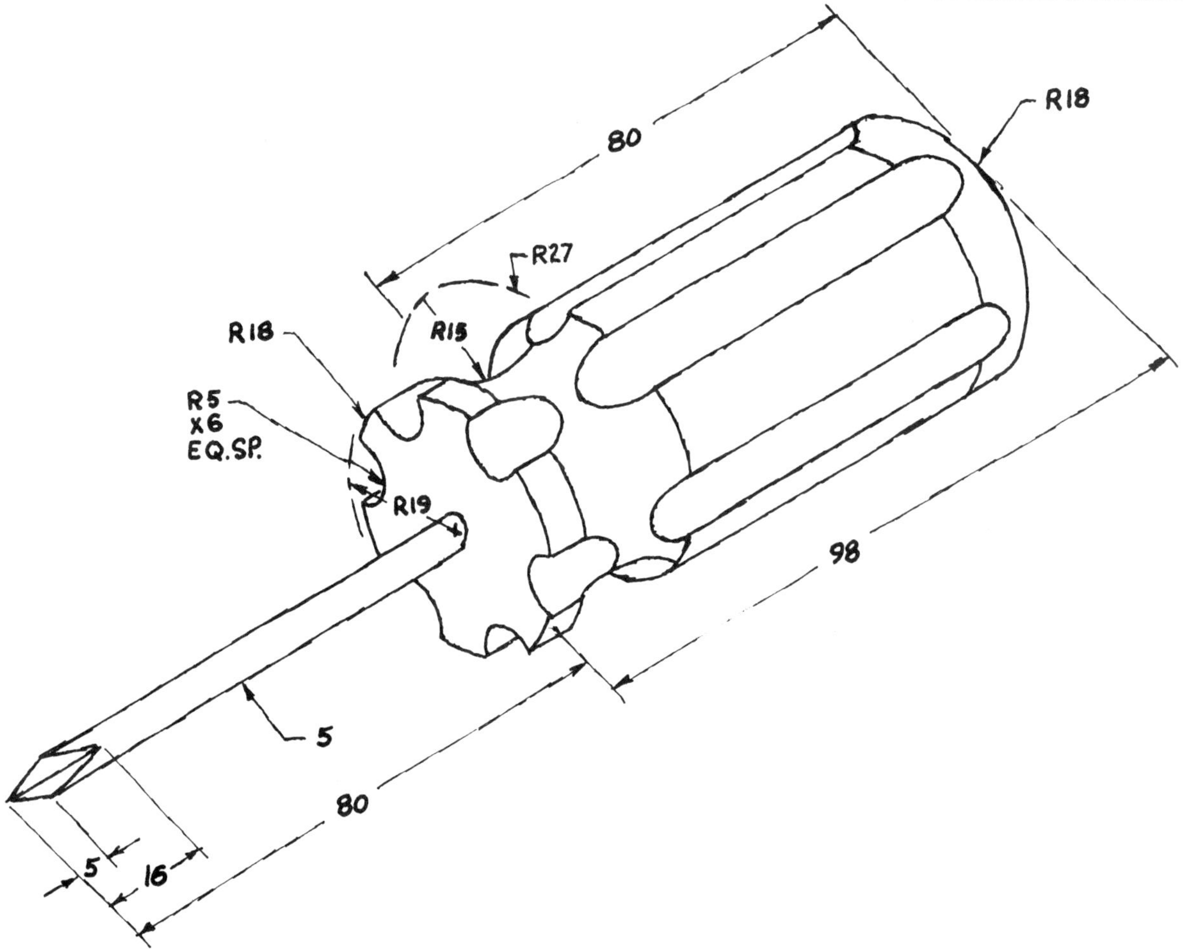

6-7 WORKING DRAWING OF SCREWDRIVER. Lay out the border and title block. Use the sketch provided to create a working drawing which includes a revolved section view. Use plastic or aluminum symbol for the section lining. Draw to the 1:1 metric scale and dimension.

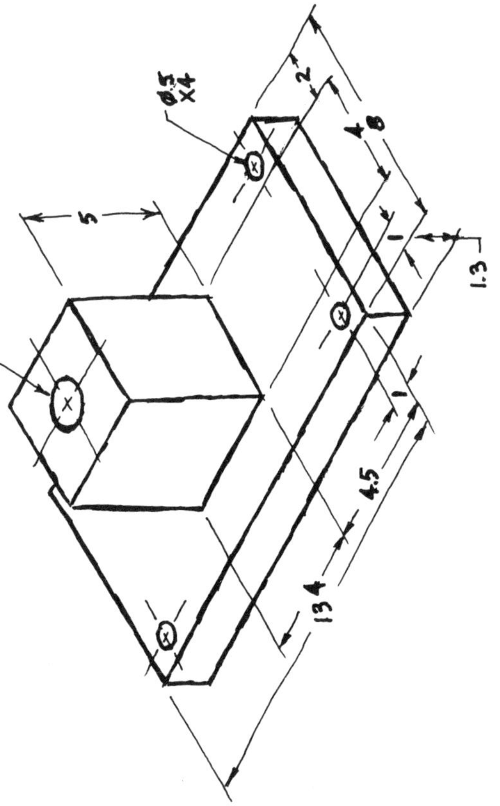

6-8 WORKING DRAWING OF OFFSET BRACKET. Lay out border and title block. Use the sketch provided to create a working drawing which includes an offset section. Use steel or brass symbol for the section lining. Draw to the 40 scale and dimension.

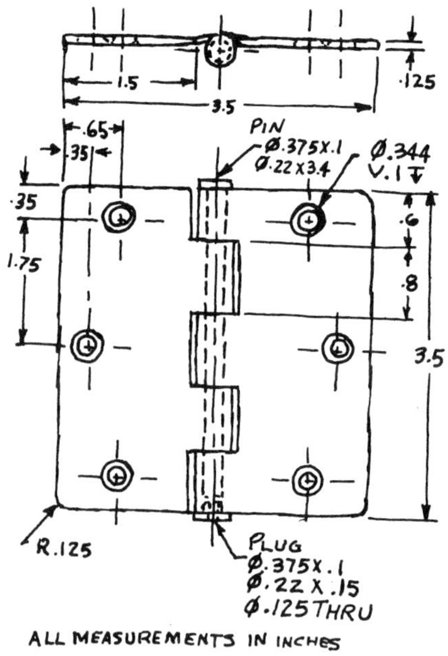

6-9 EXLODED ISOMETRIC VIEW OF DOOR HINGE. Lay out the border and the title block. Draw and dimension an exploded isometric view using the sketch of the door hinge. Use the 10 scale on the engineer's scale.

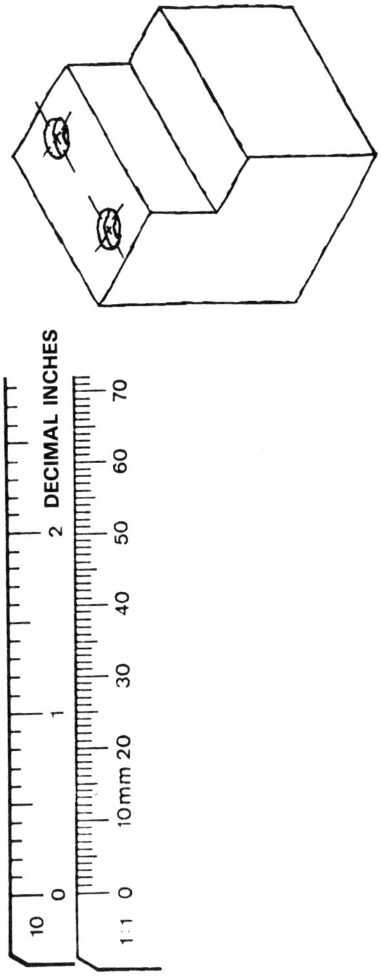

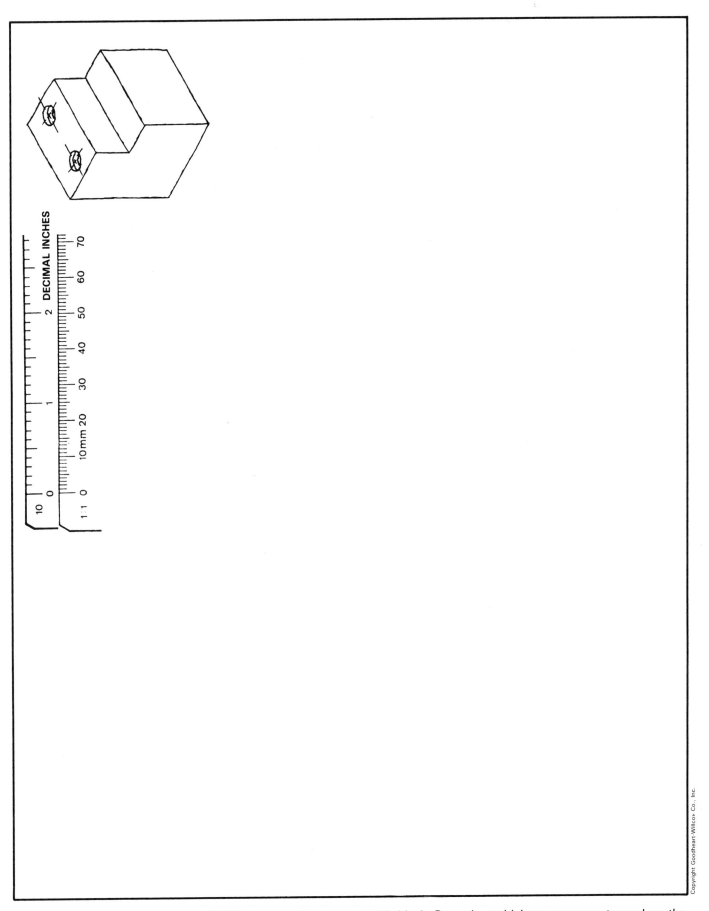

6-10 WORKING DRAWING OF FIXTURE. Lay out a border and a title block. Draw the multiviews necessary to produce the fixture. Use geometric dimensioning and tolerancing with either the metric or decimal inch scales provided. Use datums and tolerances related to form, profile orientation, and location. Consider using 1st angle projection for this drawing.

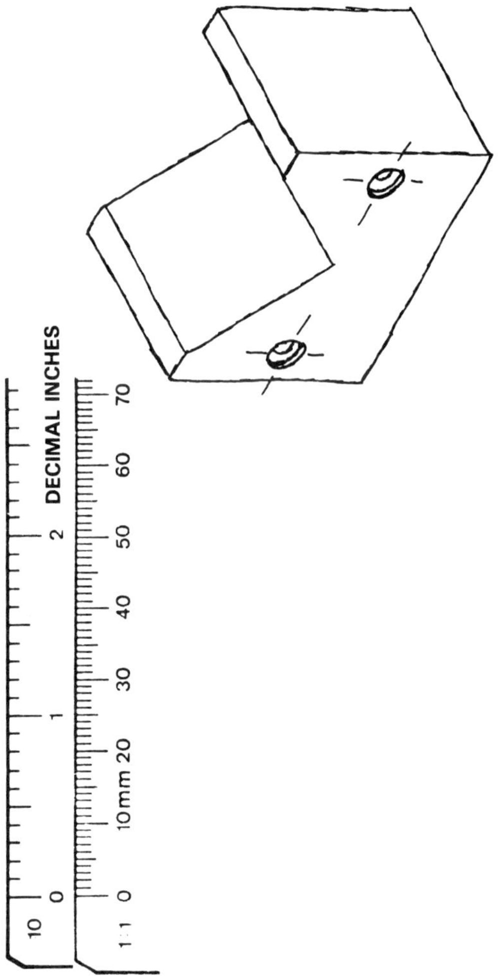

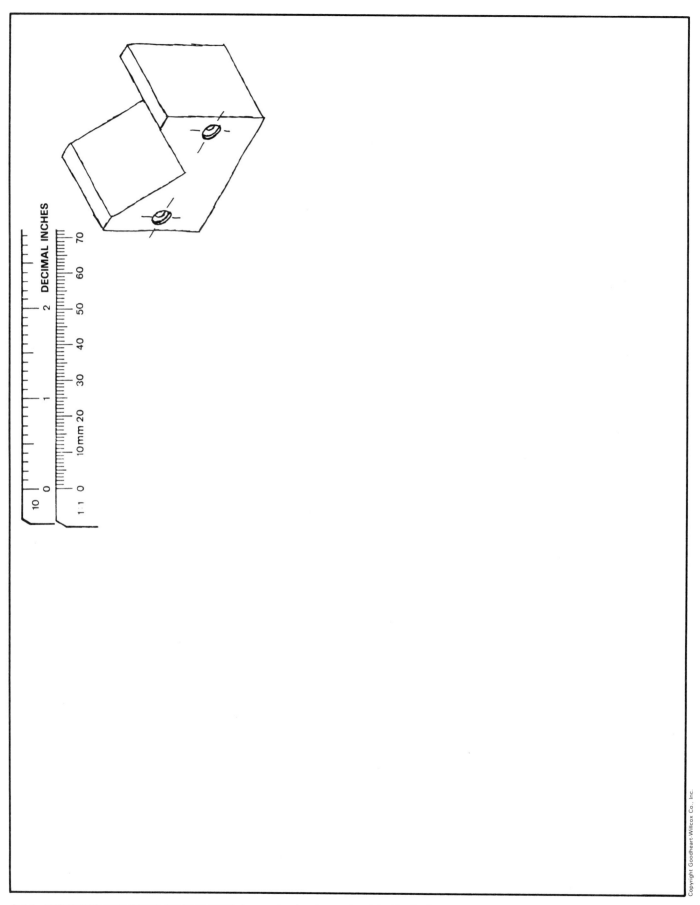

6-11 WORKING DRAWING OF V-BLOCK. Lay out a border and a title block. Draw the multiviews necessary to produce the V-block. Use geometric dimensioning and tolerancing with either the metric or the decimal inch scales provided. Use datums and tolerances related to form, profile orientation, and location. Consider using 1st angle projection for this drawing.

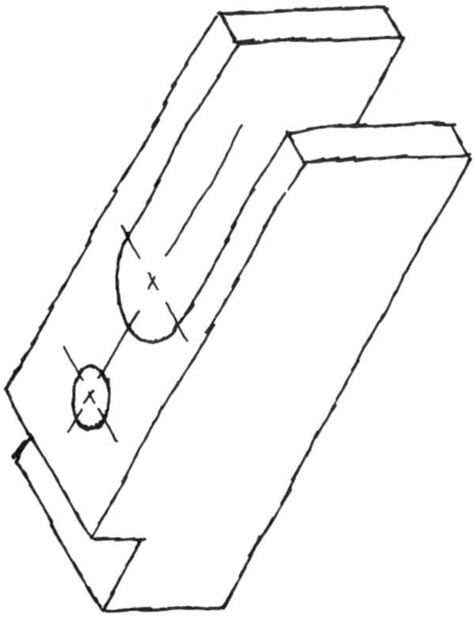

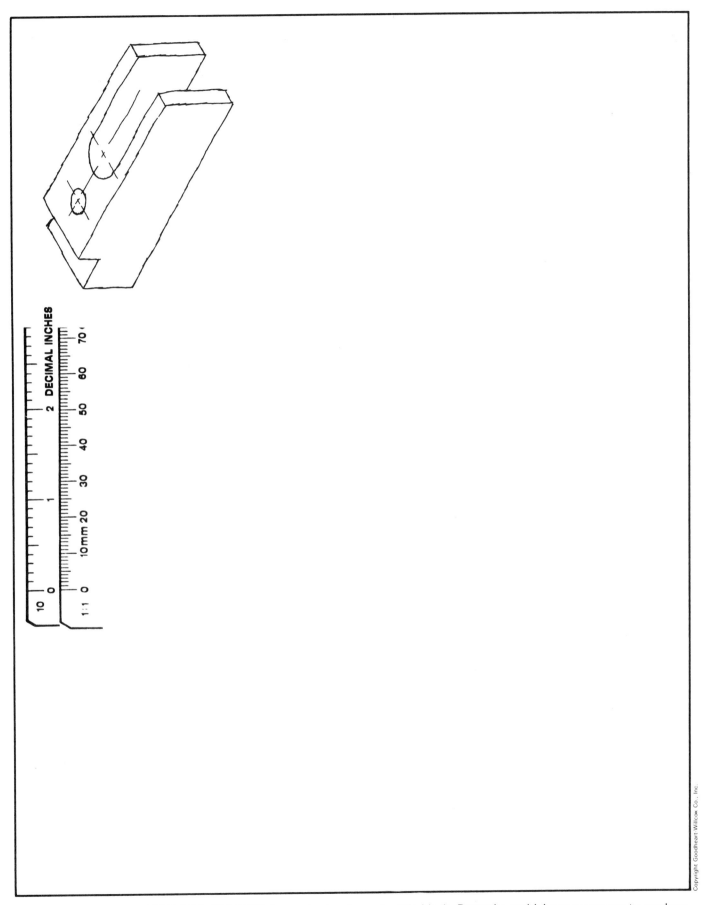

6-12 WORKING DRAWING OF C-BRACKET. Lay out a border and a title block. Draw the multiviews necessary to produce the C-block. Use geometric dimensioning and tolerancing with either the metric or the decimal inch scales provided. Use datums and tolerances related to form, profile orientation, and location. Consider using 1st angle projection for this drawing.

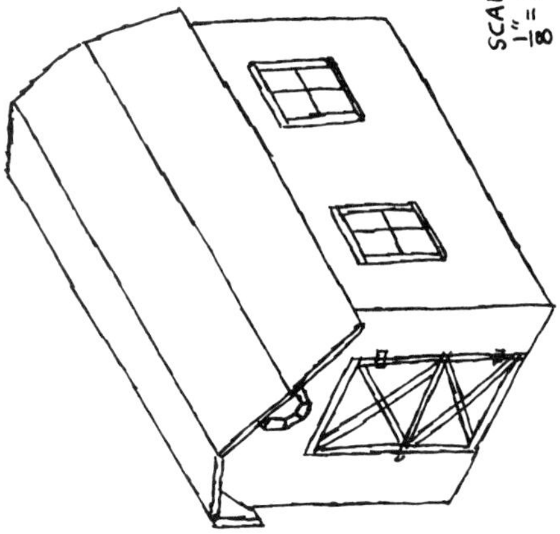

6-13 WORKING DRAWING OF STORAGE SHED. Lay out a border and a title block. Draw and dimension a front elevation, side elevation, and floor plan of the sketched storage shed. Use the architect's scale. Locate and label storage areas for lawn tools, mowers, bicycles, etc. Scales to be 1/8' = 1'.

Chapter 7

COMPUTER-ASSISTED DRAFTING AND DESIGN

OBJECTIVES

After completing this chapter in COMPUTER-ASSISTED DRAFTING AND DESIGN, you will be able to:

- ☐ *Recognize the advantages of the computer in design and drafting.*
- ☐ *Demonstrate access procedures for your specific system.*
- ☐ *Label points with X, Y, and Z coordinates.*
- ☐ *Draw various types of lines, arcs, and circles.*
- ☐ *Complete two-dimensional views of rectangular objects.*
- ☐ *Complete three-dimensional views of rectangular objects.*
- ☐ *Select standard view options to draw multiviews and isometrics.*
- ☐ *Select and use dimensioning, sectioning, and lettering capabilities.*
- ☐ *Store data and print approved drawings.*

The computer has revolutionized our culture including the way we design and draw. Systems of hardware and software have emerged that allow the hobbyist to design and create drawings with a personal computer. On the other end of the continuum, corporations make substantial investments in mainframe computers and advanced software to aid in the design, drawing, and control of manufactured products.

The primary advantage of Computer-Assisted Drafting and Design (CADD) is that it allows the designer to remove, replace, modify, and manipulate drawings instantly as images on the screen. This process is entertaining, saves the designer time, and allows for tremendous flexibility.

The computer and its software allow the designer to create images on a screen, Fig. 7-1. Changes may be made on the screen before images are drawn on paper by a plotter. Prior to using the computer for designing and drafting, an understanding of the basic drafting language must be acquired and understood. This language includes the selection and arrangement of views, correct dimensioning procedures, and the provision of appropriate notes as reviewed in the previous chapters. This learning experience may be gained through traditional board work or through CADD exercises.

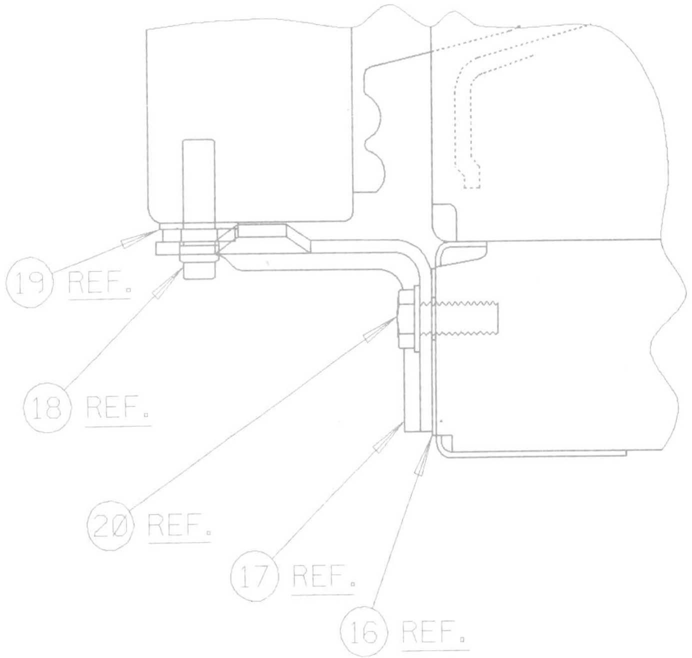

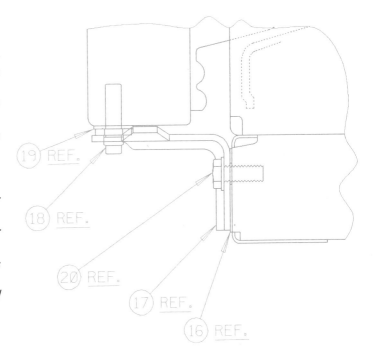

Fig. 7-1. Refrigerator door hinge drawn with an industrial CADD system. This hard copy plot is the same example used in previous chapters of this text.

Many experts feel board work, followed by CADD experiences, is the most efficient method of learning drafting. This method is supported by the idea that a certain amount of "soaking time" is needed to absorb the basic language without the addition of friendly or unfriendly messages from a computer.

Difficult decisions are required in determining the real cost effectiveness of computer-assisted drafting and design. The initial investment in hardware, software, and training is either absorbed by the individual or passed along to consumers. Consideration must also be given to the expenses related to routine service, system updates, and continuing education to keep up with trends and developments.

FUNDAMENTALS

CADD systems include a variety of hardware and software components. The hardware components include input devices, a central processing unit (CPU), data storage devices, and output devides, Fig. 7-2.

With a personal computer, the input device would be the keyboard and may include a light pen, mouse, or graphics tablet. The central processing unit (CPU) is the computer. The storage device with most systems is the disk drive. The output devices include the video monitor (screen), and a printer or plotter. Software includes a program stored on a floppy disk and an instruction manual.

The larger and more expensive systems used in industry utilize a light pen and graphic tablets almost exclusively as input devices. The CPU is usually expensive and capable of a wide range of options. The CPU may be located either near the input devices or at another location and connected to the input device by telephone modem or dedicated wiring. Output devices may include a screen along with various types and sizes of plotters. The software includes programs stored and accessed from the CPU. Storage apparatus may be on magnetic tape or hard disk located near the CPU.

Each CADD system has a unique procedure for usage that is explained in the written manual provided with the system. Numerous classes and seminars are available to support learning about CADD systems.

Access procedures for personal CADD systems include turning on the computer, printer, screen, and disk drive in the proper sequence. This is followed by loading and accessing the software

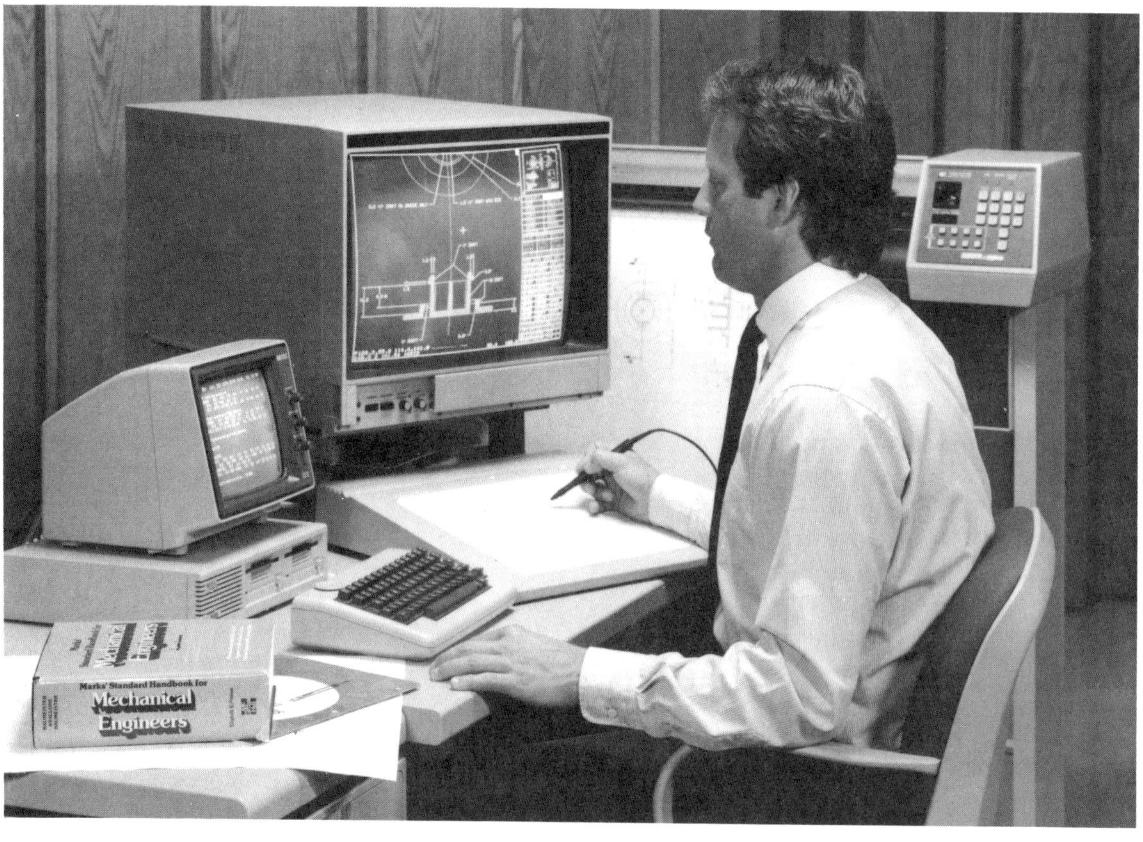

Fig. 7-2. Typical CADD system showing the central processing unit (CPU) set on the floor next to the desk, a dual disk drive unit for reading the disks, a keyboard and a digitzer tablet and styles for input, a monitor for viewing and progress being made on the drawing, and a plotter in the background. Note the reference manuals and the microfilm reader as resources for the drafter. (Hewlett-Packard)

from the disk. Images of lines, arcs, circles, and notes may then be created. Drawings are made by interacting with menu options. These options are explained in the written manual provided with your system. After completing drawings, you may store and/or print them. Access, usage, and exit procedures must be followed explicitly to avoid frustration and "unfriendly" messages. As you learn more about CADD systems and their capabilities, remember to SAVE your work!

Accessing the larger and more expensive systems requires specific log-on procedures. These systems often include coded messages. User-identification numbers and other coded information are often needed to access the mainframe CPU.

By selecting and completing options from the menu, your mental images are recorded on the screen. These options are chosen from the menu with the light pen or mouse. Additional input, such as coordinate points, distances, angles, and positions, is then provided. The images appear on the screen as lines, arcs, and circles. These images may be modified by returning to the menu and changing the distances, angles, and positions. The ability to make these changes represents an advantage of CADD compared with conventional drafting practices. These changes are instantaneous, while changes made on the drawing board may be very time consuming. This flexibility gives the CADD drafter more options and more creative freedom to experiment.

COMMON CADD PRACTICES

You may gain experience with CADD procedures similar to drawing on a board with traditional drafting tools. These procedures involve learning to draw lines, arcs, and circles. These elements are then connected to form the front view of an object. As you have learned, the front view of an object shows the length and height, but no depth.

You should practice drawing a variety of front views which include horizontal, vertical, and slanted lines, combined with arcs and circles. This practice will provide exposure to the various menu options as well as interactions with input and output devices.

As a beginner, you will learn a tremendous amount of information in a short period of time. You will gain confidence in your CADD skills so you can

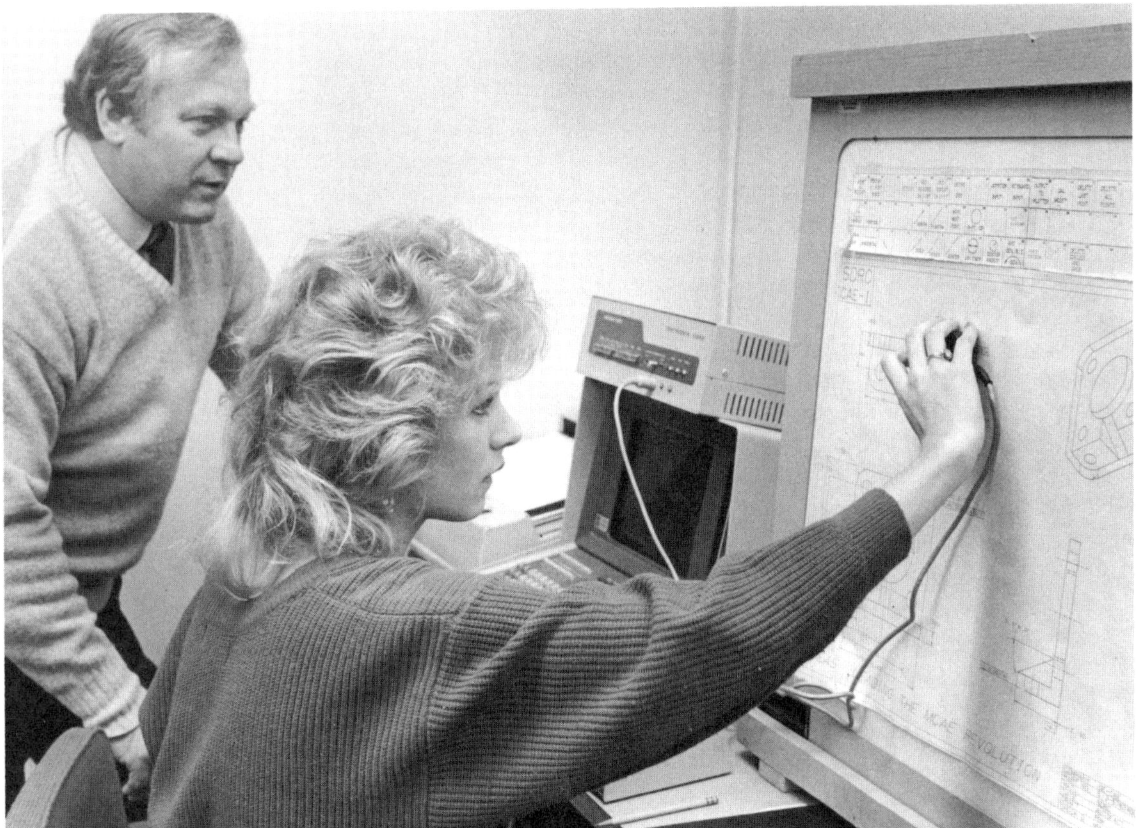

Fig. 7-3. Student using a "puck" to enter the points off a drawing taped to a graphics table. The information stored in the CADD system can be called up and manipulated to revise or alter the drawing at anytime in the future.

confront more complex or difficult problems. The next step is to work in three dimensions by adding depth to the front views which you have completed. After you become familiar with the menu and the basic operations of your system, you will be ready to draw images in three dimensions.

Before printing or plotting, drawings are often modified, revised, or "cleaned up." These modifications may require several days and a CADD system will allow you to save your drawings within its memory. You should determine at what point your work should be saved and outline the specific procedures you must follow to create a storage file.

When a print of the drawing is needed, a plotter is used to transfer the image from the screen to the paper (hard copy). After the hard copy is made, decide whether or not to save your work in storage for future use or to delete it from the file.

Another advantage of CADD systems is the ability to work on one drawing for a while, store it, and then work on a different drawing. Storage and retrieval is virtually instantaneous. However,you must remember to file your work precisely.

You will be amazed at the speed and accuracy of CADD systems in creating standard views from multiview drawings, Fig. 7-3. In the larger CADD systems, standard views include pictorials that can be rotated in space to view the part from various directions. Plotters can then print a hard copy of the drawings with remarkable speed and accuracy.

USING X, Y, AND Z COORDINATES

A two-dimensional CADD drawing uses coordinates on the X and Y axes. The X and Y coordinates determine the length and width of an object. Three-dimensional CADD drawings utilize coordinates on the X, Y, and Z axes. The Z coordinates add depth, making the drawing three dimensional.

To understand the coordinate system, imagine yourself in an empty room facing one wall, Fig. 7-4. The lower left corner of the wall, called the origin, is the intersection of the X, Y, and Z axes. The horizontal line which joins the front wall to the floor represents the X-axis. The vertical line which joins the front wall to the adjacent wall represents the Y-axis. The edge formed by the adjacent wall and the floor represents the Z-axis.

On the X-axis, movement away from the origin to the right indicates positive X values, Fig. 7-5. On the Y-axis, movement away from the origin upward indicates positive Y values. On the Z-axis, movement forward from the origin along the floor indicates positive Z values. Conversely, movement from the origin to the left along the X-axis indicates negative X values. Downward movement along the Y-axis indicates negative Y values. Movement away from you on the Z-axis indicates negative Z values.

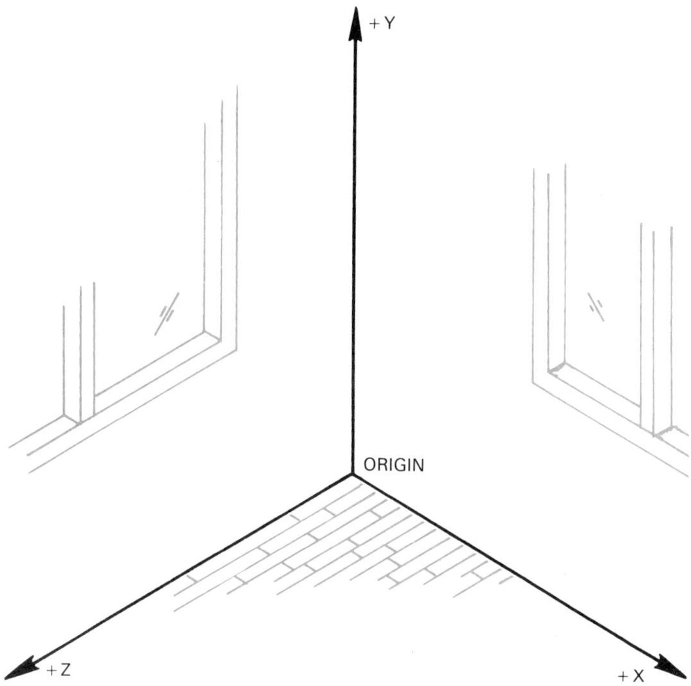

Fig. 7-4. Relating the X, Y, and Z coorindates to the corner of a room.

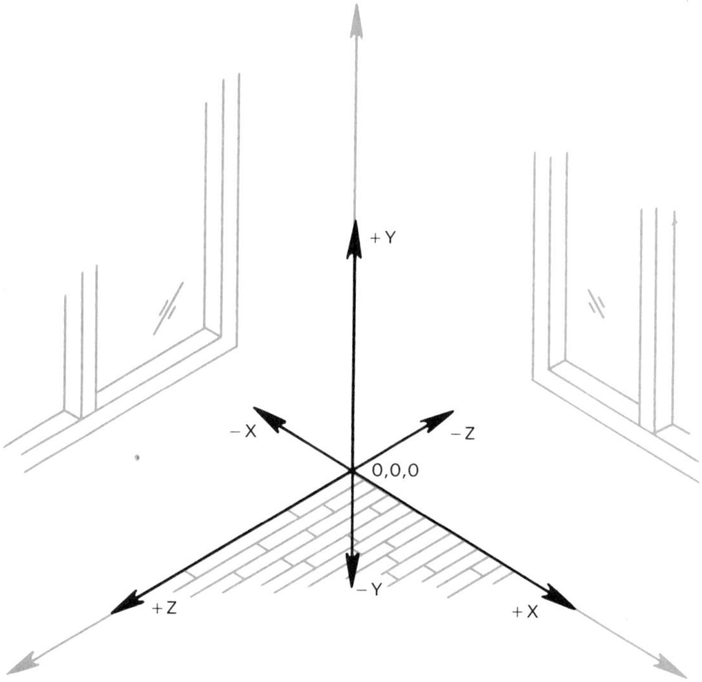

Fig. 7-5. Coordinate system showing X, Y, and Z coordinates. Note how values may be either positive or negative.

These values are always arranged in alphabetical order, (X,Y,Z). For example, to locate (1,2,0), move 1 unit to the right of the origin along the X-axis, move 2 units above the origin along the Y-axis, and move 0 units along the Z-axis, Fig. 7-6. If the coordinates

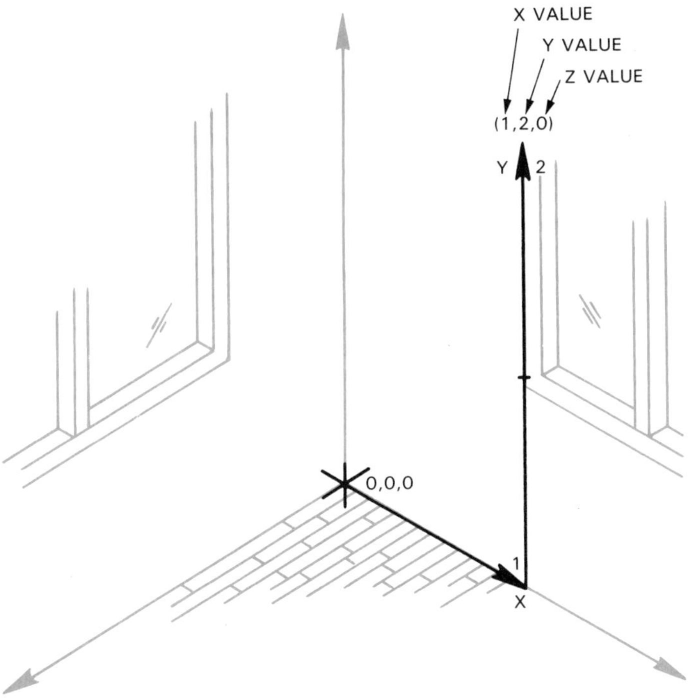

Fig. 7-6. Starting at the origin (0,0,0), move one unit to right and two units up to plot point (1,2,0).

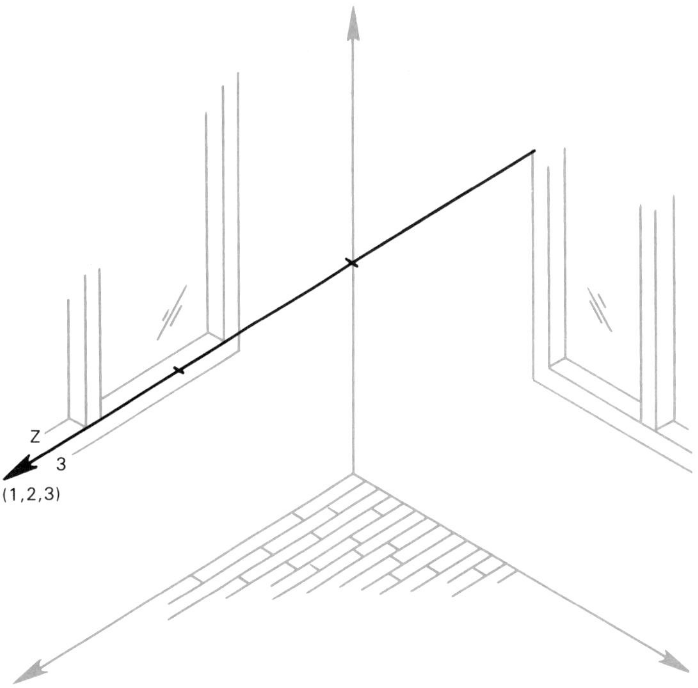

Fig. 7-7. Starting at the origin (0,0,0), follow the example above to plot (1,2,0). Then by moving three units forward, plot point (1,2,3).

are (1,2,3), follow the steps above, and then move 3 units toward you along the Z-axis, Fig. 7-7. If the coordinates are (1,2, −1), follow the steps above to find the X and Y coordinates, then move 1 unit away from you along the Z-axis, Fig. 7-8.

The use of coordinates related to three-dimensional space must become spontaneous in CADD drawing. Practice locating points with X, Y, and Z values until you can use the method automatically. Drawing a line will require two points $(X_1Y_1Z_1)$ $(X_2Y_2Z_2)$. Drawing an arc or circle will require at least one point $(X_1Y_1Z_1)$, as its center. As you can see, creating a drawing could involve hundreds of points. Next, you will learn how to create these elements in a CADD system.

Drawing Lines

The computer program has several types of lines available for use. These include object lines, centerlines, dashed lines, section lines, and lines used in dimensioning. This selection of lines is identical to those you learned too draw by traditional methods earlier in this text.

Lines are commonly created by joining two points located by their coordinates. To do this, X and Y coordinate values are keyed in on the keyboard. The points are then joined, forming a line. Lines may also be created from a single point with a command such as vertical, horizontal, or at a specific angle through the given point. Instructions are provided in the menu for constructing these lines.

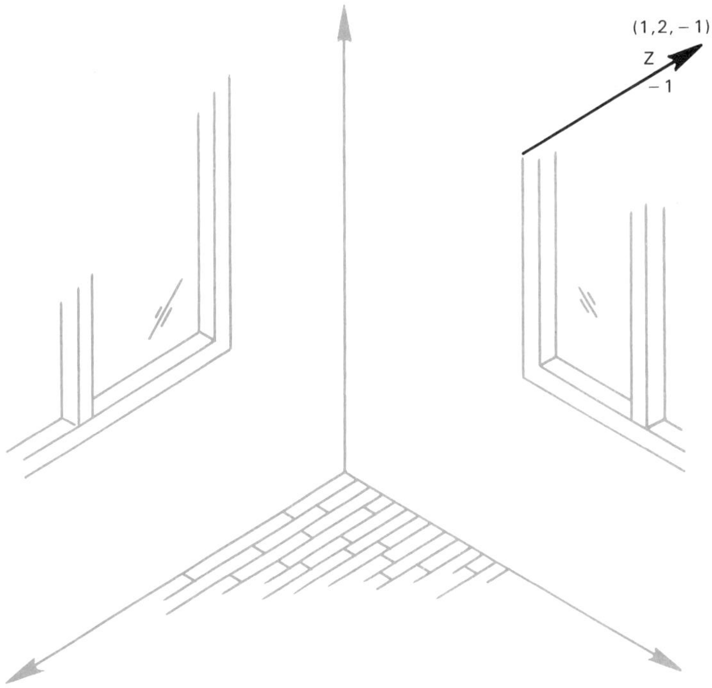

Fig. 7-8. Starting at the origin (0,0,0), follow the example in Fig. 7-6 to plot point (1,2,0). Then by moving one unit back along the Z-axis, you can plot point (1,2, −1).

"Screen position" is another way to create lines. After selecting screen position as a menu option, the location of either a light pen or mouse can be seen as a cursor on the screen. Points are then located by depressing the light pen or mouse at chosen positions. By using a light pen or mouse, end points of a line can be located and placed on the screen thus automatically drawing the line.

Lines can also be repeated by identifing the line to be copied and indicating a command such as ''parallel at a distance'' or ''perpendicular to a line through a given point.''

Drawing Arcs and Circles

The computer program has several ways to draw arcs and circles. The most common method requires a center point and a radius. Locate the center point on the screen and then enter the radius value.

A circle is usually drawn in a counterclockwise direction from 0 to 360 degrees by ''default.'' Default indicates programmed values built into the software program. The default values can be changed if necessary. An arc is also drawn in a counterclockwise direction, but the desired starting and ending degrees must be provided.

Other methods of drawing arcs and circles include using the center point and diameter, or three points on the circumference of the circle.

Mistakes are corrected quite easily for any of the lines, arcs, and circles by deleting, redrawing, and reentering the data.

Connecting Lines to Form a Rectangular Front View Surface

Rectangular surfaces can be created by locating and connecting points similar to a child's ''dot-to-dot'' book. Choose a method for locating points and drawing lines from the options available in your system. Arcs and circles can be added to a surface by using one of the available options, Fig. 7-9.

Again, a major advantage in CADD drawing is in the ability to delete and redraw boundaries instantaneously.

Adding Depth to a Surface with Top and Side Views

When a part or product has been created in the X and Y plane, it has no thickness. Thickness or depth is provided by adding a Z value, which appears in the top and side views, Fig. 7-10. This Z value provides depth in the isometric views.

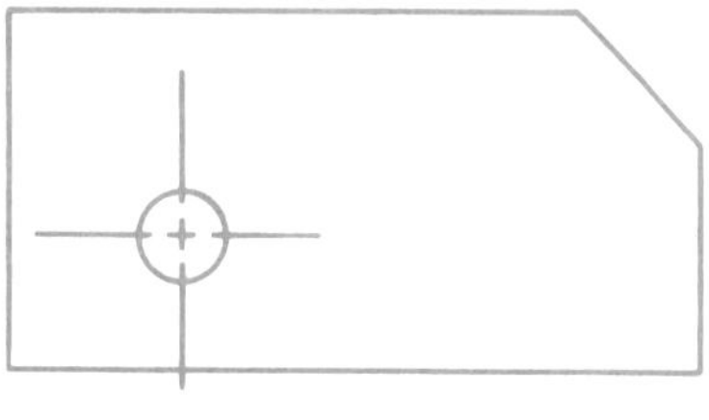

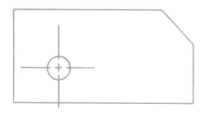

Fig. 7-9. Plotted front view drawn using horizontal lines, vertical lines, slanted line, and circular lines.

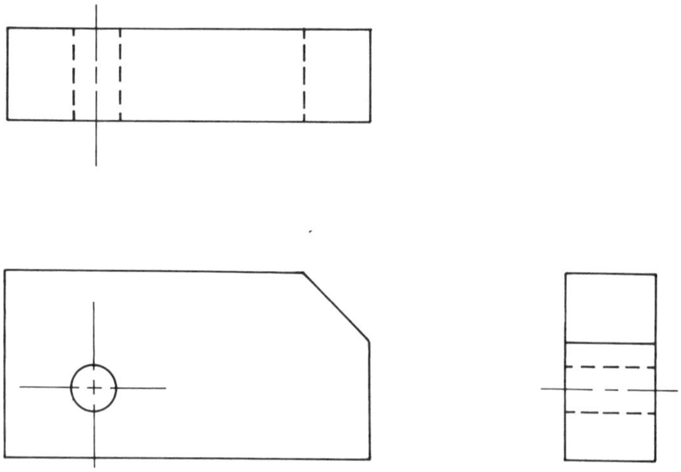

Fig. 7-10. The top view and the side view may be drawn using the Z-coordinate values. These view depth or thickness.

Add the Z value by selecting a depth command from the menu and keying in the value. Many systems draw the top, front, right side, and isometric views by selecting a multiview option from the menu, Fig. 7-11.

The more sophisticated systems have a standard view option that may be selected from the menu. The computer will draw eight standard views. These standard views include: top, front, right side, left side, and isometric.

Dimensioning, Sectioning, and Lettering

As a first step in CADD dimensioning, sketch the type and location of the dimensions that you intend to use. Next, choose the appropriate dimensioning option from the menu and follow the commands with regard to arrowheads and numerical values, Fig. 7-12.

Section views often appear in standard multiview positions, but may be located where space is available. Wherever the section view is located, a cutting plane line must be labeled consistently with the section view. Follow the guidelines you learned in Chapter 6 on drawing section views. Section lining is supplied by selecting the appropriate option from the menu and following its commands.

Numerals and notes may be supplied in designated areas by selecting the appropriate option from the menu and keying in the values and messages. Automatic dimensioning is another option. The computer calculates and displays distances and dimensions the object.

Storing Data and Printing Drawings

Drawings may be stored by filing the data according to the name or number of the drawing file. The software manual will provide you with the necessary information for filing your drawings.

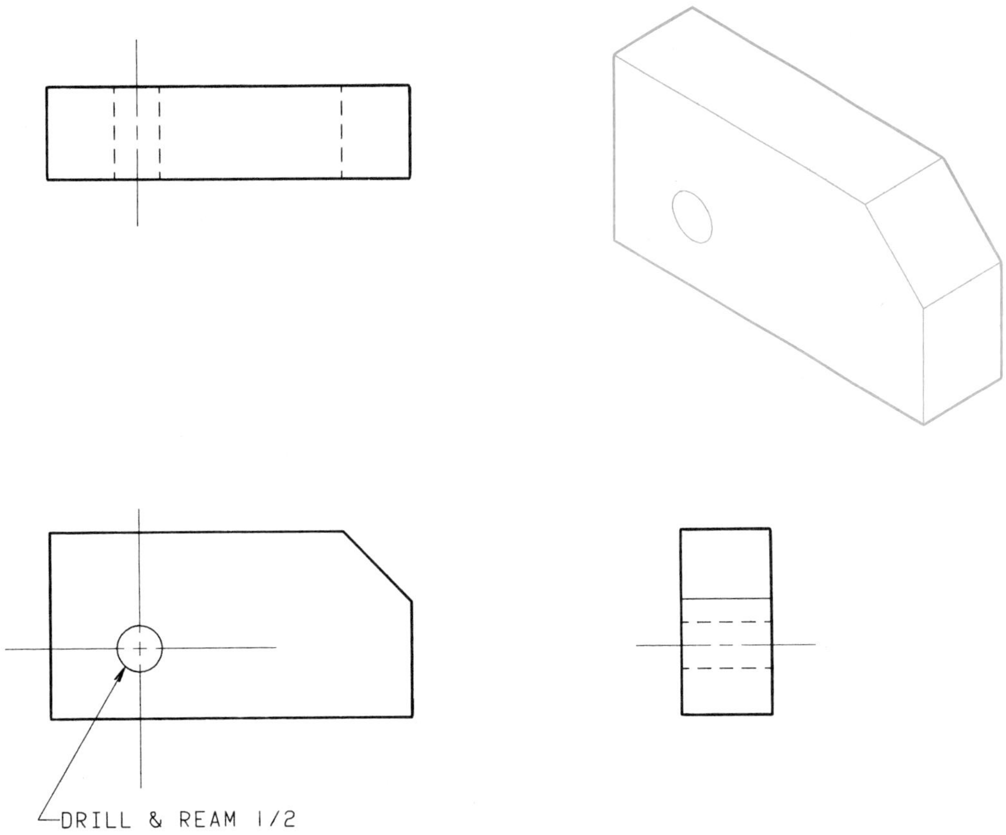

Fig. 7-11. Using the front view, top view, and side view, some CADD programs will create the isometric view.

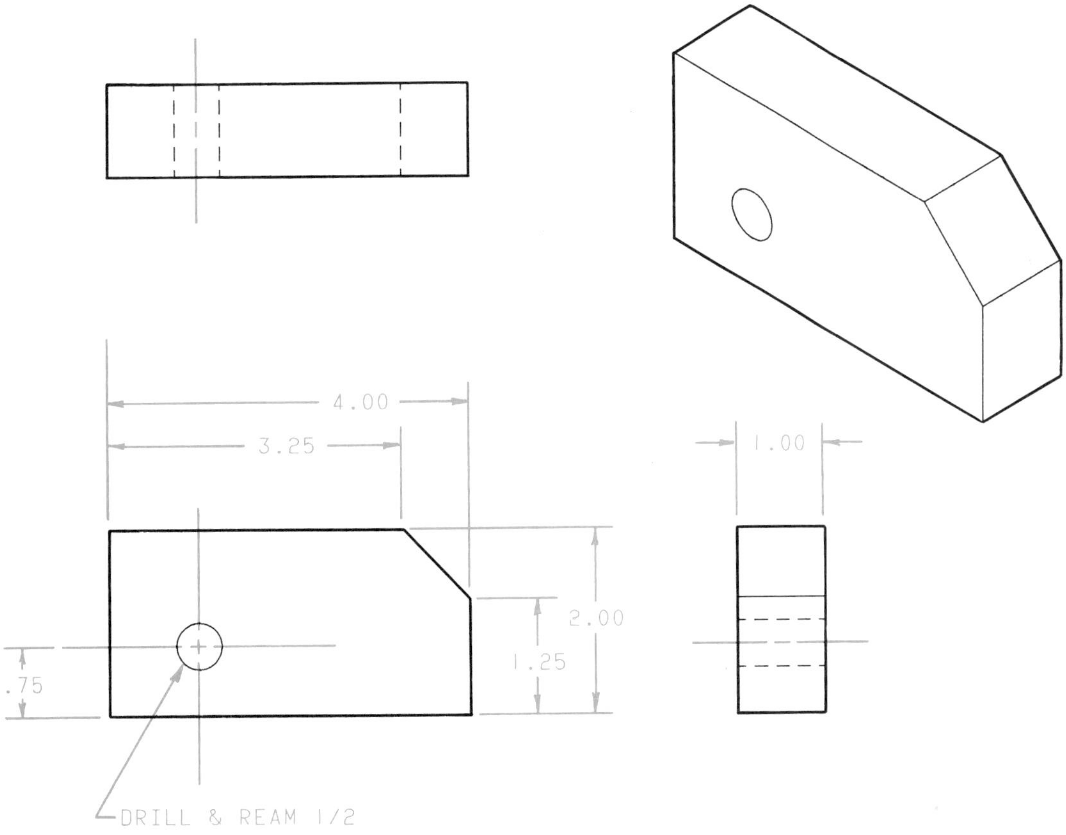

Fig. 7-12. Working drawings must have dimension lines, arrowheads, and numerical values to be useful.

When a drawing is completed, it is good practice to have hardcopy printed for your review.

CADD SUMMARY

The following series of suggestions and exercises will acquaint you with CADD. Suggestions before you begin:

1. Take notes and make sketches showing the steps of development as you learn about CADD on the computer.
2. Create a file to store your drawings by using easy to remember codes, such as "IED1" (Industrial Education Drawing 1).
3. Store each drawing in your file with an easy to remember code.
4. Print or plot each of your CADD exercises.
5. Keep each of your exercises for future reference.

Exercise 1:

After you understand how to open your system, practice using X and Y coordinates by laying out a border line and title block for future drawings. The worksheet shown in Fig. 7-13 indicates modified ANSI standard sheet layouts as an example. You may want to create a different format for your drawings. Your border and title block should be printed and stored for future CADD drawings.

Exercise 2:

Try a variety of main menu commands to complete geometric constructions figures. Create and then print vertical, horizontal, and angular lines. Include solid lines, dashed lines, and centerlines. Next, create and then print arcs and circles by using a variety of the menu options available.

Exercise 3:

Use the system's "DRAW" command to create a series of isometric views. Begin with a rectangular block, Fig. 7-14. Then, create a rectangular block that has one or more offset surfaces, Fig. 7-15. Next, create a block with slanted surfaces, Fig. 7-16. Fig. 7-17 provides some good examples of drawings with holes and curved surfaces. Each sketch should be printed on paper containing your border line/title block. Save your sketches on the computer for future reference.

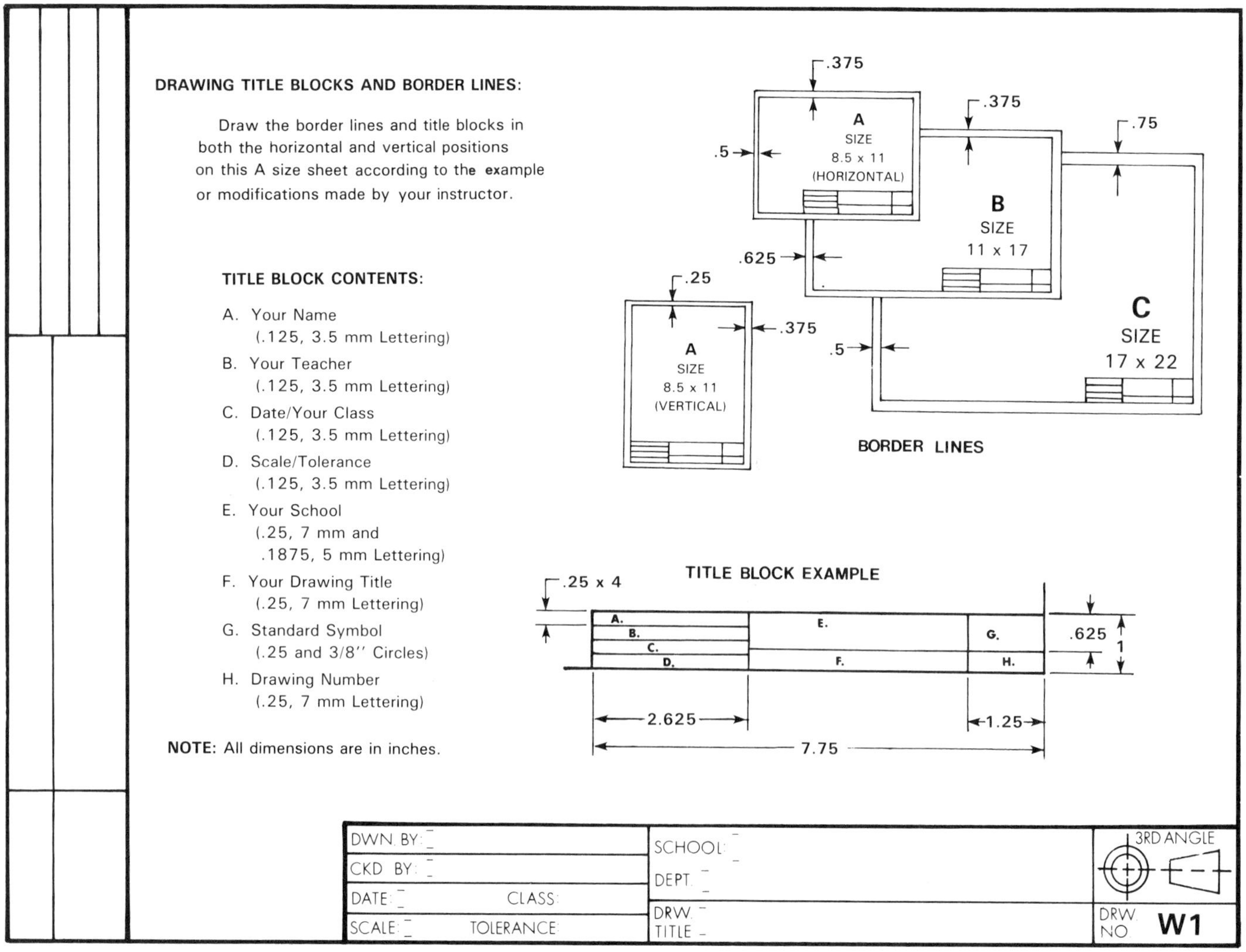

Fig. 7-13. Suggested layout for border lines and title blocks for future use in CADD drawings.

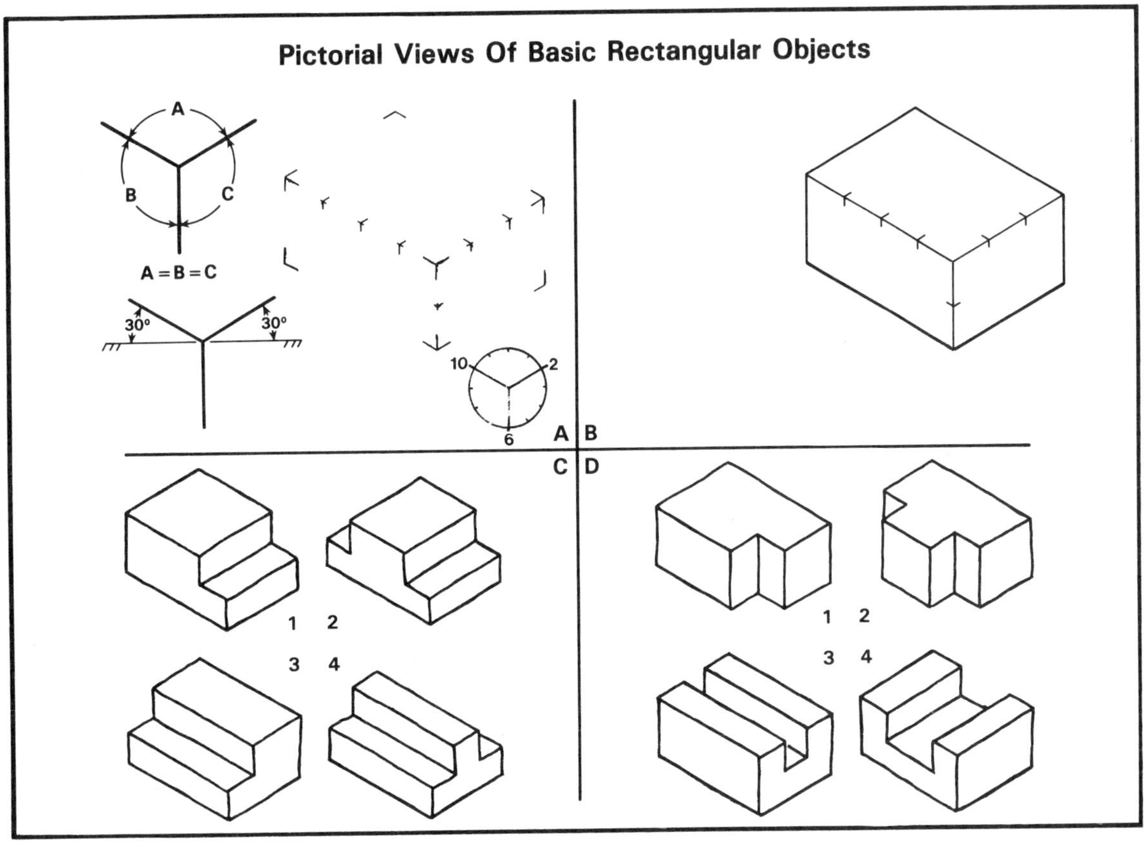

Fig. 7-14. Suggested exercises for CADD drawings using rectangular block and offset surfaces.

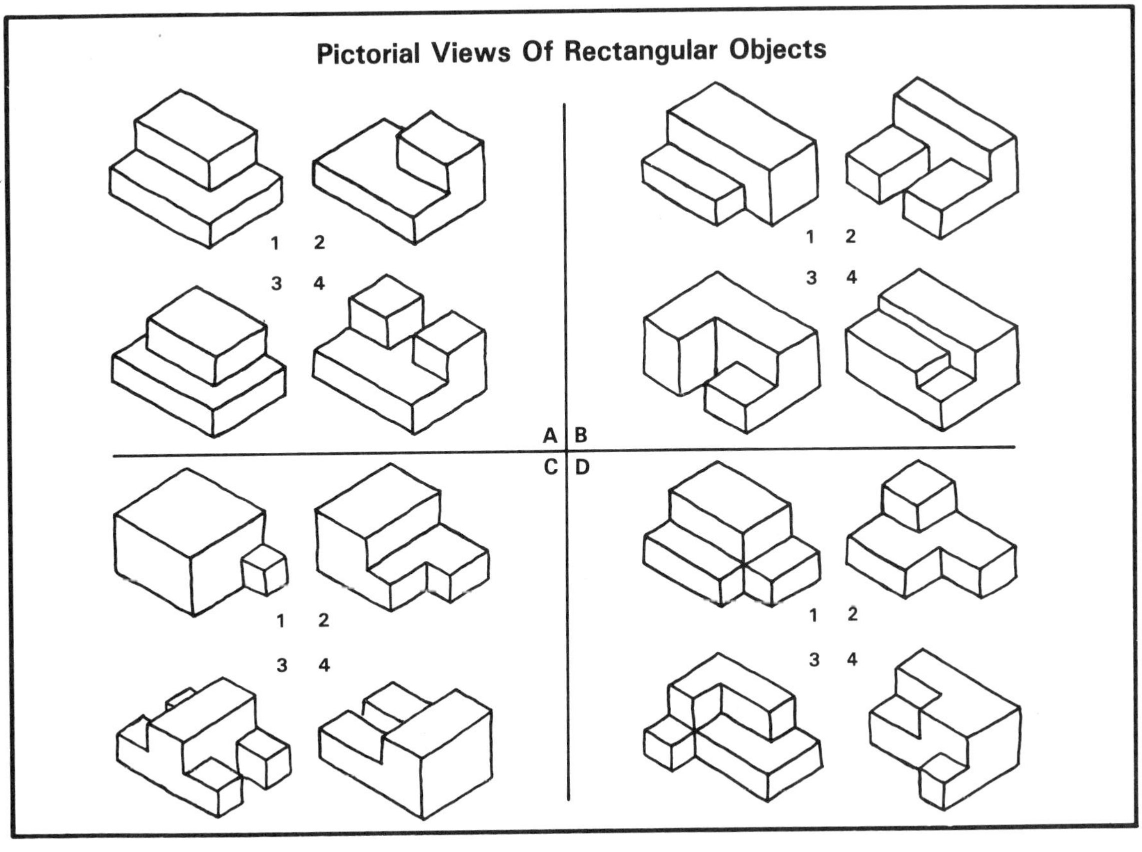

Fig. 7-15. Suggested exercises for CADD drawings incorporating more complex horizontal and vertical surfaces.

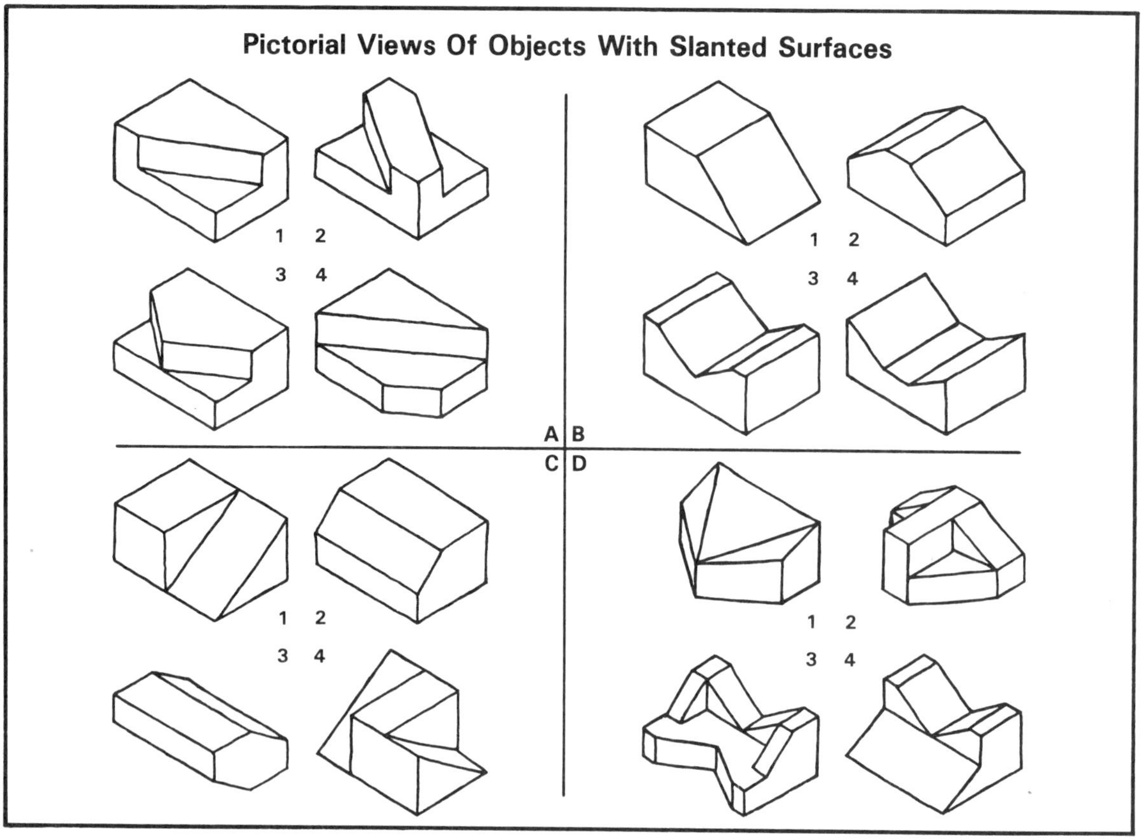

Fig. 7-16. Suggested exercises for CADD drawings incorporating slanted surfaces.

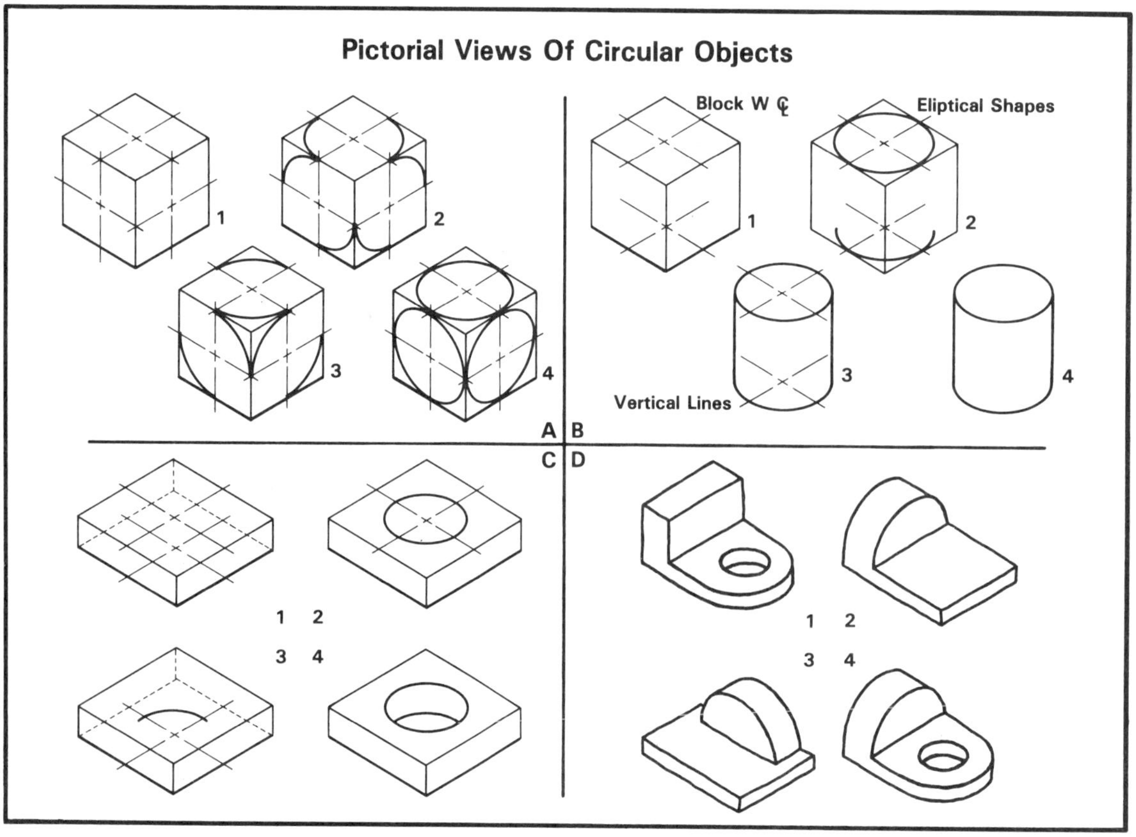

Fig. 7-17. Suggested exercises for CADD drawings incorporating holes and curved surfaces.

Exercise 4:

Create multiview drawings from one of your stored isometric sketches. Begin with a block and lay out its top, front, and side views. Next, select one of your original sketches with slanted surfaces and complete the top, front, and side views. Remember, add dashed lines for the hidden surfaces. Continue by drawing sketches with circular features. Remember both the dashed and center lines. Store and print each of your multiview drawings.

Exerices 5:

Open one of your previously stored multiview drawings for adding dimensions. Use extension lines, dimension lines, and arrowheads to give accurate and complete size/shape information. Next, select and dimension your stored drawings containing slanted surfaces and circular features.

Exercise 6:

Create working drawings of products from the workbook or objects that you want to create from your environment. Include an isometric sketch, a multiview drawing, dimensioning, and sectioning when necessary.

As you complete the CADD drawings, keep in mind that you should:

1. Include all necessary views.
2. Supply accurate dimensions in appropriate locations.
3. Include section views when needed.
4. Provide adequate notes in appropriate locations.
5. Consider rearranging, rescaling views, or repositioning notes and dimensions to improve clarity and appearance.

Chapter 7—COMPUTER-ASSISTED DRAFTING AND DESIGN

Review What You Have Learned

Write your answers on a separate sheet of paper. Do not write in this textbook.

Essay:

1. Discuss the advantages and disadvantages of computer-assisted drafting and design compared to traditional drafting and design. You may find this topic could be presented using charts to compare and contrast various points.
2. Using your own words, explain in a couple of paragraphs why it is important to understand the basics of drafting before operating a computer assisted drafting system.
3. Make a comparison among three to four major software packages. Use the library as a resource. You will find that many software programs have been reviewed in professional magazines and these may provide you with additional background for your paper.

Multiple Choice: Carefully read the statements below and write the letter of the best answer for each of the items on your answer sheet.

4. CADD hardware includes all but which of the following?
   a. Input devices.
   b. Transverse devices.
   c. Storage devices.
   d. Central processing unit.
   e. Output devices.
5. When using the "X,Y,Z coordinate system," a point three units to the right of the origin would have which of the following X, Y, and Z coordinates?
   a. 1,2,3.
   b. 3,2,1.
   c. 0,3,0.
   d. 3,0,0.
   e. 0,0,3.
6. When using the "X,Y,Z coordinate system," a point one unit above and two units to the right of the origin would have which of the following X,Y, and Z coordinates?
   a. 1,2,3.
   b. 1,2,0.
   c. 0,1,2.
   d. 1,0.2.
   e. 2,1,0.
7. When using the "X,Y,Z coordinate system," a point three units above, two units to the right, and one unit toward you from the origin would have which of the following X, Y, and Z coordinates?
   a. 1,2,3.
   b. 2,3,1.
   c. 3,1,2.
   d. 3,2,1.
   e. 1,3,2.
8. When using the "X,Y,Z coordinate system," a point two units below, one unit to the left, and three units toward you from the origin would have which of the following X,Y, and Z coordinates?
   a. 2, −1, 3.
   b. −2, 1, −3.
   c. 2, 1, 3.
   d. −2, −1, −3.
   e. −2, −1, 3.

True or False: Carefully read the statements below. Write a "T" on your answer sheet for the statements which are true. For the statements which are false, write an "F." Rewrite each false statement so it becomes true.

9. Knowing the basic drafting language is necessary before completing computer assisted drawings. True or False?
10. CADD drawings are less expensive to produce than conventional drawings. True or False?

11. Lines may be created with a light pen or mouse by using a "screen position" option. True or False?
12. Each CADD system uses its own procedures for creating drawings. True or False?
13. Since a CADD system is so easy to use and since an operator can create drawings so fast, it is not necessary to make back-up disks of the drawings. True or False?

Completion: After studying this chapter, read the incomplete sentences below. Write the missing word or words on your separate answer sheet.

14. A typical CADD system includes hardware such as ________, ________, ________, and ________.
15. Circles are usually drawn in a ________ direction by default.
16. The options that a CADD system has available are displayed as a ________.
17. One of the most enjoyable characteristics of CADD is to see the drawing ________ on the screen making necessary changes.
18. The x,y,z, coordinate that relates to the height of a product is ________.
19. The most common method used to draw circles using a software program is to require a ________ point and a radius.

Matching: Read the numbered positions in column A and match up the corresponding direction from column B. Write your selection on your answer sheet.

Column A	Column B
20. x +	a. Upward.
21. x −	b. Downward.
22. y +	c. To the right.
23. y −	d. To the left.
24. z +	e. Toward you.
25. z −	f. Away from you.

Practice What You Have Learned: Depending upon the CADD equipment and software available, demonstrate your understanding and operation of the system by completing the working drawings you constructed in Chapter 6 under the heading of Practice What You Have Learned. This exercise will allow you to gain experience in many different constructions.

USEFUL INFORMATION

SOME COMMON ABBREVIATIONS/SYMBOLS

ENGLISH		METRIC	
UNIT	ABBREVIATION	UNIT	SYMBOL
inch	in	kilometre	km
feet	ft	hectometre	hm
yard	yd	dekametre	dam
mile	mi	metre	m
grain	gr	decimetre	dm
ounce	oz	centimetre	cm
pound	lb	millimetre	mm
teaspoon	tsp	cubic centimetre	cm^3
tablespoon	tbsp	kilogram	kg
fluid ounce	fl oz	hectogram	hg
cup	c	dekagram	dag
pint	pt	gram	g
quart	qt	decigram	dg
gallon	gal	centigram	cg
cubic inch	in^3	milligram	mg
cubic foot	ft^3	kilolitre	kl
cubic yard	yd^3	hectolitre	hl
square inch	in^2	dekalitre	dal
square foot	ft^2	litre	L
square yard	yd^2	centilitre	cl
square mile	mi^2	millilitre	ml
Fahrenheit	F	dekastere	das
barrel	bbl	square kilometre	km^2
fluid dram	fl dr	hectare	ha
board foot	bd ft	are	a
rod	rd	centare	ca
dram	dr	tonne	t
bushel	bu	Celsius	C

MEASURING SYSTEMS

ENGLISH	METRIC
LENGTH	
12 inches = 1 foot	1 kilometre = 1000 metres
36 inches = 1 yard	1 hectometre = 100 metres
3 feet = 1 yard	1 dekametre = 10 metres
5,280 feet = 1 mile	1 metre = 1 metre
16.5 feet = 1 rod	1 decimetre = 0.1 metre
320 rods = 1 mile	1 centimetre = 0.01 metre
6 feet = 1 fathom	1 millimetre = 0.001 metre
WEIGHT	
27.34 grains = 1 dram	1 tonne = 1,000,000 grams
438 grains = 1 ounce	1 kilogram = 1000 grams
16 drams = 1 ounce	1 hectogram = 100 grams
16 ounces = 1 pound	1 dekagram = 10 grams
2000 pounds = 1 short ton	1 gram = 1 gram
2240 pounds = 1 long ton	1 decigram = 0.1 gram
25 pounds = 1 quarter	1 centigram = 0.01 gram
4 quarters = 1 cwt	1 milligram = 0.001 gram
VOLUME	
8 ounces = 1 cup	1 hectolitre = 100 litres
16 ounces = 1 pint	1 dekalitre = 10 litres
32 ounces = 1 quart	1 litre = 1 litre
2 cups = 1 pint	1 decilitre = 0.1 litre
2 pints = 1 quart	1 centilitre = 0.01 litre
4 quarts = 1 gallon	1 millilitre = 0.001 litre
8 pints = 1 gallon	1000 millilitre = 1 litre
AREA	
144 sq. inches = 1 sq. foot	100 sq. millimetres = 1 sq. centimetre
9 sq. feet = 1 sq. yard	100 sq. centimetres = 1 sq. decimetre
43,560 sq. ft. = 160 sq. rods	100 sq. decimetres = 1 sq. metre
160 sq. rods = 1 acre	10,000 sq. metres = 1 hectare
640 acres = 1 sq. mile	

TEMPERATURE

FAHRENHEIT		CELSIUS
32 degrees F	Water freezes	0 degree C
68 degrees F	Reasonable room temperature	20 degrees C
98.6 degrees F	Normal body temperature	37 degrees C
173 degrees F	Alcohol boils	78.34 degrees C
212 degrees F	Water boils	100 degrees C

USEFUL CONVERSIONS

WHEN YOU KNOW:	MULTIPLY BY:	TO FIND:
TORQUE		
Pound - inch	0.11298	newton-metres (N-m)
Pound - foot	1.3558	newton-metres
LIGHT		
Foot candles	1.0764	lumens/metres^2 (lm/m^2)
FUEL PERFORMANCE		
Miles/gallon	0.4251	kilometres/litre (km/L)
SPEED		
Miles/hour	1.6093	kilometres/hr (km/h)
FORCE		
kilogram	9.807	newtons (n)
ounce	0.278	newtons
pound	4.448	newtons
POWER		
Horsepower	0.746	kilowatts (kw)
PRESSURE OR STRESS		
Inches of water	0.2491	kilopascals (kPa)
Pounds/sq. in.	6.895	kilopascals
ENERGY OR WORK		
BTU	1055.0	joules (J)
Foot - pound	1.3558	joules
Kilowatt-hour	3600000.0	joules (J = one W/s)

CONVERSION TABLE
METRIC TO ENGLISH

WHEN YOU KNOW	MULTIPLY BY: * = Exact		TO FIND
	VERY ACCURATE	APPROXIMATE	
LENGTH			
millimetres	0.0393701	0.04	inches
centimetres	0.3937008	0.4	inches
metres	3.280840	3.3	feet
metres	1.093613	1.1	yards
kilometres	0.621371	0.6	miles
WEIGHT			
grains	0.00228571	0.0023	ounces
grams	0.03527396	0.035	ounces
kilograms	2.204623	2.2	pounds
tonnes	1.1023113	1.1	short tons
VOLUME			
millilitres		0.2	teaspoons
millilitres	0.06667	0.067	tablespoons
millilitres	0.03381402	0.03	fluid ounces
litres	61.02374	61.024	cubic inches
litres	2.113376	2.1	pints
litres	1.056688	1.06	quarts
litres	0.26417205	0.26	gallons
litres	0.03531467	0.035	cubic feet
cubic metres	61023.74	61023.7	cubic inches
cubic metres	35.31467	35.0	cubic feet
cubic metres	1.3079506	1.3	cubic yards
cubic metres	264.17205	264.0	gallons
AREA			
square centimetres	0.1550003	0.16	square inches
square centimetres	0.00107639	0.001	square feet
square metres	10.76391	10.8	square feet
square metres	1.195990	1.2	square yards
square kilometres		0.4	square miles
hectares	2.471054	2.5	acres
TEMPERATURE			
Celsius	*9/5 (then add 32)		Fahrenheit

CONVERSION TABLE
ENGLISH TO METRIC

WHEN YOU KNOW	MULTIPLY BY: * = Exact		TO FIND
	VERY ACCURATE	APPROXIMATE	
LENGTH			
inches	* 25.4		millimetres
inches	* 2.54		centimetres
feet	* 0.3048		metres
feet	* 30.48		centimetres
yards	* 0.9144	0.9	metres
miles	* 1.609344	1.6	kilometres
WEIGHT			
grains	15.43236	15.4	grams
ounces	* 28.349523125	28.0	grams
ounces	* 0.028349523125	.028	kilograms
pounds	* 0.45359237	0.45	kilograms
short ton	* 0.90718474	0.9	tonnes
VOLUME			
teaspoons		5.0	millilitres
tablespoons		15.0	millilitres
fluid ounces	29.57353	30.0	millilitres
cups		0.24	litres
pints	* 0.473176473	0.47	litres
quarts	* 0.946352946	0.95	litres
gallons	* 3.785411784	3.8	litres
cubic inches	* 0.016387064	0.02	litres
cubic feet	* 0.028316846592	0.03	cubic metres
cubic yards	* 0.764554857984	0.76	cubic metres
AREA			
square inches	* 6.4516	6.5	square centimetres
square feet	* 0.09290304	0.09	square metres
square yards	* 0.83612736	0.8	square metres
square miles		2.6	square kilometres
acres	* 0.40468564224	0.4	hectares
TEMPERATURE			
Fahrenheit	* 5/9 (after subtracting 32)		Celsius

INDEX

Q

R

S

T

U

V

W